Oxford
KS3 Science

Activate 1
Question • Progress • Succeed

Teacher Handbook

Simon Broadley
Mark Matthews
Victoria Stutt
Nicky Thomas

Assessment Editor
Dr Andrew Chandler-Grevatt

Contents

Physics P1

Introduction

About the series

Activate is designed to match the 2014 Key Stage 3 Programme of Study and to help prepare your students for success in the new GCSEs and equivalent Key Stage 4 qualifications. Across the Student Books, Teacher Handbooks, and Kerboodle courses *Activate* allows you to track your students' progress through Key Stage 3 using innovative and reliable assessment and learning resources.

Activate is also flexible to suit your preferred route through Key Stage 3. The Programme of Study is covered in *Activate 1* and *Activate 2*, making it a perfect match for a two-year course. If you're continuing Key Stage 3 into Year 9, *Activate 3* offers consolidation and extension of core concepts through engaging contexts, with plenty of practice in the skills needed for success at Key Stage 4.

All of the content in the *Activate* series has been written and reviewed by our expert author and editor teams, all of whom have significant teaching experience, and our Assessment Editor is a school-assessment expert. You can be confident that *Activate* provides the best support for the new curriculum.

Your Teacher Handbook

This Teacher Handbook aims to save you time and effort by offering lesson plans, differentiation suggestions, and assessment guidance on a page-by-page basis that is a direct match to the Student Book.

You can use the Unit Openers to see the knowledge required of students from Key Stage 2 for each topic at a glance. You can also use the Checkpoint Lessons at the end of each chapter to support students who have yet to grasp a secure knowledge of the outcomes covered in each chapter. Lesson plans are written for 55-minute lessons but are flexible and fully adaptable so you can choose the activities that suit your classes best.

Unit Opener

Overview

The Unit Opener provides an overview of the unit (Biology, Chemistry, or Physics) and how it links to Key Stage 2 and Key Stage 4.

Curriculum links

An overview of the chapters in this unit, and the Key Stage 3 topics they link to.

Preparing for Key Stage 4 success

This table provides an overview of the Key Stage 4 skills and underpinning knowledge that are covered in the unit. It also provides details of where Key Stage 4 style assessment questions can be found throughout the unit.

Key Stage 2 catch-up

This table outlines the Key Stage 2 knowledge that is a pre-requisite for this unit. This can be assessed using the automarked Unit Pre-test on Kerboodle.

For each Key Stage 2 statement, a suggestion for how you can help students to catch up is provided, as well as an index of which topic each statement links to.

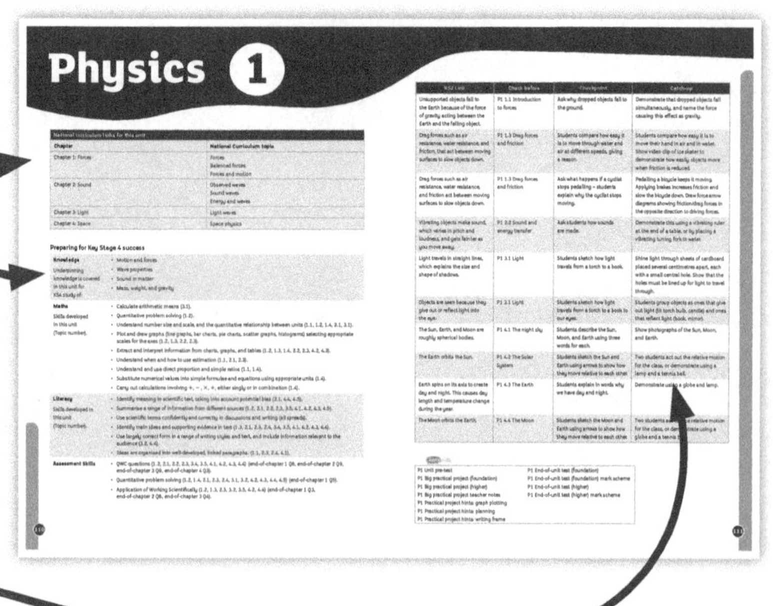
Physics 1

Lesson

Curriculum links

This indicates the area of the 2014 Programme of Study this lesson covers. A Working Scientifically link is also given for most lessons. This indicates the main Working Scientifically focus of the lesson.

Differentiated outcomes

This table summarises the possible lesson outcomes. They are ramped and divided into three ability bands. Levels for each outcome are given in brackets. The three ability bands are explained on the following page.

An indication of where each outcome is covered is given in the checkpoint table, helping you to monitor progress through the lesson.

Maths and Literacy

These boxes provide suggestions of how Maths and Literacy skills can be developed in the lesson. They also indicate when a Maths or Literacy activity is given in the Student Book.

Maths and Literacy skills are ramped through *Activate*. A Progression Grid and Progress Tasks are supplied on Kerboodle.

Assessing Pupil Progress (APP)

Opportunities for integration of APP (based on the 2009 APP framework) are included in the APP box.

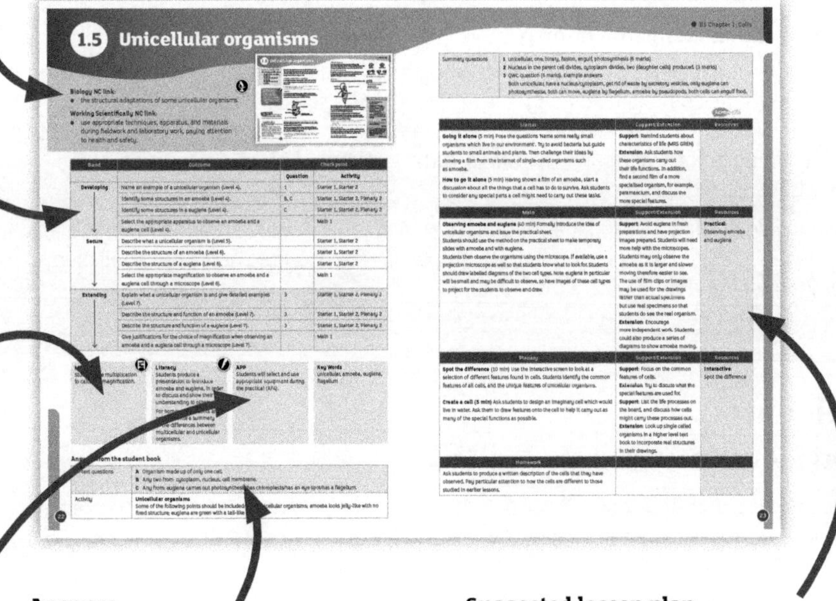

Answers

Answers to the Student Book activities and questions can be found here.

Suggested lesson plan

A suggested route through the lesson is provided, including ideas for support, extension, and homework. The right-hand column indicates where Kerboodle resources are available.

Each lesson plan is supported by an editable lesson presentation on Kerboodle.

Checkpoint and Summary Lessons

Overview

The Checkpoint Lesson is a suggested follow-up lesson after students have completed the automarked Checkpoint Assessment on Kerboodle. There are two routes through the lesson, with the route for each student being determined by their mark in the assessment. Route A helps students to consolidate what they have learnt through the chapter, whilst Route B offers extension for students who have already grasped the key concepts.

Answers

Answers to the End-of-Chapter questions in the Student Book.

Checkpoint routes

A summary of the two suggested routes through the lesson.

Progression table

This table summarises the outcomes covered in the Revision Lesson, and provides guidance for how students can make progress to achieve each outcome.

The tasks outlined in the table, resources for the Extension Lesson, and detailed Teacher Notes are all available on Kerboodle.

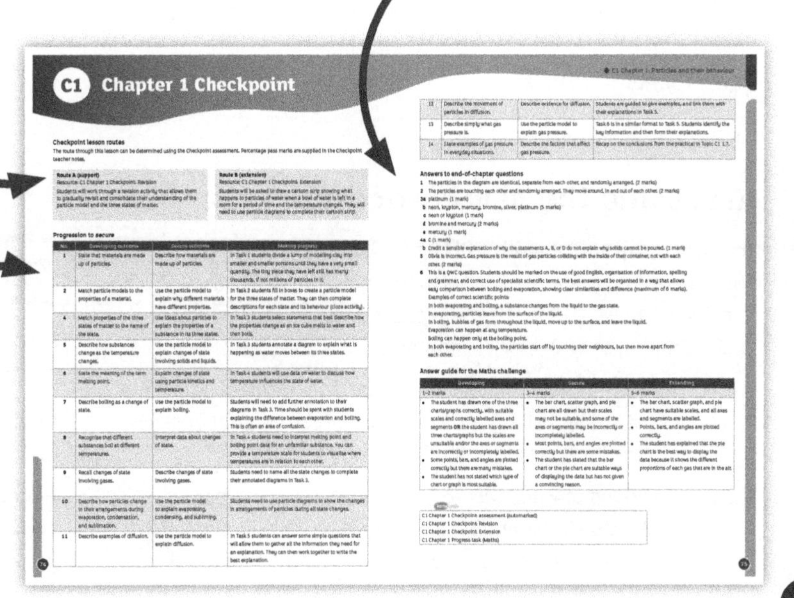

Assessment and progress

About the Assessment Editor

Dr Andrew Chandler-Grevatt has a doctorate in school assessment, and has a real passion for science teaching and learning. Having worked as a science teacher for ten years, of which five was spent as an AST, Andy has a real understanding of the pressures and joys of teaching in the classroom. This stays at the forefront of his mind during all of his work in education.

Alongside his national and international research in school assessment, Andy is a teaching fellow on the PGCE course at the University of Sussex, and is a successful published assessment author.

Welcome

from the Assessment Editor

Welcome to your *Activate 1* Teacher Handbook. The Teacher Handbooks, together with Kerboodle, and the Student Books, provide comprehensive assessment support for the new curriculum.

The new Key Stage 3 curriculum has no prescribed assessment framework. Our assessment model will help your school monitor progress and attainment against the new curriculum, whether you want to continue using levels, or adopt a new model based on curriculum statements. Throughout *Activate*, formative assessment has been made easy, and we have followed a set of guiding assessment principles.

Activate assessment principles

Assessment in *Activate* aims to:

- inform teaching and/or learning directly (have a formative function)
- assess agreed and shared objectives
- provide opportunities for peer- and self-assessment
- provide opportunities for specific feedback to be given to and acted upon by individual students
- provide usable data or information that informs teachers of progress of classes and individuals.

I have been working closely with our expert author teams across all components of *Activate* to ensure consistency in the assessment material, meaning you can be confident when using *Activate* to monitor your students' progress.

Assessing the new curriculum

The current system of levels will be removed from the National Curriculum. Schools are expected to set their own methods of tracking progress, whilst ensuring students gain a secure level of understanding of each block of content.

The *Activate* assessment model is based on bands; the middle band indicates that students have a *secure* grasp of the content or skills specified in the Programme of Study.

The band working towards *secure* is *developing*, and the band moving past *secure* is *extending*. The bands have been matched to levels and grades, meaning you can adopt a system that works for your school.

Activate bands	**Developing**		**Secure**		**Extending**	
Level equivalent	3	4	5	6	7	8
Grade indicator	To ensure grade indicators are up-to-date with KS4 qualifications, the information is stored on Kerboodle.					
Bloom's Taxonomy links	Remembering & Understanding		Application & Analysing		Evaluation & Creating	

Flexible assessment that works for you

Assessment in *Activate* is designed to be flexible, formative, and summative, allowing you to choose what best suits your students and school. All paper assessments are fully editable for you to adapt to your chosen approach.

All automarked assessments have the option of providing either formative feedback (where students receive feedback on each question and additional attempts) or summative feedback (with one attempt at each question and feedback at the end).

Bands	Levels	Grades	Comment only
All outcomes are banded throughout this book and in progress tasks. Use this model to assess students on their grasp of curriculum statements and set improvement targets, with a focus on ensuring students are always aiming for a *secure* band or higher.	All outcomes are matched to levels in this book and in progress tasks. This means you can continue using levels with *Activate* content, as well as integrating content you already have with *Activate*. This enables progress to be monitored and targets to be set.	Grade indicators are provided in Kerboodle. This enables progress to be monitored with reference to KS4 qualifications.	Some schools have adopted the 'no grades or marks' approach to assessment, opting for comment-only feedback. Interactive assessments provide comments and feedback to facilitate progression, and all paper assessments are fully editable, so banding and levelling can be removed.

The Checkpoint system

At the end of each chapter, there is an automarked online assessment. It will help you to determine if your students have a *secure* understanding of the chapter.

Activities for a follow-up Checkpoint Lesson are provided on Kerboodle. There are two recommended routes through the lesson for students, depending on the percentage they achieve in the assessment. Revision and Extension routes can be followed in the same lesson, allowing students to either consolidate their understanding or attempt an extension task.

Each lesson also includes informal checkpoints to track progress through a lesson.

Follow assessment with learning

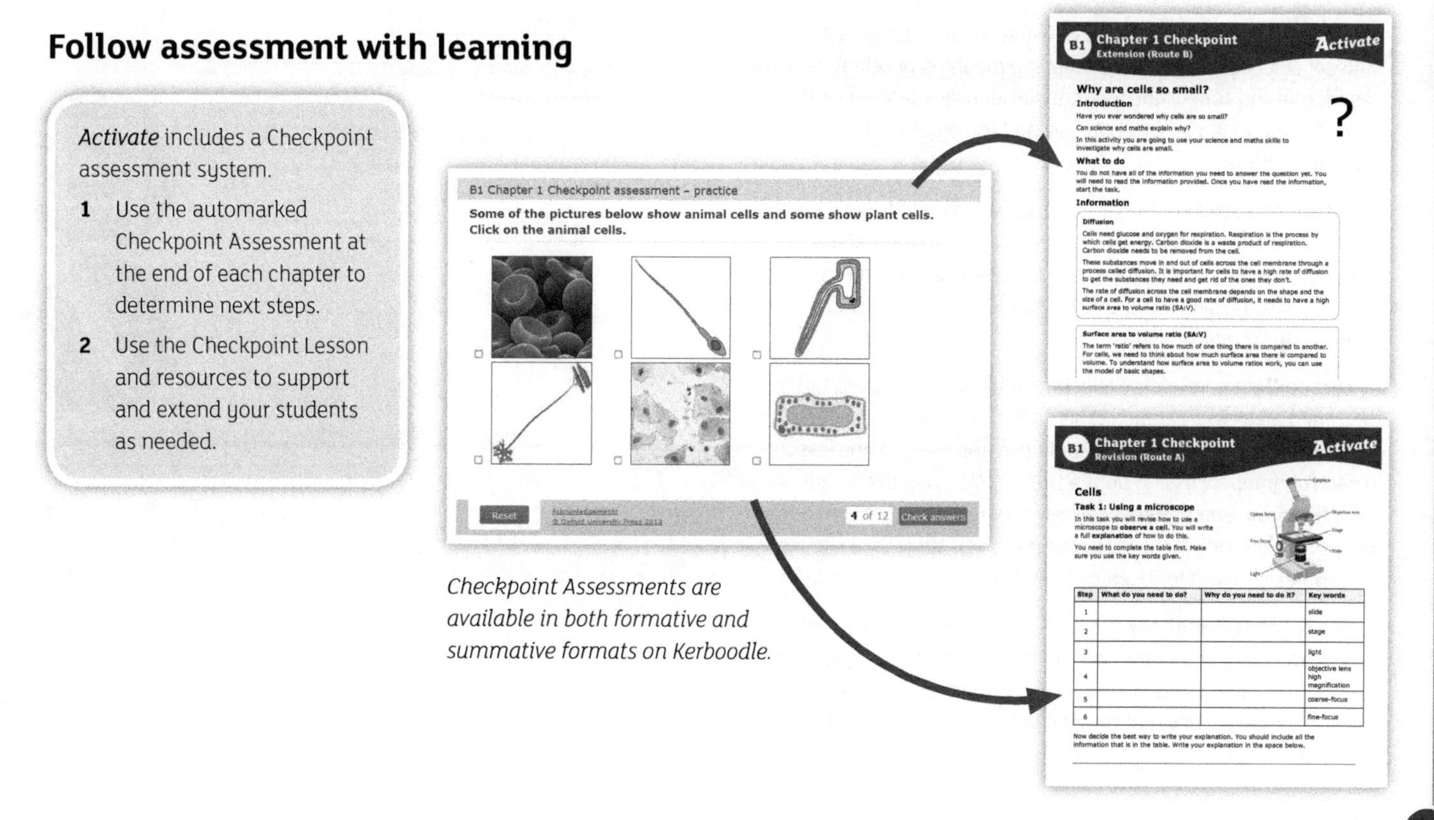

Activate includes a Checkpoint assessment system.

1. Use the automarked Checkpoint Assessment at the end of each chapter to determine next steps.
2. Use the Checkpoint Lesson and resources to support and extend your students as needed.

Checkpoint Assessments are available in both formative and summative formats on Kerboodle.

Differentiation and skills

Maths skills

Maths skills have always been important for science but with the introduction of the new GCSEs competence in maths in scientific contexts will be vital for success.

Key Maths skills for science include quantitative problem solving, use of scientific formulae, and the calculation of arithmetic means. Each skill has been integrated across components in *Activate*, with progress in each skill mapped out. You can view the Progression Grid for Maths in Kerboodle.

The **Student Books** contain maths activities and hints to support and develop Maths skills as students work from their books. There are also Maths challenges at the end of some chapters, focussing on quantitative problem solving skills.

In **Kerboodle**, you will find maths Skills Interactives that are automarked and provide formative feedback. Maths questions are also incorporated into other assessments where appropriate, and designated Progress Tasks for Maths will help you track progress.

In this **Teacher Handbook**, you will find maths suggestions for most lessons, linking to the Student Book where relevant. By using *Activate* resources, students will gain plenty of experience in a range of Maths skills that have been identified as vital for success at Key Stage 4.

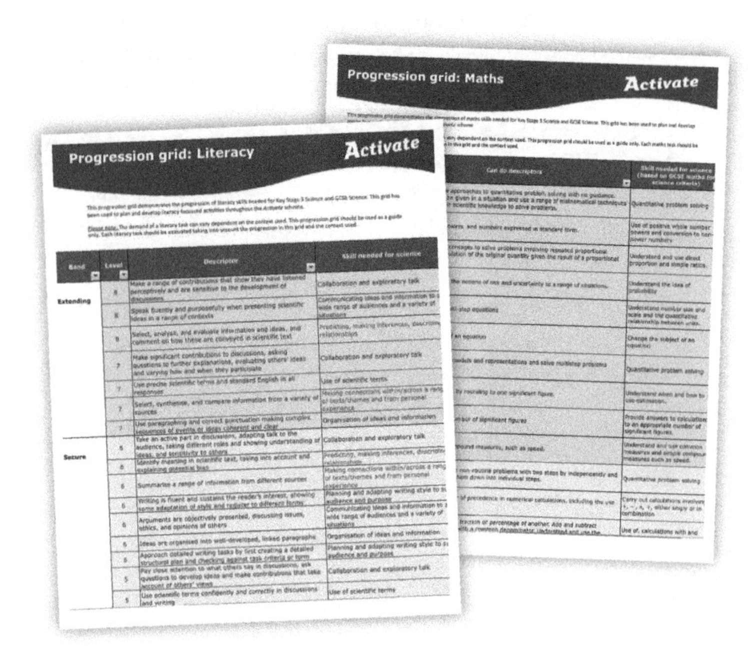
Progression grid: Maths
Activate

Progression grid: Literacy
Activate

Literacy skills

Literacy skills enable students to effectively communicate their ideas about science, and access the information they need. Since the introduction of extended writing at GCSE Literacy skills are now more important than ever.

Literacy skills are vital for success in any subject but key Literacy skills for science include understanding meaning of scientific texts and identifying supporting ideas and evidence, adapting writing styles to suit audience and purpose, and the organisation of ideas and information.

The **Student books** contain literacy activities and hints to support and develop Literacy skills as students work from their books. There are also Big Writes at the end of some chapters, focussing on extended writing skills. Key Words and a Glossary help students get to grips with scientific terms.

In **Kerboodle** you will find Skills Interactives and Progress Quizzes that will help assess Literacy skills, including spelling of key words. Question-led Lessons offer an alternative approach to one lesson in each chapter, focussing on the Literacy skills needed to answer a Big Question, and Progress Tasks for Literacy will help you track progress in key skill areas throughout the key stage. You can view the Progression Grid for Literacy in Kerboodle.

In this **Teacher Handbook**, you will find Literacy suggestions for most lessons, linking to the Student Book where relevant. By using *Activate* resources, students will gain plenty of experience in a range of Literacy skills that have been identified as vital for success at Key Stage 4.

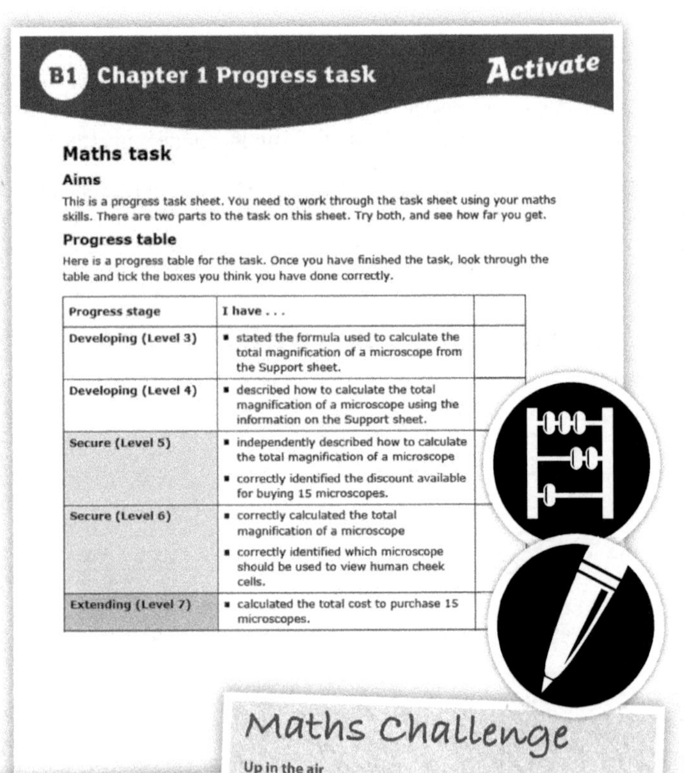
B1 Chapter 1 Progress task
Activate

Maths task

Aims

This is a progress task sheet. You need to work through the task sheet using your maths skills. There are two parts to the task on this sheet. Try both, and see how far you get.

Progress table

Here is a progress table for the task. Once you have finished the task, look through the table and tick the boxes you think you have done correctly.

Progress stage	I have . . .	
Developing (Level 3)	• stated the formula used to calculate the total magnification of a microscope from the Support sheet.	
Developing (Level 4)	• described how to calculate the total magnification of a microscope using the information on the Support sheet.	
Secure (Level 5)	• independently described how to calculate the total magnification of a microscope • correctly identified the discount available for buying 15 microscopes.	
Secure (Level 6)	• correctly calculated the total magnification of a microscope • correctly identified which microscope should be used to view human cheek cells.	
Extending (Level 7)	• calculated the total cost to purchase 15 microscopes.	

Maths Challenge

Up in the air

The air is a mixture of substances. The table shows the percentages of the substances in the air.

Substance	Percentage of substance in dry air
nitrogen	78.08
oxygen	20.95
argon	0.93
others, including carbon dioxide	0.04

Task

Draw a graph or chart to represent the data in the table. Decide which type of chart is best, and explain why.

Mission to Mars

NASA's Curiosity rover landed on Mars ... the first astronauts have just returned f...

Task

You were one of the astronauts on the ... covers the whole mission. Start from ... Earth and finish with splash down wh...

Tips

- Explain the motion of the rocket d... journey to and from Mars.
- Use what you have learnt about where forces come from and how they affect motion.

Working Scientifically

Working Scientifically is new to the 2014 Key Stage 3 Programme of Study and the new GCSE criteria. It is divided into four areas, and is integrated into the teaching and learning of Biology, Chemistry, and Physics. The four areas are:

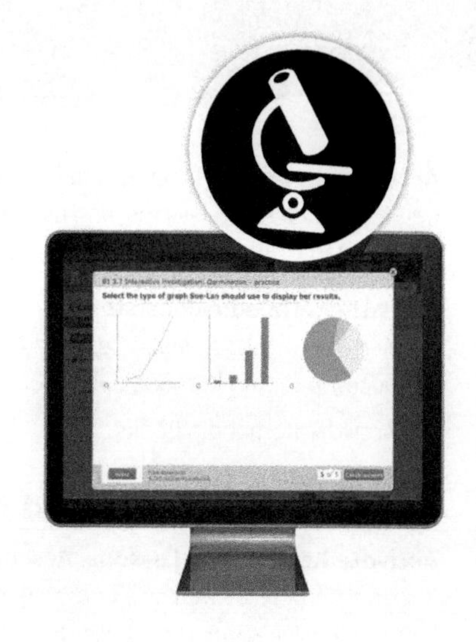

Scientific attitudes, in which students need to be aware of accuracy, precision, repeatability, and reproducibility, and demonstrate understanding of scientific methods and the scientific process.

Experimental skills and investigations, in which students ask scientific questions based on observations, make predictions using scientific knowledge and understanding, carry out investigations to test predictions, make and record measurements, and evaluate methods.

Analysis and evaluation, in which students apply mathematical concepts and calculate results, present and interpret data using tables and graphs, draw conclusions, and evaluate data.

Measurement, in which students calculate results using scientific formulae, using basic data analysis, SI units, and IUPAC chemical nomenclature where appropriate.

Working Scientifically is integrated throughout the **Student Book** , and it also contains activities and hints to help students build their investigative skills and understand the process of working scientifically. A dedicated Working Scientifically chapter is also provided in *Activate 1*.

In **Kerboodle** you will find Practicals and Activities, each with their own Working Scientifically objectives, as well as Interactive investigations, Skills Interactives, Skill Sheets and Progress Tasks.

The **Teacher Handbook** lessons often have one Working Scientifically focus in mind for the activities of that lesson. Working Scientifically outcomes are ramped and included as part of the lesson outcomes.

Differentiation

Activate will help you to support students of every ability through Key Stage 3. A variety of support is available, combining opt-in differentiation, ramped questions and tasks, and differentiation by task, as appropriate for each type of activity.

Differentiation using the Checkpoint system

- The end-of-chapter Checkpoint lessons will help you to progress students of every ability.
- The revision tasks are designed to be used with students in need of support. Teacher input will help them grasp important concepts from the chapter.
- The extension tasks provide an opportunity to stretch students who require an extra challenge. Students can work independently.

Teacher Handbook

Lesson outcomes are differentiated, including Working Scientifically. Suggestions for activities throughout lesson plans are also accompanied by support and extension opportunities.

Student Book

The Summary Questions and End-of-Chapter Questions in the Student Book are ramped. The level of demand of each question is indicated by the number of conical flasks depicted at the beginning of the question.

Practicals and Activities

Each Practical or Activity includes an extension task. Support Sheets or Access Sheets are available as an extra resource for most Practicals and Activities. Support Sheets offer opt-in differentiation, providing additional support with a difficult area of the task. Access Sheets offer alternative lesson activities where the main Practical or Activity is not accessible by some students.

Skill Sheets may also be used in tandem with Practicals and Activities to provide extra support. These can be found in Additional support in Kerboodle.

Interactive Assessments

Interactive Assessments are ramped in difficulty and support is provided in the feedback.

Written assessments

- End-of-Unit Tests and Big Practical Projects have Foundation and Higher versions.
- Progress Tasks each contain two tasks and a progress ladder to cater for all abilities.

Kerboodle

***Activate* Kerboodle** is packed full of guided support and ideas for running and creating effective Key Stage 3 Science lessons, and assessing and facilitating students' progress. It's intuitive to use, customizable, and can be accessed online.

***Activate* Kerboodle consists of**:

- *Activate* Lessons, Resources, and Assessment (includes teacher access to the accompanying Kerboodle Book)
- *Activate* Kerboodle Books.

Lessons, Resources, and Assessment

***Activate* Kerboodle – Lessons**, **Resources**, and **Assessment** provides hundreds of engaging lesson resources as well as a comprehensive assessment package. Kerboodle offers flexibility and comprehensive support for both the *Activate* course and your own scheme of work.

You can **adapt** many of the resources to suit your students' needs, with all non-interactive activities available as editable Word documents. You can also **upload** your existing resources so that everything can be accessed from one location.

Kerboodle is online, allowing you and your students to access the course anytime, anywhere. Set homework and assessments through the Assessment system, and **track** progress using the Markbook.

Lessons, Resources, and Assessment provide:

- Lessons
- Resources
- Assessment and Markbook
- Teacher access to the Kerboodle Book.

Lessons

Click on the **Lessons tab** to access the *Activate* Lesson Plan and Presentations (with accompanying notes).

Ready-to-play Lesson Plan and Presentations complement every spread in the Teacher Handbook and Student Book. Each lesson presentation is easy to launch and features lesson objectives, settlers, starters, activity guidance, key diagrams, plenaries, and homework suggestions. You can further **personalize** the lessons by adding in your own resources and notes. This means that the Lesson Presentations and accompanying notes sections are 100% customizable. Your lessons and notes can be accessed by your whole department and they are ideal for use in cover lessons.

Every lesson is accompanied by teacher notes that provide additional support and extension opportunities, to fully support lesson delivery.

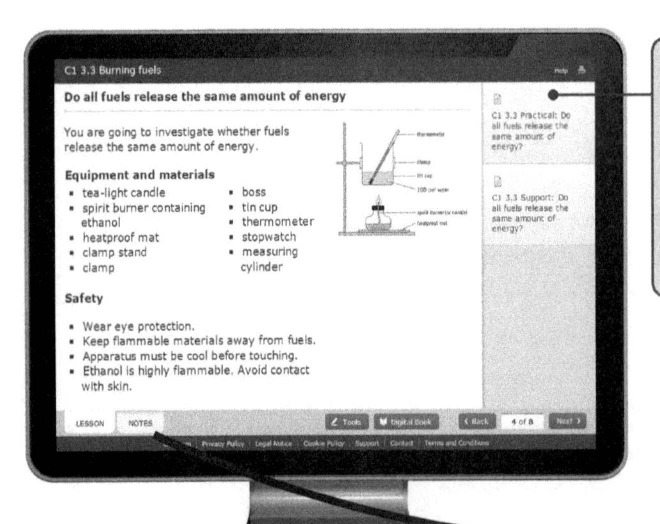

Resources are built into each lesson presentation so that associated interactive content, practical, or activity worksheets are ready to launch.

Energy transfers in different fuels (25 min)

Students will carry out a simple calorimetric experiment to compare the effectiveness of a candle and a spirit burner water.

A support sheet is available with a suggested table of results.

As an extension, students should consider if the method they used can give conclusive data on which fuel transfers and suggest how it can be improved.

Fully-editable resources and Teacher and Technician Notes (offering further guidance on this practical and answers the practical sheet) are available from the resources tab on Kerboodle, under Activate 1 > Chemistry 1 > C1, 3 Burning fuels.

Resources

Click on the **Resources tab** to access the full list of *Activate* lesson resources.

Fully customizable content to cater all your classes. Resources can be created using the create button.
Existing resources can be uploaded onto the platform using the upload button.
Page navigator shows resources matching to particular pages in the Student Book and Kerboodle Book.
Navigation panel and search bar allow for easy navigation between resources by book, unit, and chapter.
Resources matching every lesson in the Activate series are shown here.

The resource section contains:

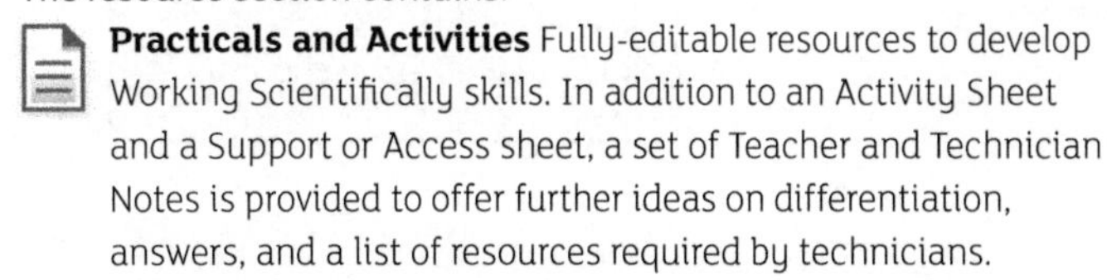

Practicals and Activities Fully-editable resources to develop Working Scientifically skills. In addition to an Activity Sheet and a Support or Access sheet, a set of Teacher and Technician Notes is provided to offer further ideas on differentiation, answers, and a list of resources required by technicians.

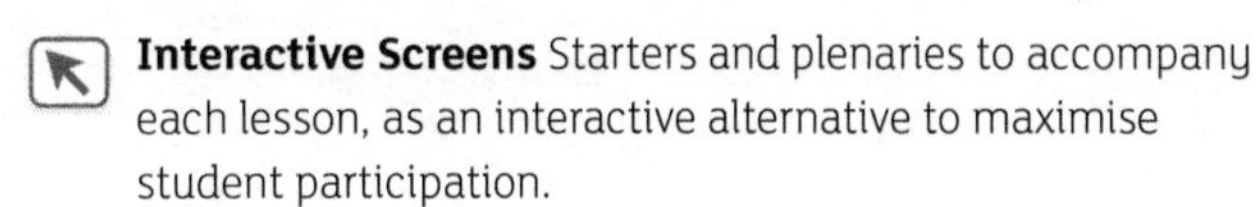

Interactive Screens Starters and plenaries to accompany each lesson, as an interactive alternative to maximise student participation.

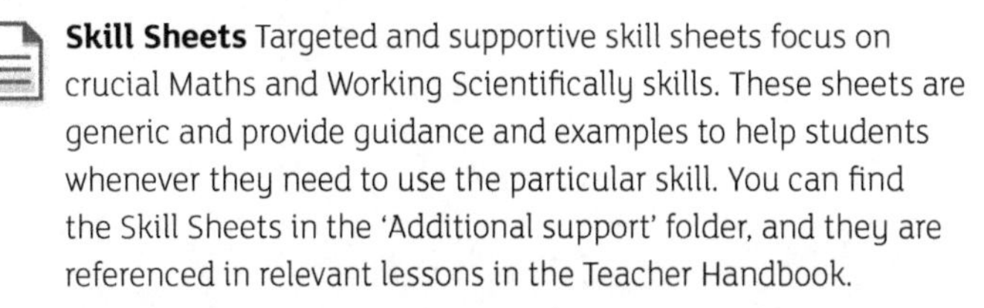

Skill Sheets Targeted and supportive skill sheets focus on crucial Maths and Working Scientifically skills. These sheets are generic and provide guidance and examples to help students whenever they need to use the particular skill. You can find the Skill Sheets in the 'Additional support' folder, and they are referenced in relevant lessons in the Teacher Handbook.

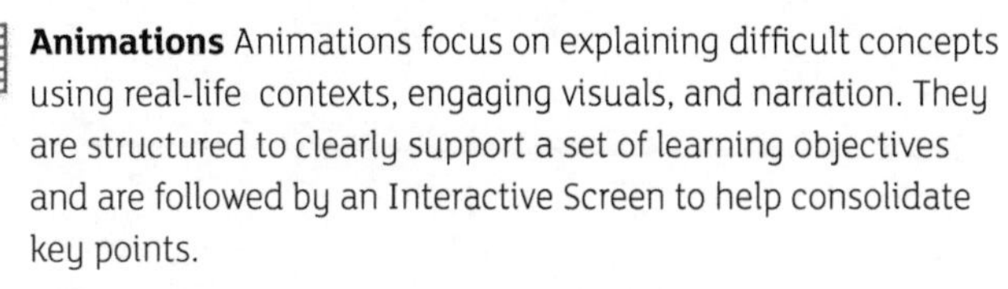

Animations Animations focus on explaining difficult concepts using real-life contexts, engaging visuals, and narration. They are structured to clearly support a set of learning objectives and are followed by an Interactive Screen to help consolidate key points.

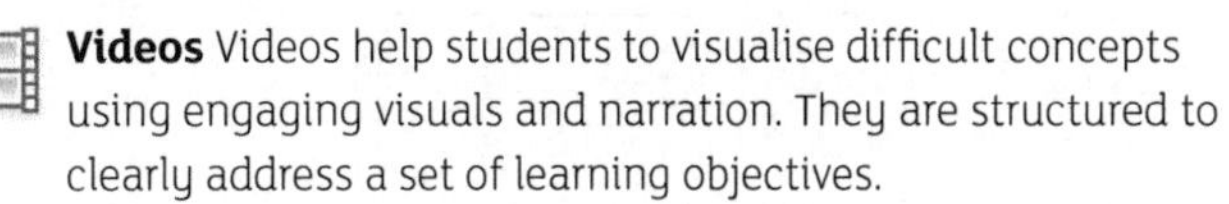

Videos Videos help students to visualise difficult concepts using engaging visuals and narration. They are structured to clearly address a set of learning objectives.

Skills Interactives Automarked interactive activities with formative feedback focus on key Maths, Literacy, and Working Scientifically skills. You can use these activities in class to help consolidate key skills relevant to the lesson. They can also be set as homework by accessing them through the Assessment tab.

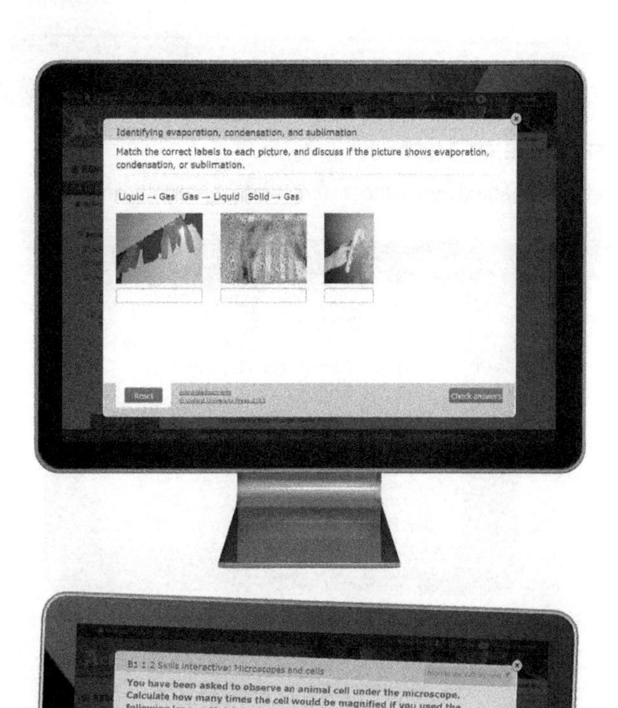

Kerboodle

Assessment and Markbook

All of the Assessment material in Kerboodle has been quality assured by our expert Assessment Editor. Click on the **Assessment tab** to find a wide range of assessment materials to help you deliver a varied, motivating, and effective assessment programme.

It's easy to import class registers and create user accounts for your students. Once your classes are set up, you can assign them assessments to do at home, individually, or as a group.

A **Markbook** with reporting function helps you to keep track of your students' results. This includes both automarked assessments and work that needs to be marked by you.

A Markbook and reporting function help you track your students' progress.

Assign assessments with 'practice' in the title if you want your students to get formative feedback on each answer before having another go.

Assign assessments with 'test' in the title if you want your students to have summative feedback, with only one attempt at each question.

Practice or test?

Each automarked assessment in *Activate* is available in formative or summative versions.

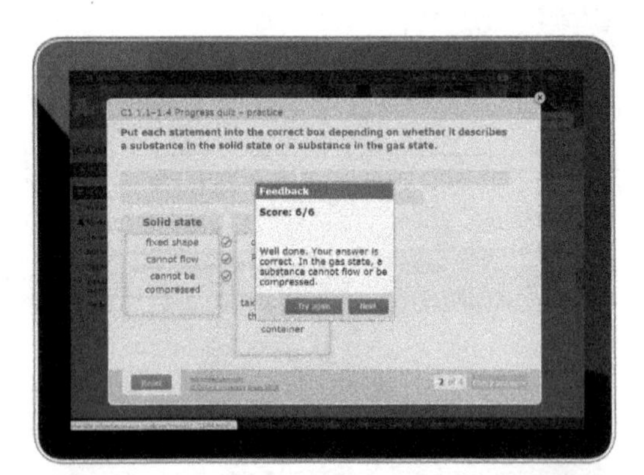

Practice versions of the assessment provide screen-by-screen feedback, focussing on misconceptions, and provide hints for the students to help them revise their answer. Students are given the opportunity to try again. Marks are reported to the Markbook.

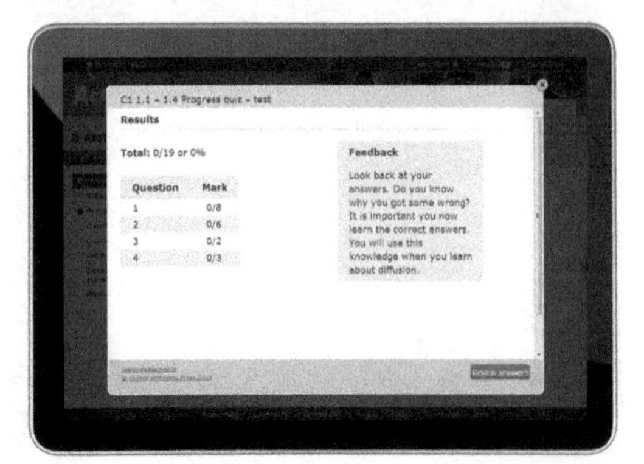

Test versions of the assessment provide feedback on performance at the end of the test. Students are only given one attempt at each screen but can review them and see which answers they got wrong after completing the activity. Marks are reported to the Markbook.

The Assessment section provides ample opportunity for student assessment before, during, and after studying a unit.

Before each unit

Unit Pre-tests These automarked tests revise and assess students' knowledge of Key Stage 2 content. Students are given feedback on their answers to help them correct gaps and misconceptions.

Through each chapter

Progress Quizzes These automarked assessments focus on content midway through a chapter to help you keep track of students as they move through the course.

Skills Interactives These automarked interactives focus specifically on Maths, Literacy, and Working Scientifically skills.

Interactive Investigations These automarked assessments are set in the context of an investigation. Each screen assesses a different Working Scientifically skill.

Progress Tasks These written task-based assessments focus on progress in Maths, Literacy, and Working Scientifically skills. Each task uses a real-life scenario and comes with a progress ladder for students to self- or peer-assess their work.

Checkpoint Assessments These automarked assessments determine whether students have a secure grasp of concepts from the chapter. These assessments are ramped in difficulty and can be followed up by the Checkpoint Lesson revision and extension activities.

End-of-Chapter Tests These paper-based tests mimic examination-style questions, and can be used in conjunction with the End-of-Chapter Summary questions in the Student Book to give a comprehensive offline alternative to end-of-chapter assessments.

After each unit

End-of-Unit Revision Quizzes These automarked assessments are ramped and focus on revising content from the unit. They can be assigned to students as homework revision ahead of formal end-of-unit testing.

End-of-Unit Tests These written assessments mimic examination-style questions. Working Scientifically and quantitative problem-solving questions are available in two tiers. The Foundation paper contains developing and secure questions. The Higher paper has a full range of questions, stretching to extending. You can use the Raw Score Converter to convert scores to levels, bands, or grades.

Big Practical Projects These written assessments focus on Working Scientifically and Literacy skills. Students plan and complete an investigation based on a given scenario. The Foundation paper contains developing and secure questions. The Higher paper has a full range of questions, stretching to extending.

Kerboodle Book

The *Activate* Kerboodle Book provides a digital version of the Student Book for you to use on your students at the front of the classroom.

Teacher access to the Kerboodle Book is automatically available as part of the Lessons, Resources, and Assessment package. You can also purchase additional access for your students.

A set of tools is available with the Kerboodle Book so you can personalize your book and make notes.

Like all other resources offered on Kerboodle, the Kerboodle Book can also be accessed using a range of devices.

Zoom in and spotlight any part of the text

Use different tools such as sticky notes, bookmarks, and pen features to personalize each page

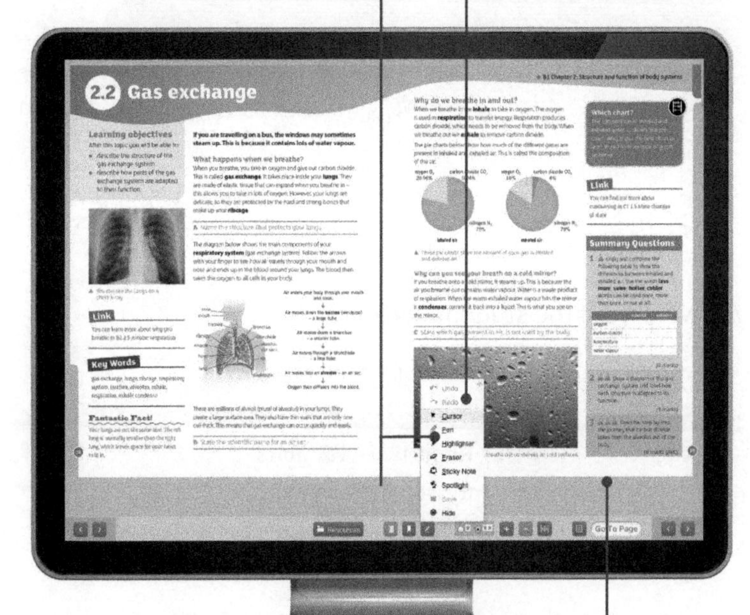

Every teacher and student has their own digital notebook for use within their Kerboodle Book. You can even choose to share some of your notes with your students, or hide the from view – all student notes are accessible to themselves only

Navigate around the book quickly with the contents menu, key word search, or page number search

1.1 Asking scientific questions

Working Scientifically NC link:

- ask questions and develop a line of enquiry based on observations of the real world, alongside prior knowledge and experience
- select, plan, and carry out the most appropriate types of scientific enquiries to test predictions, including identifying independent, dependent, and control variables, where appropriate.

Band	Outcome	Checkpoint	
		Question	**Activity**
Developing	State some questions that can be investigated (Level 4).		Starter 2, Main 1
	Name things that can vary in an investigation (Level 4).		Starter 1, Main 1
	State that some questions cannot be investigated (Level 4).		Starter 2
Secure	Describe how scientists develop an idea into a question that can be investigated (Level 5).	2	Starter 2, Main 1
	Identify independent, dependent, and control variables (Level 5).	A, B	Main 1
	Explain that some questions can be investigated and others cannot (Level 6).	3	Starter 2, Main 1
Extending	Explain why some questions cannot be investigated (Level 7).	3	Main 1
	Suggest examples of independent, dependent, and control variables in an unfamiliar situation (Level 7).		Main 1, Plenary 1
	Explain in detail why a specific question cannot be investigated, suggesting alternative questions that can be investigated (Level 8).		Main 1

Literacy
Use of scientific terms when asking questions.

APP
Students find questions to investigate, and recognise scientific questions that do not yet have definitive answers (AF1).

Students recognise a range of variables from investigations (AF4).

Key Words
observation, investigation, data, variable, independent variable, dependent variable, control variable, prediction

Answers from the student book

In-text questions	**A** independent, dependent **B** control
Activity	**Name those variables** **a** dependent: how high the ball bounces, independent: the size of the ball **b** controls: surface the ball is dropped on, height it is dropped from, type of ball

Summary questions	**1** idea, question, questions, data, observations, variables, some (7 marks) **2a** For example, how does the temperature of the water affect how long it takes the ice cube to melt? (1 mark) **b** It is a question that you can collect data for by measuring the temperature and the time. (2 marks) **3** 6 mark question. Example answers: What is the energy content each food? Because you could measure the energy content to answer it. What is the vitamin content of different foods? Because you could measure the vitamin content to answer it. What type of foods do different animals eat? Because you could watch different animals to answer it. What is the best food? Because it depends on what you mean by best – you cannot collect data. Why do different people like different food? Because you could not collect data to answer it – it is a matter of opinion. Is there enough food to feed everyone in the future? Because you could not collect data to answer it.

Starter	Support/Extension	Resources
What varies? (5–10 min) Students make a list of things that could change in an investigation. The investigation could be one they have done or are planning to do, for example, 'How quickly does a drink cool?'. **Asking questions** (10 min) Students make lists of questions they could ask if they were given something to investigate, for example, 'Melting ice-cream' or 'Floating or sinking'. Pick out examples of questions that can be investigated and examples that cannot.	**Support**: Provide a list of different things connected with an investigation for students to choose from.	
Main	**Support/Extension**	**Resources**
Asking scientific questions (35 min) Introduce the idea that investigations need to answer questions, using examples from the starter. For each example, introduce the independent variable, dependent variable, and control variable. Explain that the type of variable something belongs to depends on the question and how it is asked. Work though the activity sheet and encourage students to share their ideas.	**Support**: A support sheet is available where students focus on the ideas, questions, and variables of two stations, instead of four. Try to decrease the number of technical terms used. For example, teachers can ensure students understand that you can choose the values of some variables, rather than stressing the term independent variable.	**Activity**: Asking scientific questions
Plenary	**Support/Extension**	**Resources**
Identifying variables (5–10 min) Students are given a hypothetical investigation for which they must categorise variables as independent, dependent, and control using the interactive resource. **Grouping variables** (5–10 min) Provide a list of 12 variables and a scientific question. Students identify which variables are independent, dependent, and control.	**Extension**: Students make up their own questions based on variables given.	**Interactive**: Identifying variables
Homework		
Students write down variables linked to things they can investigate in everyday life, for example, boiling a kettle, kicking a football, or getting a seat on the tube.		

1.2 Planning investigations

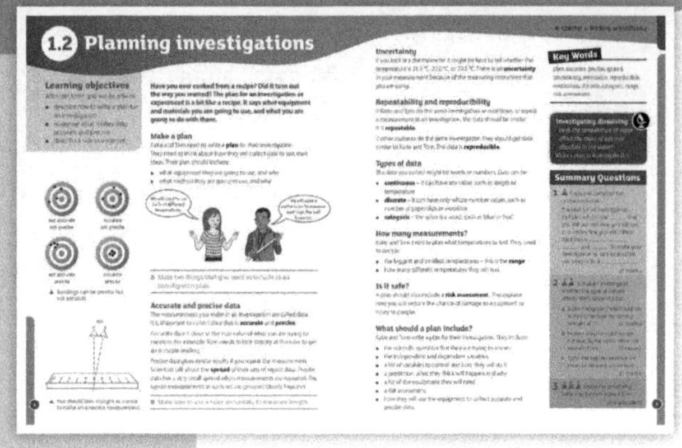
1.2 Planning investigations
Key Words
Summary Questions

Working Scientifically NC link:

- select, plan, and carry out the most appropriate types of scientific enquiries to test predictions, including identifying independent, dependent, and control variables, where appropriate
- use appropriate techniques, apparatus, and materials during fieldwork and laboratory work, paying attention to health and safety.

Band	Outcome	Checkpoint	
		Question	**Activity**
Developing	State what should be included in the plan for an investigation (Level 3).	A, 1	Main 1
	Identify data as accurate or precise (Level 4).		Main 1
	State what is meant by a risk assessment (Level 4).	1	
Secure	Describe how to write a plan for an investigation (Level 5).	1	WS
	Recognise what makes data accurate and precise (Level 6).	2	Main 1
	Describe a risk assessment (Level 5).	C	Main 1
Extending	Write a detailed plan for a hypothetical investigation (Level 7).		WS, Main 1
	Explain the difference between accurate and precise data (Level 7).	3	Main 1
	Identify risks in an experiment and write an appropriate risk assessment for an investigation (Level 7).	C	WS, Main 1

Literacy
Students adopt the appropriate writing style when writing a plan for an investigation; presenting ideas in structured sentences, and in a coherent manner.

APP
Students apply scientific knowledge and understanding in the planning of investigations, identifying significant variables, and recognising which are independent and which are dependent (AF4).

Key Words
plan, accurate, precise, spread, uncertainty, repeatable, reproducible, continuous, discrete, categoric, range, risk assessment

Answers from the student book

In-text questions	**A** What equipment and method you are going to use and why. **B** Align the object for measurement with the zero mark on the ruler. Ensure the ruler is straight. Read the scale on the ruler by looking straight at it.
Activity	**Investigating dissolving** Independent: temperature of the water Dependent: mass of salt that dissolves Control: volume of water, time allowed for salt to dissolve, type of beaker, stirring or not stirring Plan to include: method of changing temperature, method of measuring mass of salt, variables to control, range of temperature, need to repeat measurements, risk assessment

Summary questions	1 equipment, accurate, precise, repeatable, reproducible, risk assessment (6 marks) **2a** To get an accurate reading of the height and avoid parallax error. (2 marks) **b** There is an uncertainty in all measurements that produces a spread of results. (2 marks) **c** All experiments require a risk assessment for safety, for example, to reduce the chance of someone falling because of a rolling ball on the floor. (2 marks) **3** 6 mark question. Example answers: The scientific question that they are trying to answer. The independent and dependent variables. A list of all the variables that they need to control and how they will do it. A prediction: what they think will happen and why. A list of the equipment they will need. A risk assessment. How they will use the equipment to collect precise, accurate, and repeatable data.

Starter	Support/Extension	Resources
Planning (5 min) Remind students of occasions they had to plan, for example, packing their bags for school. Students state what they need to plan, consequences of not planning, and how they can tell their plan was good enough.	**Support**: Help students by asking questions, for example, 'What did you do next?'or 'What happens if you forget to bring something?'.	
Risks (10 min) Students state different risks they took that day, for example, crossing the road or jumping the queue at lunch. Ask them to classify the consequences as minor and severe, and the likelihood as likely or unlikely. Discuss whether a severe but unlikely risk is worth taking.	**Extension**: Students discuss why people are more worried about unfamiliar risks, for example, flying compared with familiar risks, for example, driving.	
Main	**Support/Extension**	**Resources**
Planning investigations (40 min) The activity sheet leads students through structured questions so they come across the main ideas and terminology used when planning. It is important to keep circulating around the groups to ask them why they are carrying out an activity in a certain way. You can help them compare their method or equipment at the time they carry out the activity.	**Support**: The support sheet includes a suggested table of results. The emphasis of the teacher should be to help students understand the ideas rather than worrying about remembering terminology.	**Activity**: Planning investigations **Skill sheet**: Accuracy and precision **Skill sheet**: Recording results
Plenary	**Support/Extension**	**Resources**
Accurate or precise? (10 min) Students are presented with four sets of data on the interactive resource and must decide whether each set of data is accurate, precise, or neither. Students can then suggest why these uncertainties have occurred and suggest ways to improve data collection.		**Interactive**: Accurate or precise?
Planning revisited (5 min) Students look again at their plans and suggest improvements based on what they have covered in the lesson.	**Support**: Demonstrate several ways to collect data, for example, measuring the volume of water using a beaker or a measuring cylinder. Students decide if the data is precise, accurate, or neither.	
Homework		
Students write a plan including a risk assessment for a simple activity, for example, preparing a meal or measuring how quickly a hot drink cools in different containers.		

1.3 Recording data

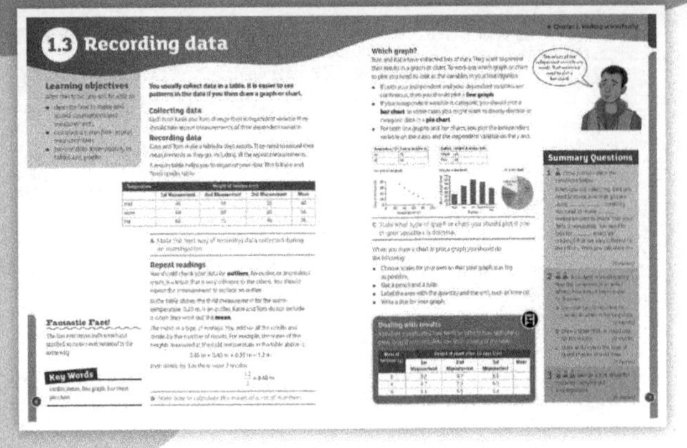
1.3 Recording data

Learning objectives

Collecting data

Recording data

Repeat readings

Fantastic Fact!

Key Words

Which graph?

Dealing with results

Summary Questions

Working Scientifically NC link:

- use appropriate techniques, apparatus, and materials during fieldwork and laboratory work, paying attention to health and safety
- present observations and data using appropriate methods, including tables and graphs.

Band	Outcome	Checkpoint	
		Question	**Activity**
Developing ↓	State an example of how data can be recorded (Level 4).	A	Starter 2
	With help, calculate a mean of two values (Level 4).		Maths, Main 1, Plenary 2
	Add data to a graph or chart (Level 4).		Main 1
Secure ↓	Describe how to make and record observations and measurements (Level 5).	1, 2	Starter 1, Starter 2, Main 1, Plenary 1
	Calculate a mean from three repeat measurements (Level 6).		Maths, Main 1, Plenary 2
	Present data appropriately as tables and graphs (Level 5).		Main 1
Extending ↓	Explain how to collect and record accurate and precise data (Level 7).	3	Main 1, Plenary 1
	Calculate a mean for repeat readings in a range of situations (Level 7).		Maths, Main 1, Plenary 2
	Design an appropriate table or graph (Level 7).		Main 1

Maths
In the student-book activity students calculate arithmetic means based on data given from an experiment.

Literacy
Students are required to summarise what they have learnt in their approach to collecting and presenting data to a range of audiences.

APP
Students choose the best method to obtain precise and accurate data in their experiment (AF4).

Experimental data obtained are presented in the appropriate graph or chart (AF3).

Key Words
outlier, mean, line graph, bar chart, pie chart

Answers from the student book

In-text questions	**A** In a table with clearly labelled headings with units. **B** Add them all together and divide by the number of numbers. **C** bar chart (or sometimes pie chart)
Activity	**Dealing with results** 3.5, 4.85, 5.3

Summary questions	
	1 measuring, instruments, repeat, outliers, mean (5 marks) **2a** repeat his reading, use the thermometer correctly (2 marks) **b** (2 marks)

	Time to dissolve (s)			
Temperature of water (°C)	**1st measurement**	**2nd measurement**	**3rd measurement**	**Mean**

c A line graph, both the variables are continuous. (2 marks)

3 Example answers (6 marks):

The seven elements of a plan from the corresponding student-book spread.

Draw a table for your results.

Include columns for your repeat readings.

Include a column for the mean.

Starter	Support/Extension	Resources
Equipment (5 min) Students describe how to use equipment to collect precise and accurate data. This reinforces the work in the previous lesson, for example, measuring volumes accurately using a measuring cylinder.	**Extension**: Students suggest the advantages of using different equipment, for example, ease of use and precision of reading.	
Using tables (5 min) Draw a table showing results from a mock investigation. Include incomplete headings. Ask students to identify what is missing and why the missing data is important, for example, missing units.	**Support**: Give students missing items to choose from. **Extension**: Give students a context and ask them to draw a results table from scratch.	
Main	**Support/Extension**	**Resources**
Collecting and presenting data (40 min) Remind students of the terminology (independent, dependent, and control variables). It is important at this stage to introduce ways to display data – line graphs for continuous data and bar charts or pie charts if data is discrete or categoric. Students carry out a straight forward experiment dropping different types of ball onto the floor from a vertical height of 1 metre. Students then measure how high the balls bounce. They prepare a suitable table to record the data and draw a graph to display their results.	**Support**: An access sheet is available with simplified questions. Tables and graph grids have also been partially filled in to help students with complex skills. **Extension**: Students can see if they can spot a pattern, attempt a conclusion, and explain why it is important to display data as graphs/charts (to display patterns).	**Practical**: Collecting and presenting data **Skill sheet**: Calculating means **Skill sheet**: Choosing scales **Skill sheet**: Recording results **Skill sheet**: Drawing graphs
Plenary	**Support/Extension**	**Resources**
'Good' data (10 min) Use examples from real-life to discuss issues raised by 'bad' use of data, for example, to compare different medical approaches including alternative medicine. The website www.badscience.net is a rich source of examples of misused data.	**Extension**: Students take a question, for example, 'Should doctors prescribe homeopathic medicine?' to suggest what data is needed to answer this question.	
Calculating means (10 min) Example data sets are provided in the interactive resource for students to calculate arithmetic means, given multiple choice answers.		**Interactive**: Calculating means
Homework		
Students collect data at home, for example, timing how long they take to do certain activities. They record the data in a suitable table for discussion in the next lesson.		

1.4 Analysing data

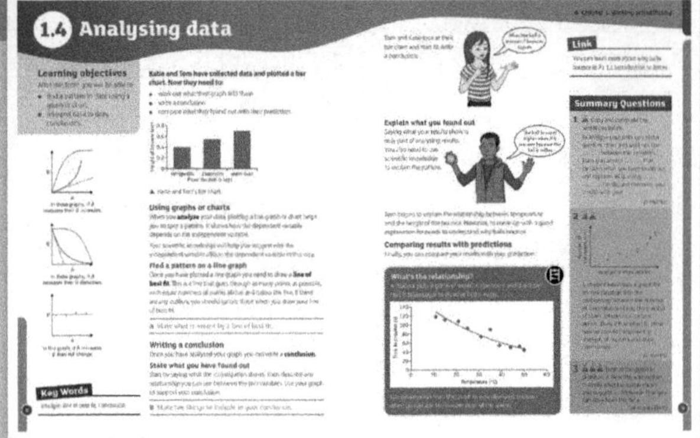

Working Scientifically NC link:

- interpret observations and data, including identifying patterns and using observations, measurements, and data to draw conclusions
- present observations and data using appropriate methods, including tables and graphs.

Band	Outcome	Checkpoint	
		Question	**Activity**
Developing ↓	State what is meant by a line of best fit (Level 4).	A	Plenary 1
	List what should be included in a conclusion (Level 4).	B, 1	Main 1
Secure ↓	Find a pattern in data using a graph or chart (Level 5).	3	WS, Main 1
	Interpret data to draw conclusions (Level 5).	3	WS, Main 1
Extending ↓	Plot data on a graph and draw the line of best fit (Level 7).		Main 1, Plenary 1
	Analyse data from an investigation to draw up a detailed conclusion, giving quantitative examples in data (Level 8).	3	WS, Main 1, Plenary 1

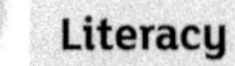

Maths
Students construct and interpret graphs to find a relationship between data.

Literacy
Students select and analyse information, presenting conclusions using scientific terms.

APP
Students interpret data in a variety of formats, spotting inconsistencies such as outliers (AF5).

Identify relationships between variables to draw conclusions (AF5).

Key Words
analyse, line of best fit, scatter plot, scatter graph, correlation, conclusion

Answers from the student book

In-text questions	**A** A line that goes through most of the points and has the same number of points above and below the line. **B** What you have found out, why you think this has happened.
Activity	**What's the relationship?** If you double the temperature of the water, the time it takes to dissolve does not halve, it is more than half.
Summary questions	**1** relationship, conclusion, scientific, knowledge, prediction (5 marks) **2** Draw a line of best fit, find the pattern on the graph, state what you have found out, explain what you have found out. (4 marks) **3** 6 mark question. Example answers: The graph shows the relationship between shark attacks and ice cream sales. There is an outlier when approximately 65 ice creams are sold. The line shows that if there are more ice creams sold there are more shark attacks. If you double the sales of ice creams, the number of shark attacks approximately doubles. Conclusion: There is a correlation between the sales of ice cream and the number of shark attacks. There is no scientific reason to suggest why this is the case. The shark attacks don't depend on ice cream sales. There is a third variable – the temperature. Both ice cream sales and shark attacks increase in the summer.

Starter	Support/Extension	Resources
Is there a relationship? (10 min) Students are presented with a range of statements on the interactive resource, for which they must decide whether the relationship in the statement is likely or unlikely.		**Interactive**: Is there a relationship?
What stages? (10 min) Show students data, for example, from a previous experiment stretching springs. Students will find it hard to state a relationship simply. Ask students to suggest the missing stages needed to analyse data.	**Support**: Provide a list of stages of analysis for students to put in order.	
Main	**Support/Extension**	**Resources**
Analysing data (35 min) Use the activity sheet to plot graphs showing different relationships. Part of this skill is choosing correct scales and drawing the axes. This is a written task, but students could use results from their own experiments. This will increase relevance and engagement for the students. Alternatively, graph axes could be drawn on the floor in chalk and students can demonstrate the shapes of their graphs by walking over the graph area.	**Support**: A support sheet is available where students are given pre-labelled graph grids to plot their data. An alternative source of support is to use the skill sheet for choosing scales instead of the accompanying support sheet. **Extension**: Encourage students to give numerical examples when describing patterns in graphs. Non-linear graphs are discussed in the extension.	**Activity**: Analysing data **Skill sheet**: Choosing scales **Skill sheet**: Drawing graphs
Plenary	**Support/Extension**	**Resources**
Line of best fit (10 min) Draw a graph with data plotted on it. Ask one student to draw a line of best fit. Other students decide if this is good enough or draw an improved line.	**Extension**: Describe the relationship shown by the graph in detail, encouraging students to give quantitative relationships.	
What does the graph show? (10 min) Show different graphs and ask students to suggest suitable variables to go on the axes (e.g., height of student and their age or speed of runner and distance travelled).		
Homework		
Provide students with further data to practise drawing graphs and ask students to describe different relationships.		

1.5 Evaluating data (extending)

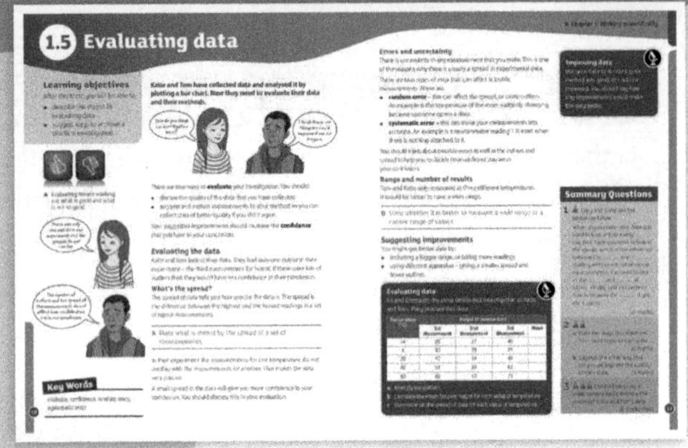

The content of this spread is aimed at extending students.

Working Scientifically NC link:

- evaluate data, showing awareness of potential sources of random and systematic error
- evaluate the reliability of methods and suggest possible improvements.

Band	Outcome	Checkpoint	
		Question	**Activity**
Developing	State how to evaluate data (Level 4).	1	
↓	Suggest one improvement to an investigation (Level 4).	2	Main 1
Secure	Describe the stages in evaluating the data (Level 5).	1	Main 1
↓	Suggest ways of improving a practical investigation (Level 5).	B, 2	Main 1
Extending	Compare and contrast data, suggesting reasons why the data may be different (Level 7).	3	Main 1
↓	Explain ways of improving data in a practical investigation (Level 7).	4	Main 1

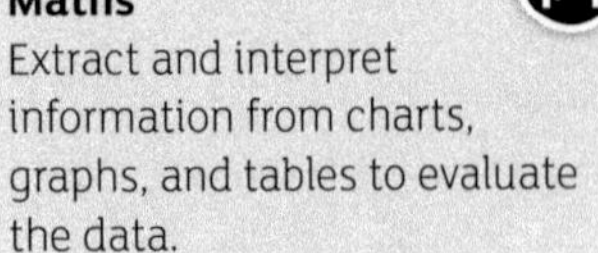

Maths
Extract and interpret information from charts, graphs, and tables to evaluate the data.

Literacy
Students describe stages in evaluating data using scientific terminology and summarise information from scientific methods.

APP
Students evaluate information and evidence from different sources, comparing the two data sets and explaining their limitations (AF3).

Students make valid comments on the quality of data and evaluate working methods, suggesting different ways to improve results (AF5).

Key Words
evaluate, confidence, random error, systematic error, valid

Answers from the student book

In-text questions	**A** The difference between the highest and lowest value of the repeat measurements. **B** wide range
Activity	**How good is that?** **a** 3rd measurement for -4, 2nd measurement for 60 **b** 0.26, 0.27, 0.50, 0.58, 0.68 **c** The spreads overlap for all the readings, the spreads are large.

Summary questions	**1** outliers, highest, lowest, range, number, data (6 marks) **2a** Any two of the following: measure temperature using a thermometer, include a bigger range, take more readings, or use different apparatus to give smaller spread and fewer outliers. **b** Ask other people to do the experiment using their method to see if their results are reproducible. (3 marks) **3** 6 mark question. Example answers: A video camera takes lots of photographs in a short time period. If they put a ruler against the wall while they were bouncing the ball they could measure height. They could pause the video at exactly the point where the ball reached the highest point of the bounce. They could take accurate readings (it is the height of the bounce). Repeat readings would have a much smaller spread that makes the data more precise. High-quality data is more precise than low-quality data.

kerboodle

Starter	Support/Extension	Resources
Do you believe it? (10 min) Provide students with examples of statistics, for example, 9 out of 10 cats prefer a certain brand of cat food. Encourage students to ask questions to judge whether to believe the data or not, for example, who prepared the data or how many cats were tested.		
Improving data (10 min) Students look at data from previous experiments, or on the activity sheet Analysing data. They suggest ways to improve the quality of the data, for example, repeat experiments or measure a bigger range of the independent variable.	**Support**: Provide cloze suggestions for students to complete, for example, take fewer/more results, show data on a graph/in a table, take one/two sets of readings.	
Main	**Support/Extension**	**Resources**
Evaluating data (35 min) Students consider the collected data when they all measure one event, for example, you dropping a ball. Then complete the activity sheet to compare two different experiments and identify differences that make one experiment better than another. Suggest how to evaluate data and the importance of evaluating data carefully.	**Support**: The support sheet offers students a simplified text to summarise when considering differences between two experiments.	**Activity**: Evaluating data
Plenary	**Support/Extension**	**Resources**
What if? (10 min) Students consider problems if data is not evaluated correctly using real-life examples. For example, ask if a cough sweet will really stop students coughing? Students suggest why it is important that we know if medicines really work and what the side effects are.	**Extension**: This is a rich topic for in-depth discussion, for example, do placebos and alternative medicines work? Is global warming really happening? Does following the five-a-day principle really reduce cancer risk?	
Patrick's claim (10 min) In the interactive resource, students decide what scientists would want to know from a list of possible options in order to decide whether to trust a claim made by a fertiliser company.		**Interactive**: Patrick's claim
Homework		
Write a paragraph explaining ways to evaluate food data information correctly or stating reasons why this is important. For example, nutritional content from a food label; horse-meat scandal; why Mars changed their slogan from 'A mars a day helps you work rest and play' to 'Work rest play your part for England'.		

Biology 1

National curriculum links for this unit	
Chapter	**National Curriculum topic**
Chapter 1: Cells	Cells and organisation
Chapter 2: Structure and function of body systems	The skeletal and muscular systems Gas exchange systems
Chapter 3: Reproduction	Reproduction

Preparing for Key Stage 4 success

Knowledge

Underpinning knowledge is covered in this unit for KS4 study of:

- Growth and development of cells
- Transport in cells
- Transport systems in multicellular organisms
- Transport systems in plants
- Reproduction

Maths

Skills developed in this unit (Topic number).

- Understand number size and scale and the quantitative relationship between units (1.1, 2.2, 2.5).
- Understand when and how to use estimation (2.3).
- Use of and calculations with percentages (2.2).
- Plot and draw graphs (line graphs, bar charts, pie charts, scatter graphs, histograms) selecting appropriate scales for the axes (2.2).
- Understand and use common measures and simple compound measures such as speed (2.3, 2.5, 2.7).
- Carry out calculations involving +, −, ×, ÷, either singly or in combination (1.1).

Literacy

Skills developed in this unit (Topic number).

- Identify meaning in scientific text, taking into account potential bias (1.3, 3.5, 3.8, 3.9).
- Summarise a range of information from different sources (3.2, 3.5, 3.9).
- Use of scientific terms and spelling of complex key words are generally correct in discussions and writing (1.2, 1.4, 1.5, 1.6, 2.4, 2.5, 2.7, 3.1, 3.2, 3.3, 3.4, 3.5, 3.6, 3.7, 3.8, 3.9).
- Identify ideas and supporting evidence in text (3.9).
- Taking different roles in discussion and show understanding of ideas and sensitivity to others (2.6, 3.4, 3.5, 3.8).
- Use largely correct form in a range of writing styles and texts and include information relevant to the audience (1.4, 1.5, 1.6, 2.3, 2.5, 2.6, 2.7, 3.1, 3.2, 3.5, 3.6, 3.8, 3.9).
- Sentences and paragraphs are coherent, clear, and well developed. Alternative ways of presenting ideas and information are used appropriately (tables, lists) (1.4, 1.5, 1.6, 2.2, 2.3, 2.4, 2.5, 2.6, 2.7, 3.1, 3.3, 3.5, 3.6, 3.7, 3.8, 3.9).

Assessment Skills

- Quantitative problem solving (1.1, 2.2, 2.5)
- Application of Working Scientifically (1.1, 2.3, 3.7, 3.8) (end-of-chapter 1 Q3, end-of-chapter 2 Q3)

KS2 Link	Check before	Checkpoint	Catch-up
The functions of different parts of flowering plants: roots, stem, leaves, and flowers.	B1 1.3 Specialised cells	Students label a diagram of a flowering plant, including the functions of each part.	Card sort of the main parts of a flowering plant and their functions.
Some animals have skeletons and muscles for support, protection, and movement.	B1 2.4 Skeleton	Discussion on 'Why do humans have skeletons and muscles?'.	List the three functions of skeletons. Ask students to put their hand around their upper arm, and bend the arm at the elbow and describe what they feel happening.
The changes as humans develop from birth to old age.	B1 3.1 Adolescence	Ask students 'What is the difference between a child and an adult?'.	List obvious differences between boys and men, girls and women.
The life cycles of a mammal, an amphibian, an insect, and a bird.	B1 3.1 Adolescence	Name parts of the life cycle of different animals. What do they have in common?	Group stages in the lifecycle into a table. Column headings: mammals only, amphibians only, insects only, birds only, common to all.
The life process of reproduction in some plants and animals.	B1 3.2 Reproductive systems	Pose the question 'Where do babies come from?'.	Spot the difference in biological artwork of men and women. Link back to B1 2.3 Specialised cells for the specialised features of a sperm cell.
The part that flowers play in the life cycle of flowering plants, including pollination, seed formation, and seed dispersal.	B1 3.6 Structure of a flower and pollination	Name the main parts of a flower. What is the flower of a plant for?	Show a picture of a half flower. Identify the parts and what they are needed for.
The requirements of plants for life and growth (air, light, water, nutrients from soil, and room to grow) and how they vary from plant to plant.	B1 3.7 Fertilisation and germination	Discussion on 'What conditions do plants need to grow? Is this different for seeds growing to seedlings?'.	Link back to MRS GREN for all living things.

kerboodle

- B1 Unit pre-test
- B1 Big practical project (foundation)
- B1 Big practical project (higher)
- B1 Big practical project teacher notes
- B1 Practical project hints: writing frame
- B1 Practical project hints: planning
- B1 End-of-unit test (foundation)
- B1 End-of-unit test (foundation) mark scheme
- B1 End-of-unit test (higher)
- B1 End-of-unit test (higher) mark scheme

Answers to Picture Puzzler

Key Words

chin, egg, leaf, leg

The key word is **cell**.

Close Up

an amoeba cell

1.1 Observing cells

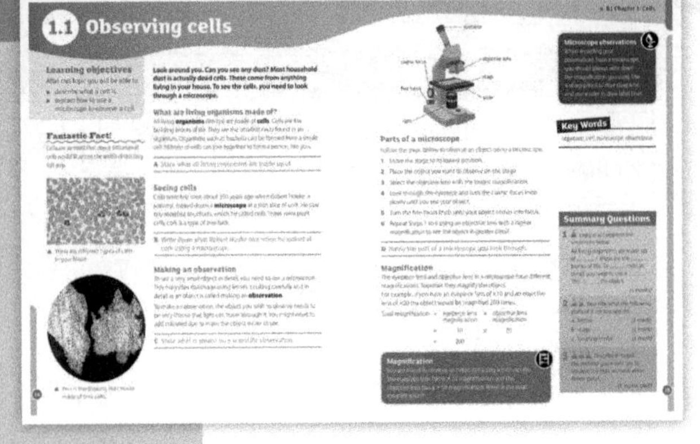

Biology NC link:

- cells as the fundamental unit of living organisms, including how to observe, interpret, and record cell structure using a light microscope.

Working Scientifically NC link:

- use appropriate techniques, apparatus, and materials during fieldwork and laboratory work, paying attention to health and safety.

Band	Outcome	Checkpoint	
		Question	**Activity**
Developing	State what a cell is (Level 3).	A	Starter 1, Starter 2
	Describe how to use a microscope to observe a cell (Level 4).	B, C	Main 1
	Use a microscope to observe a prepared slide, with assistance (Level 4).		Main 1
Secure	Describe what a cell is (Level 5).		Starter 2
	Explain how to use a microscope to observe a cell (Level 5).	2	Main 1
	Use a microscope to observe a prepared slide and state the magnification (Level 6).		Maths, Main 1
Extending	Explain what all living organisms are made of (Level 6).		Starter 1, Starter 2
	Explain what each part of the microscope does and how it is used (Level 6).	3	Main 1
	Use a microscope to observe a prepared slide calculating a range of magnifications (Level 7).		Maths, Main 1

Maths
In the student-book activity, students use multiplication to calculate magnification.

Literacy
In the student-book activity, students organise ideas and information to explain how to use a microscope.

APP
When using the microscope, students will explain why particular pieces of equipment are appropriate for the questions or ideas under investigation (AF4).

Key Words
organisms, cells, microscope, observe

Answers from the student book

In-text questions	**A** cells **B** Cork cells, that looked like tiny rooms. **C** Looking carefully/in detail at an object. **D** eye piece
Activity	**Magnification** $(10 \times 50 =) \times 500$

Summary questions	**1** cells, building, observe, microscope, magnifies (5 marks) **2a** magnifies object (1 mark) **b** holds microscope slide (or object) you are observing (1 mark) **c** produce a clear image of the object (1 mark) **3** 6 mark question. Example answers: Plant and animal cells share several components. They each have a nucleus, cytoplasm, cell membrane, and mitochondria. Plant cells also have a cell wall, chloroplasts, and a vacuole. Both cell types can respire. This is due to the presence of mitochondria in both types of cells. Only plant cells can photosynthesise . This is because only plant cells have chloroplasts.

Starter	Support/Extension	Resources
A scaly problem (5 min) Ask students to draw an insect (or any small organism) on the board. Lead discussion to consider size. If the student makes a small drawing, extract the idea that it is difficult to see so should be drawn bigger. If the student makes a large drawing to start, ask why. Try to extract the idea that increasing the size of the object makes it easier to see. **Magnifying lenses** (5 min) Issue hand lenses and some object, for example, insect wings. Ask students to look at the object. Ask students what has happened and why it has happened. Has the object changed size? What is the advantage of increasing the image size? In both cases, introduce the idea that all living things are made up of cells.	**Support**: Clearly focus on the idea that increasing size helps to see objects. Write key words for of magnification on the board. **Extension**: Consider how much bigger the image is, introduce the idea of quantifying magnification.	
Main	**Support/Extension**	**Resources**
Discovering the microscope (45 min) Issue microscopes to small groups of the class. Provide only basic safety information; do not tell them how it works. Ask the students to use the microscope, and find out how it works. Set a time limit of approximately 5 minutes. Initiate a class discussion to establish what they have found out. Try to extract the basic ideas about the parts, their names, and how to use these parts. Now issue each group with some slides, either pre-made or locust wings and a pair of glass slides. Ask students to use the microscope to observe the details of the object issued. Ask how they were able to see the object. Then issue practical sheets and ask the students to complete the tasks included.	**Support**: The support sheet lists parts of a microscope. Instead of producing a full leaflet, students can instead write a simple statement for each part of the microscope. **Extension**: Students label the sheet alone and produce a detailed leaflet. Lead students to calculate the magnification used during the practical. Encourage students to consider the different levels of magnification.	**Practical**: Discovering the microscope
Plenary	**Support/Extension**	**Resources**
What's in a name? (5 min) Use the interactive resource to check the students' knowledge of the names of the parts of the microscope. **Ordering game** (5 min) Produce a set of cards, each with a statement about how to use a microscope. Deal them out to the class. Each student needs to stand up and read their card when they think it is their turn.	**Extension**: Ask students to explain what each part does. **Support**: Identify the first card player.	**Interactive**: What's in a name?
Homework		
Complete the production of the leaflet. An alternative WebQuest homework activity is also available on Kerboodle where students research the development of the microscope.		**WebQuest**: Development of the microscope

1.2 Plant and animal cells

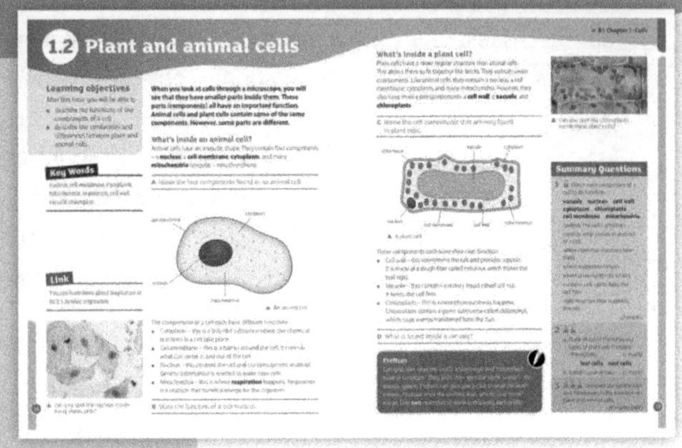

Biology NC link:

- cells as the fundamental unit of living organisms, including how to observe, interpret, and record cell structure using a light microscope
- the functions of the cell wall, cell membrane, cytoplasm, nucleus, vacuole, mitochondria, and chloroplasts.

Working Scientifically NC link:

- use appropriate techniques, apparatus, and materials during fieldwork and laboratory work, paying attention to health and safety.

Band	Outcome	Checkpoint	
		Question	**Activity**
Developing	Identify one similarity and one difference between a plant and an animal cell (Level 4).	A, C, 1	
	Match some components of a cell to their functions (Level 4).	B, C, 1	Starter 1
	With support, prepare and observe a microscope slide safely (Level 4).		Starter 2, Main 1
Secure	Describe the similarities and differences between plant and animal cells (Level 5).	2	
	Describe the functions of the components of a cell (Level 6).	1–3	
	Prepare and observe cells on a microscope slide safely (Level 5).		Starter 2, Main 1
Extending	Explain the similarities and differences between plant and animal cells (Level 7).	3	
	Explain the functions of the components of a cell by linking them to life processes (Level 7).		Starter 1, Plenary 2
	Prepare and observe cells on a microscope slide safely, using scale and magnifications (Level 7).		Starter 2, Main 1, Plenary 1

Maths
In the student-book activity students use multiplication to calculate magnification.

Literacy
Students access information to ascertain meaning, using word skills and comprehension strategies when reading instructions for preparing a slide for a microscope.

APP
When using the microscope, students will explain why particular pieces of equipment are appropriate for the questions or ideas under investigation (AF4).

Key Words
nucleus, cell membrane, cytoplasm, mitochondria, respiration, cell wall, vacuole, chloroplasts

Answers from the student book

In-text questions	**A** nucleus, cell membrane, cytoplasm, mitochondria **B** Controls the cell/contains genetic material. **C** cell wall, chloroplast, vacuole **D** cell sap
Activity	**Prefixes** Bio- = life; biology, biography Photo- = light; photograph, photographer Micro- = small; microscope, microwave

Summary questions	**1** vacuole – contains cell sap to keep the cell firm nucleus – controls the cell's activities cell wall – rigid structure that supports the cell cytoplasm – where chemical reactions take place chloroplast – where photosynthesis occurs cell membrane – controls what comes in and out of a cell mitochondria – where respiration occurs (7 marks) **2a** leaf cells (1 mark) **b** Leaf cells require chlorophyll to be able to photosynthesise. (1 mark) **3** 6 mark question. Example answers: Animal cells and plant cells have a nucleus, cytoplasm, cell membrane, and mitochondria. Plant cells also have a cell wall, chloroplasts, and a vacuole. Both cell types can respire (due to the presence of mitochondria). Only plant cells can photosynthesise (due to the presence of chloroplasts).

kerboodle

Starter	Support/Extension	Resources
Parts of a cell (5 min) Ask students to read the corresponding student-book spread and then use the interactive screen to name the parts of an animal cell.	**Support**: Write a list of the parts of the cell on the board, and leave it on the board throughout the lesson. **Extension**: Ask students to explain the roles of the parts of the cell.	**Interactive**: Parts of a cell
Seeing cells (10 min) Ask students why we can't see cells. Then lead them into explaining how scientists do see cells.		
Main	**Support/Extension**	**Resources**
Making an onion slide (40 min) It is important at this point to formally introduce students to the different parts of plant and animal cells. Issue the practical sheet with instructions explaining how to make an onion slide. Ask students to read the sheet, and then list at least two health and safety risks. Students then make an onion slide and set up the microscope. Students observe their slide through the microscope and produce a labelled diagram of an onion cell.	**Support**: First, demonstrate the making of the slide, then help students to make the slide and set up the microscope if necessary. **Extension**: Ask students to calculate the magnification they are using.	**Practical**: Making an onion slide
Plenary	**Support/Extension**	**Resources**
Another cell (10 min) If time permits make a second slide using Spirogyra. Students observe this and draw another diagram.	**Extension**: Extension work only.	
Missing parts! (5 min) Discuss with the students what they could observe in the onion cell and what they could not see, for example, mitochondria. Why couldn't they see some parts? Why are some parts not present at all in an onion cell? What parts would you not see in the animal cell?	**Support**: Return to the list of words on the board. Start as a check list for drawing diagrams. **Extension**: Target able students with more probing questions.	
Homework		
Ask students to draw a summary table for the different components of both animal and plant cells, including their functions.		

1.3 Specialised cells

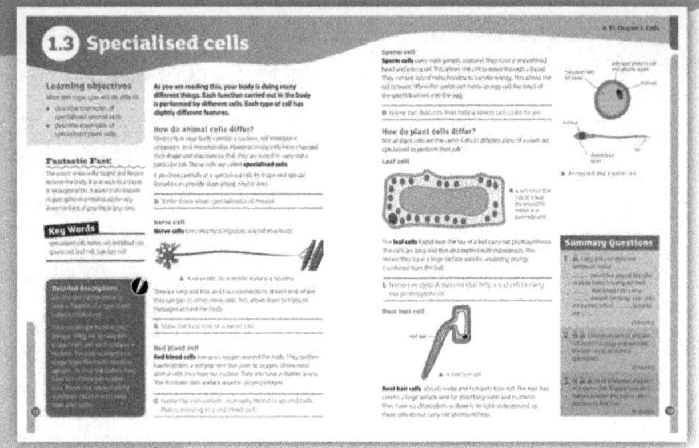

Biology NC link:

- the similarities and differences between plant and animal cells.

Working Scientifically NC link:

- present observations and data using appropriate methods, including tables and graphs.

Band	Outcome	Checkpoint	
		Question	**Activity**
Developing ↓	Name some examples of specialised animal cells (Level 4).	A–D, 1	Starter 1, Starter 2, Main 1, Main 2, Plenary 1
	Name some examples of specialised plant cells (Level 4).	A, E, 1	Starter 1, Starter 2, Main 1, Main 2, Plenary 1
	State specialised features of plant and animal cells, summarising this in a table or as a model (Level 4).	C–E	Main 1, Main 2
Secure ↓	Describe examples of specialised animal cells (Level 6).	2	Starter 1, Starter 2, Main 1, Main 2, Plenary 1
	Describe examples of specialised plant cells (Level 6).	2	Starter 1, Starter 2, Main 1, Main 2, Plenary 1
	Describe specialised features of plant and animal cells, summarising this in a table or as a model (Level 6).		Main 1, Main 2
Extending ↓	Describe examples of specialised animal cells, linking structure and function (Level 7).	2, 3	Starter 1, Starter 2, Main 1, Main 2, Plenary 2
	Describe examples of specialised plant cells, linking structure and function (Level 7).	2, 3	Starter 1, Starter 2, Main 1, Main 2, Plenary 2
	Compare and contrast specialised features of plant and animal cells, summarising this in a table or as a model (Level 7).		Main 1, Main 2

Literacy

Students read a paragraph describing ciliated cells, interpreting the information given to draw a diagram of ciliated cells.

In the activities students need to read information to extract meaning and to talk about their own cells in a presentation.

APP

Students will need to build models of cells to aid a presentation (AF1).

Key Words

specialised cell, nerve cell, red blood cell, sperm cell, leaf cell, root hair cell

Answers from the student book

In-text questions	**A** Cells that can perform particular functions/jobs. **B** Transmit messages/electrical impulses around the body. **C** nucleus **D** streamlined head and tail **E** large surface area; packed with chloroplasts
Activity	**Detailed descriptions** Ciliated cells should appear as rectangular cells with nuclei inside and hairs on top of the rectangles labelled cilia.

Summary questions	1 specialised, function, oxygen, chloroplasts, photosynthesis (5 marks) 2 correct description of specialised features, for example, a red blood cell: no nucleus, disc-like shape. (2 marks) 3 A labelled diagram for a sperm cell is drawn, with the following features: streamlined head – enable it to move through water easily, tail – to 'swim', many mitochondria – for respiration. (6 marks)

kerboodle

Starter	Support/Extension	Resources
An alternative question-led lesson is also available.		**Question-led lesson**: Specialised cells
Mix and match (5 min) Present students with a list of the main parts of plant and animal cells, and a list of the functions. Ask students to match each part to the function. This could be done with playing cards or on the board.	**Support**: Allow students to use the corresponding student-book spread. **Extension**: Ask students to give their own definition of the functions.	
Becoming different (5–10 min) The teacher shows a number of images of specialised cells from the internet. Ask the students to identify special features in these cells not familiar to them from their previous knowledge of cells. They make suggestions about what the parts might be used for.	**Extension**: Spend more time on what the parts are for.	
Main	**Support/Extension**	**Resources**
Either: **Building a cell** (40 min) Students use textbooks (provided by the teacher) to research a specialised cell. Give students a box of scrap material, such as paper, string, packaging, dried pasta, and so on, and ask them to build a model of a specialised cell. Ask students to give a short presentation to the class about their cell, focusing on the special parts and their functions. OR **Speed dating** (40 min) Select up to eight cells. Divide the class into groups of the same number as the number of selected cells. Each student in the group is given time to research about one of the selected cells, either using text books, the Internet, or an information card from the activity sheet Then divide the group in half. Make two concentric circles, each facing the other. Students should be in pairs. Give each pair about three minutes to tell the other about their cell. Then move the outer circle around by one student. Continue until all pairs have been matched.	All students should be issued with the extra activity sheet (blank table) to fill in regardless of the activity chosen. This table will be self-differentiating. **Support**: The teacher controls which cells are researched and built by which student/group. Give more difficult cells to the more able students/groups. **Extension**: Ask probing questions during the presentation and ask students to fill in the final column of the table.	**Activity**: Building a cell **Activity**: Speed dating
Plenary	**Support/Extension**	**Resources**
Matchmaking (5 min) Interactive resource where students link cells to their specialised feature and function.		**Interactive**: Matchmaking
Game of threes (5 min) Students asked to pick three specialised cells. For each, name a special part and give a special function. This could be done on a mini-whiteboard.		
Homework		
Draw and label a specialised cell. Label as many specialised parts as possible and describe the functions.		

1.4 Movement of substances

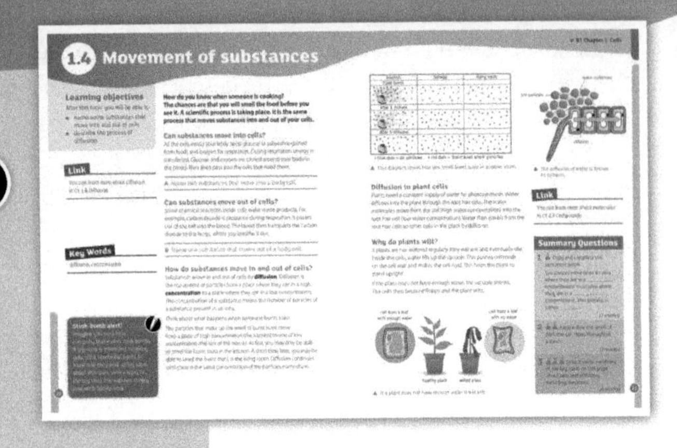
1.4 Movement of substances

Biology NC link:

- the role of diffusion in the movement of materials in and between cells.

Physics NC link:

- diffusion in liquids and gases driven by differences in concentration.

Working Scientifically NC link:

- make and record observations and measurements using a range of methods for different investigations.

Band	Outcome	Checkpoint	
		Question	**Activity**
Developing	Identify substances that move into or out of cells (Level 4).	A, B	
	State simply what diffusion is (Level 4).	1	Plenary 2
	Make sets of observations or measurements of diffusion of coloured gel, identifying the ranges and intervals used (Level 4).		Main 1, Plenary 1
Secure	Name some substances that move into and out of cells (Level 5).	A, B	
	Describe the process of diffusion (Level 6).		Plenary 2
	Collect data of diffusion of coloured gel, choosing appropriate ranges, numbers, and values for measurements and observations (Level 6).		Main 1, Plenary 1
Extending	Explain which substances move into and out of cells (Level 7).	A, B, 3	
	Explain the process of diffusion (Level 7).	3	Plenary 2
	Choose and justify data collection methods of diffusion of coloured gel that minimise error, and produce precise and reliable data (Level 8).		Main 1, Plenary 1

Maths

During the practical students will be required to measure times and volumes.

Literacy

Students use their understanding of the concept of diffusion to write a letter explaining this phenomenon to toy shop owners in the literacy task, relating this in the context of stink bombs.

During the practical students need to read the method for information on how to complete the experiment. They will discuss their results with others in the group, and listen to the ideas of others, for explanations of their findings.

APP

Students will use an abstract model to explain the ideas involved (AF1).

The students will need to supply explanations of their findings, using appropriate scientific language (AF3).

They will be asked to select equipment and make appropriate use of the equipment (AF4).

Key Words

diffusion, concentration

Answers from the student book

In-text questions	**A** food particles/glucose and oxygen **B** carbon dioxide
Activity	**Stink-bomb alert!** In diffusion, particles travel from an area of high concentration to an area of low concentration. Initially, the smell from the stink bomb is only found in the immediate vicinity but eventually, the smell will spread until the concentration of stink bomb particles becomes constant.
Summary questions	**1** high, low, diffusion (3 marks) **2** The smell diffuses from an area of high concentration to one of low concentration. (3 marks) **3** Example answers (6 marks): water in the plant is used for photosynthesis, vacuole becomes less full, less pressure on the cell wall, cell becomes floppy, therefore the plant wilts. Credit correct use of diagrams.

Starter	Support/Extension	Resources
Wanted or not (5 min) Interactive resource with a list of molecules students need to decide whether or not the cell needs. **Observation skills** (5 min) Pose two questions: 'What is the difference between an observation and a measurement?' and 'When making observations, how would you plan to make observations during an experiment?'. Give students some time to consider these questions then explore their answers. Try to lead the observations answer to a series of observations during the course of the experiment.	**Support**: Change second question to two options, 'observe at the end only' or 'observe at intervals'. **Extension**: Ask students why a series of observations would be more useful.	**Interactive**: Wanted or not
Main	**Support/Extension**	**Resources**
Observing diffusion (40 min) Give the students the practical sheet with a method. They will need to put a cube of coloured gel into water and make observations at times intervals. Do not lead students to expect any particular outcome. Group discussion of their observations. Students need to consider questions in the practical sheet to produce some explanation of the movement of molecules. Then link this to diffusion into and out of cells. For the conclusion, it is important to go through with students the definition of diffusion and what substances diffuse into and out of our cells.	**Support**: The support sheet contains a results table for students to use. Help students write in their observations by modelling good practice. **Extension**: Encourage students to explain the idea of diffusion and lead their group during the experiment. They might be able to discuss limitations with the technique or model.	**Practical**: Observing diffusion **Skill sheet**: Recording results
Plenary	**Support/Extension**	**Resources**
Class feedback (10 min) Groups feedback their ideas about what they have seen in the experiment. Notes on 'What is diffusion' written in their books. **Role play** (10 min) Arrange the chairs in a large circle around the room with gaps to represent the cell membrane. Ask all of the students to stand outside the membrane and tell them they represent oxygen. Then ask them to diffuse into the cell. They need to become evenly spread. If they don't, ask them why they have gone wrong.	**Support**: Ask weaker students to describe the observations. **Extension**: Encourage students to explain why this might have happened.	
Homework		
Ask students to produce a drawing of a red blood cell. Ask them to explain how oxygen would get into the cell. They can use a mix of labels or written prose, perhaps depending on ability.		

1.5 Unicellular organisms

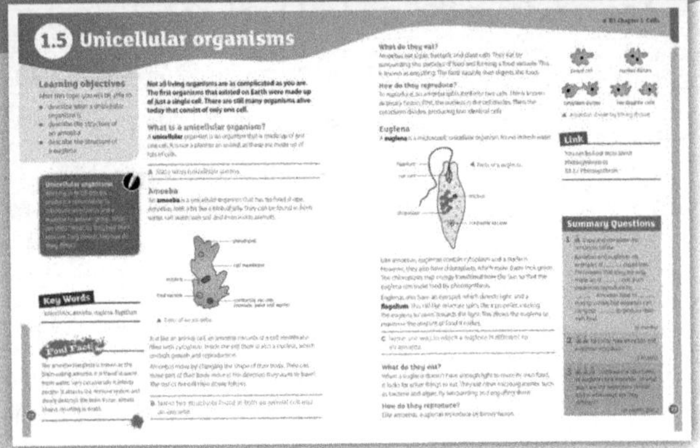

Biology NC link:

- the structural adaptations of some unicellular organisms.

Working Scientifically NC link:

- use appropriate techniques, apparatus, and materials during fieldwork and laboratory work, paying attention to health and safety.

Band	Outcome	Checkpoint	
		Question	**Activity**
Developing	Name an example of a unicellular organism (Level 4).	1	Starter 1, Starter 2
	Identify some structures in an amoeba (Level 4).	B, C	Starter 1, Starter 2, Plenary 2
	Identify some structures in a euglena (Level 4).	C	Starter 1, Starter 2, Plenary 2
	Select the appropriate apparatus to observe an amoeba and a euglena cell (Level 4).		Main 1
Secure	Describe what a unicellular organism is (Level 5).		Starter 1, Starter 2
	Describe the structure of an amoeba (Level 6).		Starter 1, Starter 2
	Describe the structure of a euglena (Level 6).		Starter 1, Starter 2
	Select the appropriate magnification to observe an amoeba and a euglena cell through a microscope (Level 6).		Main 1
Extending	Explain what a unicellular organism is and give detailed examples (Level 7).	3	Starter 1, Starter 2, Plenary 2
	Describe the structure and function of an amoeba (Level 7).	3	Starter 1, Starter 2, Plenary 2
	Describe the structure and function of a euglena (Level 7).	3	Starter 1, Starter 2, Plenary 2
	Give justifications for the choice of magnification when observing an amoeba and a euglena cell through a microscope (Level 7).		Main 1

Maths
Students use multiplication to calculate magnification.

Literacy
Students produce a presentation to introduce amoeba and euglena, in order to discuss and show their understanding to others.

For homework, students are asked to write a summary of the differences between multicellular and unicellular organisms.

APP
Students will select and use appropriate equipment during the practical (AF4).

Key Words
unicellular, amoeba, euglena, flagellum

Answers from the student book

In-text questions	**A** Organism made up of only one cell. **B** Any two from: cytoplasm, nucleus, cell membrane. **C** Any from: euglena carries out photosynthesis/has chloroplasts/has an eye spot/has a flagellum.
Activity	**Unicellular organisms** Some of the following points should be included: both unicellular organisms; amoeba looks jelly-like with no fixed structure; euglena are green with a tail-like structure.

Summary questions	1 unicellular, one, binary, fission, engulf, photosynthesis (6 marks) 2 Nucleus in the parent cell divides, cytoplasm divides, two (daughter cells) produced. (3 marks) 3 6 mark question. Example answers: Both unicellular, have a nucleus/cytoplasm, get rid of waste by excretory vesicles, only euglena can photosynthesise, both can move, euglena by flagellum, amoeba by pseudopods, both cells can engulf food.

Starter	Support/Extension	Resources
Going it alone (5 min) Pose the questions 'Name some really small organisms which live in our environment'. Try to avoid bacteria but guide students to small animals and plants. Then challenge their ideas by showing a film from the internet of single-celled organisms such as amoeba. **How to go it alone** (5 min) Having shown a film of an amoeba, start a discussion about all the things that a cell has to do to survive. Ask students to consider any special parts a cell might need to carry out these tasks.	**Support**: Remind students about characteristics of life (MRS GREN) **Extension**: Ask students how these organisms carry out their life functions. In addition, find a second film of a more specialised organism, for example, paramaecium, and discuss the more special features.	
Main	**Support/Extension**	**Resources**
Observing amoeba and euglena (40 min) Formally introduce the idea of unicellular organisms and issue the practical sheet. Students should use the method on the practical sheet to make temporary slides with amoeba and with euglena. Students then observe the organisms using the microscope. If available, use a projection microscope as well so that students know what to look for. Students should draw labelled diagrams of the two cell types. Note: euglena in particular will be small and may be difficult to observe, so have images of these cell types to project for the students to observe and draw.	**Support**: Avoid euglena in fresh preparations and have projection images prepared. Students will need more help with the microscopes. Students may only observe the amoeba as it is larger and slower moving therefore easier to see. The use of film clips or images may be used for the drawings rather than actual specimens but use real specimens so that students do see the real organism. **Extension**: Encourage more independent work. Students could also produce a series of diagrams to show amoeba moving.	**Practical**: Observing amoeba and euglena
Plenary	**Support/Extension**	**Resources**
Spot the difference (10 min) Use the interactive screen to look at a selection of different features found in cells. Students identify the common features of all cells, and the unique features of unicellular organisms. **Create a cell (5 min)** Ask students to design an imaginary cell which would live in water. Ask them to draw features onto the cell to help it carry out as many of the special functions as possible.	**Support**: Focus on the common features of cells. **Extension**: Try to discuss what the special features are used for. **Support**: List the life processes on the board, and discuss how cells might carry these processes out. **Extension**: Look up single celled organisms in a higher level text book to incorporate real structures in their drawings.	**Interactive**: Spot the difference
Homework		
Ask students to produce a written description of the cells that they have observed. Pay particular attention to how the cells are different to those studied in earlier lessons.		

B1 Chapter 1 Checkpoint

Checkpoint lesson routes

The route through this lesson can be determined using the Checkpoint assessment.

Percentage pass marks are supplied in the Checkpoint teacher notes.

Route A (support)
Resource: B1 Chapter 1 Checkpoint: Revision

Students can work through the revision activity supported by the rest of the group and by the teacher. There is a focus on descriptions, using the correct vocabulary, and including enough information. Students can keep the revision activity as a summary sheet and use it for end-of-term/year revision.

Route B (extension)
Resource: B1 Chapter 1 Checkpoint: Extension

Students will link ideas from across the chapter in this extension activity, based around the question 'Why are cells so small?'

Information is provided as an introduction to surface area to volume ratio. Students need to use their literacy and maths skills to work through the sheet, and should work together to support each other.

Progression to *secure*

No.	Developing	Secure	Making progress
1	Describe how to use a microscope to observe a cell.	Explain how to use a microscope to observe a cell.	Get out a microscope and a specimen slide and ask the group to explain to you how to use it. For each step, push the group for additional detail so that they understand the difference between a description and an explanation. Students can form their explanations using guidance in Task 1.
2	State what a cell is.	Describe what a cell is.	Students will often not provide enough information when asked for a description. In Task 2 they need to consider all of the important information they know about cells. This task is about identification of the key information, and then writing and improving a description.
3	Match some components of a cell to their functions.	Describe the functions of the components of a cell.	Each student is given the name of a cell component. They describe its function to the rest of the group, and the group need to guess what component it is. This leads into a full description of each component which can be written up in Task 3.
4	Identify one similarity and one difference between a plant and animal cell.	Describe the similarities and differences between plant and animal cells.	Discuss with students the similarities and differences in the needs of each cell (information for this is also provided). Students can use their descriptions from Task 3 to sort into 'plant cells' and 'plant/animal cells' and then write a full description.
5	Name some examples of specialised animal cells and plant cells.	Describe examples of specialised animal cells and plant cells.	Diagrams of specialised cells (and non-specialised cells for comparison) plus a structure for a description are given in Task 4. Discuss with students the key requirements of each 'job' (e.g., carrying oxygen).
6	State simply what diffusion is.	Describe the process of diffusion.	Students may not have grasped the concept of diffusion, or may not have the correct vocabulary to describe it. You can use the analogy of people moving down a train carriage. In Task 5 students can draw a diffusion diagram, and then write a full description using the key words.
7	Name an example of a unicellular organism.	Describe what a unicellular organism is.	Students may struggle understanding the difference between a unicellular organism and single cells they have seen and drawn. Emphasise that cells are usually just a unit of an organism (referring back to Task 2), and that unicellular organisms are alive with just one cell. Encourage students to look to the word for clues (uni = one).
8	Identify some structures in amoeba and euglena.	Describe the structure of amoeba and euglena.	Students may get these two organisms confused. You can show a photo of a euglena and ask students about the colour. They are green so they must contain chloroplasts. Students should draw the two organisms in Task 7.

Answers to end-of-chapter questions

1 B (A cell is the smallest unit of an organism.) (1 mark)

2a nucleus (1 mark)

b trap light/photosynthesis (1 mark)

c W (vacuole) (1 mark)

d Two from: nucleus, cytoplasm, cell membrane.

3a microscope (1 mark)

b add stain/dye/coloured liquid (1 mark)

c It could transmit a disease or cause an infection as blood is removed. (1 mark)

d Diagram should show a cell containing a nucleus, cytoplasm, and cell membrane. (3 marks)

4a A cell whose structure is adapted to suit its function. (1 mark)

b red blood cell (1 mark), transport oxygen (1 mark)
transmits messages (1 mark)
carry out photosynthesis (1 mark), packed with chloroplasts (1 mark)

c Water moves into the root hair cell by diffusion/osmosis.
It moves from an area of high water concentration to an area of low water concentration, through a cell membrane. (3 marks)

5a No, it is unicellular/consists of one cell only. Plants are multicellular organisms. (2 marks)

b Any similarity from: nucleus; cell membrane; cytoplasm. (1 mark)
Any difference from: chloroplasts; eye spot; flagellum only present in euglena. (1 mark)

c The eye spot detects light. The flagella cause euglena to move towards the light.
It has lots of chloroplasts to trap light for photosynthesis. (3 marks)

6 Students should be marked on the use of good English, organisation of information, spelling and grammar, and correct use of specialist scientific terms. The best answers will be organised in a logical sequence, with detail of how to use the microscope (maximum of 6 marks).
Examples of correct scientific points:
State source of cells (onion skin and animal source, e.g., skin cell).
Indication that the sample needs to be very thin.
Reference to use of stain/dye.
Reference to use of a microscope.
Use of lowest level of magnification first.
Focus by turning fine/coarse focus knob.
Any other relevant microscope detail.
Draw a labelled diagram of the structures you observe.
Indicate the magnification used on the diagram drawn.

Answer guide for Big Write

Developing	Secure	Extending
1–2 marks	3–4 marks	5–6 marks
• The article is not presented in a logical way, and little attention has been paid to the rules of this text type. • The student has stated at least one difference and one similarity between an amoeba and a human.	• The article is clearly presented. • The student has described at least two similarities and two differences in the structure and function of an amoeba and a human.	• The article is clearly presented and engaging, paying attention to the rules of this text type. • The student has clearly explained a number of similarities and differences in the structure and functions of an amoeba and a human.

kerboodle

B1 Chapter 1 Checkpoint assessment (automarked)
B1 Chapter 1 Checkpoint: Revision
B1 Chapter 1 Checkpoint: Extension
B1 Chapter 1 Progress task (Maths)

2.1 Levels of organisation

Biology NC link:

- the hierarchical organisation of multicellular organisms: from cells to tissues to organs to systems to organisms.

Working Scientifically NC link:

- interpret observations and data, including identifying patterns and using observations, measurements, and data to draw conclusions.

2.1 Levels of organisation

Learning objectives

Link

Fantastic Fact!

Do the trees outside look like a euglena? No, not really! As well as being much larger, they are much more complicated. They consist of many cells working together to form a multicellular organism.

What are multicellular organisms?

What is a tissue?

What is an organ?

What is an organ system?

Key Words

Summary Questions

Band	Outcome	Checkpoint	
		Question	**Activity**
Developing	State what is meant by a tissue, an organ, and an organ system (Level 4).	1	Main 1
	State the sequence of the hierarchy of organisation in a multicellular organism (Level 4).	1	Lit, Starter 2, Main 1
	Use information provided to list the organs found in a given organ system, and state the function of that system (Level 4).	2, 3	Main 1, Main 2
Secure	Define and state examples of tissues, organs, and organ systems (Level 5).	B–D, 1–3	Main 1, Plenary 1
	Explain the hierarchy of organisation in a multicellular organism (Level 5).	3	Lit, Main 1
	Interpret information provided to decide on the function of the individual organs and of the organ system (Level 5).		Main 1, Main 2
Extending	Explain in detail the hierarchy of organisation in a multicellular organism, using a range of examples (Level 7).	2	Main 1, Plenary 2
	Explain how the different tissues in an organ and the different organs in an organ system function together (Level 7).	3	Main 1, Main 2
	Interpret information to explain the functions of several organ systems (Level 6).		Main 1, Main 2

Literacy
The student-book activity asks students to apply the information they have learned about hierarchy to new information given.

APP
Students use appropriate communication skills to present scientific information when explaining the hierarchy of systems in multicellular organisms (AF3).

Key Words
multicellular organism, tissue, organ, organ system

Answers from the student book

In-text questions	**A** cell **B** for example, nervous tissue **C** for example, skin **D** for example, circulatory system
Activity	**Organise this** nerve cell, nervous tissue, brain, nervous system, chimpanzee

Summary questions	1 cell – building blocks of life; tissue – group of similar cells working together; organ – group of tissues working together; organ system – group of organs working together; organism – group of organ systems working together (5 marks) 2 For example, the digestive system is made up of the following organs: (pancreas,) stomach, liver, small intestine, large intestine. (2 marks) 3 One mark for correctly ordering the levels of organisation; one mark for each correctly linked example. For example, nerve cell (cell) → nerve tissue (tissue) → brain (organ) → nervous system (organ system) → human (multicellular organism) (6 marks)

kerboodle

Starter	Support/Extension	Resources
Working together (5–10 min) Present students (either in a group or as a class demo) with the disassembled parts of plastic building blocks, which will build into a specific object, for example, a car. Ask them to build the object. Have a discussion in which the idea is that the individual bricks work together to make the whole object work. Each block might have its own function.	**Extension**: Ask more probing questions in the discussion. Ask the students to make connections between this idea and a large plant or animal body.	
Building an organism (5 min) Present students with a picture of a cell, tissue, organ, organ system, and an organism. Ask them to put the pictures into an order and to explain their decision. Ideally use images from a related organ system sequence. In a short discussion, focus in on groups which have selected a hierarchical structure.	**Support**: Students work in groups. The images used could be more basic. **Extension**: Students explain their reasoning in detail.	
Main	**Support/Extension**	**Resources**
Organising a body (20 min) Begin by introducing the parts of the digestive system so that students can label the system on their activity sheet. Students then read through the information sheet, describing specialised cells, levels of organisation, and organ systems. Students extract information in order to answer the questions on the accompanying activity sheet.	**Support**: An access sheet is available, which includes simplified text and questions of lower demand.	**Activity**: Organising a body
Research and presentation (20 min) Provide students with a variety of text books from a range of levels, or use the Internet if available. Divide the class into groups and give them time to research the organs and functions of a different organ system. They can use the film as a model. Students should write brief notes in their books. Each group then gives a presentation about their organ system.	**Support**: Organise students into groups so that some students can lead the task. Differentiate according to the quality of the texts available. **Extension**: Students should explain the role of each organ in the system in detail.	
Plenary	**Support/Extension**	**Resources**
Cells, tissues, or organs? (5 min) Using the interactive resource, students reorganise a list of words according to the categories cells, tissues, and organs.	**Support**: Students can discuss answers in pairs before going through answers on the board.	**Interactive**: Cells, tissues, or organs?
Which system am I? (5 min) Produce a series of paper slips, each containing the name of one organ (plant or animal). Students must then find other students in the class with organs from the same organ system. They group together and name their system.		
Homework		
Ask students to create a table. The first column should have the seven life functions that students have encountered at KS2 (MRS GREN). In the second column, ask students to explain how this function is carried out in the human body, linking this to as many organs and organ systems as possible.		

2.2 Gas exchange

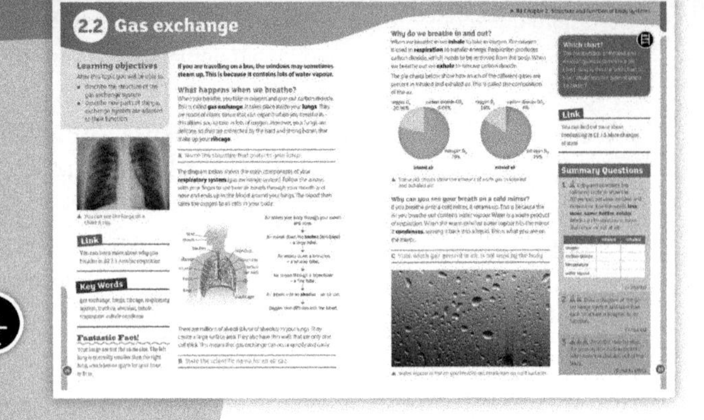

Biology NC link:

- the structure and functions of the gas exchange system in humans, including adaptations to function.

Working Scientifically NC link:

- interpret observations and data, including identifying patterns and using observations, measurements, and data to draw conclusions.

Band	Outcome	Checkpoint	
		Question	**Activity**
Developing	Name the parts of the gas exchange system (Level 4).	A, B, 2	Main
	State that the parts of the gas exchange system are adapted to their function (Level 3).	2	
	State that the composition of the air inhaled and exhaled are different using data provided (Level 4).	1	Main
Secure	Describe the structure of the gas exchange system (Level 4).	2, 3	Main
	Describe how the parts of the gas exchange system are adapted to their function (Level 5).	2	Plenary 1
	Interpret data given to compare the difference in the composition of inhaled and exhaled air (Level 5).		Main
Extending	Describe the gas exchange system as an organ system, linking the organs (Level 6).	2, 3	Plenary 1
	Explain how the adaptations of the parts of the gas exchange system help them perform their function (Level 7).	2	Plenary 1
	Interpret data given to explain the difference in the composition of inhaled and exhaled air (Level 7).		Main

Maths
Students draw an appropriate graph to display data provided, showing an understanding of number size and scale (for percentages).

Students analyse data provided interpreting graphs to draw valid conclusions for the composition of inhaled and exhaled air.

Student also consider appropriate graphs in the student-book activity.

Literacy
Students summarise key points relating to inhaled and exhaled air when presenting ideas for a novel submarine as part of their homework.

APP
Students choose the most appropriate graph to display data given (AF3).

Students use data provided to draw conclusions (AF5).

Key Words
gas exchange, lungs, ribcage, respiratory system, trachea, alveolus, inhale, respiration, exhale, condense

Answers from the student book

In-text questions	**A** ribcage **B** alveolus (plural alveoli) **C** nitrogen
Activity	**Which chart?** A pie chart makes the difference between inhaled and exhaled air clear. Bar chart could also be used.

Summary questions	**1** One mark for each correct row (4 marks).

	Inhaled	**Exhaled**
oxygen	more	less
carbon dioxide	less	more
temperature	colder	hotter
water vapour	less	more

2 Credit correctly labelled diagrams with adaptations of each part. (3 marks)

3 6 mark question. Example answers:

Carbon dioxide moves/diffuses out of the blood; moves/diffuses into an air sac (alveolus); moves through a bronchiole; moves through a bronchus; moves up the windpipe (trachea); and leaves your body (is exhaled) through your mouth/nose.

Starter	Support/Extension	Resources
The breathing system (5 min) Lead a discussion of 'What does our breathing system consist of?'. Use this opportunity to gauge the preconceptions of students.		
Comparing the air (10 min) Demonstrate the bubbling of air through a test tube of limewater. Ask students to carry out the same practical by blowing gently into a second test tube of limewater, using clean straws. Students should notice the difference between the two test tubes. Lead the discussion to what the mystery substance that causes this difference may be (CO_2 from exhaled air) and the use of limewater as a test for CO_2.	**Support**: Focus on the observations so that students see something is different between the air around us and exhaled air	

Main	Support/Extension	Resources
The composition of inhaled and exhaled air (40 min) Introduce the structure of the gas exchange system, highlighting key words for the different parts of the system. Issue students with the activity sheet. This activity requires students to label a diagram of the gas exchange system, draw a bar chart using data provided, and analyse results given to draw a valid conclusion.	**Support**: A support sheet is available with a list of key words to label the diagram and a pre-labelled graph grid for drawing the bar chart	**Activity**: The composition of inhaled and exhaled air **Skill sheet**: Drawing graphs **Skill sheet:** Choosing scales

Plenary	Support/Extension	Resources
Before or after (10 min) This game is based on the game 'Higher or lower'. Prepare a set of cards with each part of the gas exchange system written on different cards. Shuffle the cards and reveal the first and second card. Leave the rest of the cards face down. Ask the students where the second card comes in relation to the first based on the path of O_2 during gas exchange. For example, a first card of bronchus and a second card of trachea would give the answer 'before': O_2 reaches the trachea before the bronchus. Continue for all the cards available. Repeat the game for the path CO_2 gas takes.	**Support**: Students may wish to work as a team. **Extension**: Students should be able to justify their answers, explaining how different parts of the system work together and how the different parts are adapted to their function.	
The air we breathe (5 min) Interactive resource where students complete a paragraph on the composition of inhaled and exhaled air.		**Interactive**: The air we breathe

Homework		
Introduce the *Octonauts* as fictional characters who live in a submarine. Students design a submarine to maintain a constant level of O_2 and CO_2 (their gas exchange system works in the same way as ours). You can have O_2 tanks, CO_2 filters, and monitors as necessary.		

2.3 Breathing

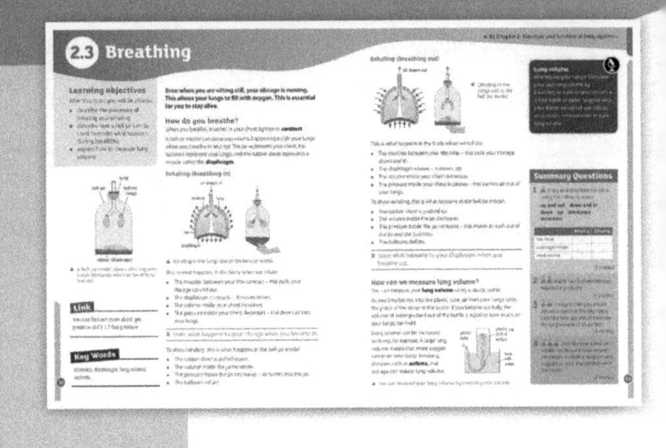

Biology NC link:

- the mechanism of breathing to move air in and out of the lungs, using a pressure model to explain the movement of gases, including simple measurements of lung volume
- the impact of exercise, asthma, and smoking on the human gas exchange system.

Working Scientifically NC link:

- use appropriate techniques, apparatus, and materials during fieldwork and laboratory work, paying attention to health and safety.

Band	Outcome	Checkpoint	
		Question	Activity
Developing	State what happens to the ribcage and diaphragm during inhaling and exhaling (Level 4).	A, B, 1	Starter 2
	State what each part of the bell jar model represents (Level 4).	3	Main
	State a value of lung volume (Level 4).		WS, Main
	Use apparatus provided to obtain a lung volume (Level 4).		Main
Secure	Describe the processes of inhaling and exhaling (Level 5).	A, B, 1	
	Describe how a bell jar can be used to model what happens during breathing (Level 5).	3	Main
	Explain how to measure lung volume (Level 6).	2	WS, Main
	Use appropriately calibrated apparatus to obtain a lung volume (Level 5).		Main
Extending	Explain how the actions of the ribcage and diaphragm lead to inhaling and exhaling (Level 7).		Starter 2
	Explain the similarities and differences between the bell jar and the breathing system (Level 7).	3	Main
	Explain in detail how to measure lung volumes (Level 7).	2	WS, Main
	Use appropriately calibrated apparatus to obtain an accurate lung volume, evaluating the precision of instruments involved (Level 8).		Main

Literacy

During the practical and in the student-book activity students must apply their understanding of accuracy and precision in their discussion of how exercise affects breathing.

APP

Students will use investigative approaches to gather evidence through collection of lung capacity data (AF4).

Students will use the data obtained to reach a conclusion and evaluate the accuracy and precision of their data (AF5).

Key Words

contract, diaphragm, lung volume, asthma

Answers from the student book

<table>
<tr><td>In-text questions</td><td>A The ribcage moves up and out. B It moves up.</td></tr>
<tr><td>Activity</td><td>Lung volume
Lung volume can be found from the practical activity.
Doctors would not use this method as the resolution of the water bottle is poor, which leads to imprecise results.</td></tr>
<tr><td>Summary questions</td><td>1 One mark for each correct row (3 marks).
<table><tr><th></th><th>Inhaling</th><th>Exhaling</th></tr><tr><td>ribs move</td><td>up and out</td><td>down and in</td></tr><tr><td>diaphragm moves</td><td>down</td><td>up</td></tr><tr><td>chest volume</td><td>increases</td><td>decreases</td></tr></table>2 Any two from: smoking, asthma, old age, other names lung condition. (2 marks)
3 Take a bottle containing a known volume of water. Turn bottle upside down so neck of bottle is underwater. Ask Bolt to breathe out through a tube inserted into the bottle. Difference in volume of water at the end and the start is his lung volume. (3 marks)
4 Example answers (6 marks):
Rubber sheet represents the diaphragm; bell jar – chest cavity; balloons – lungs; pulling sheet down – diaphragm contracting.
Volume in bell jar now increased. Decreased pressure pulls air into balloons. Balloons inflate, representing air in lungs.
At least one problem with the model. Credit suitable suggestions, for example, bell jar walls represent ribcage, but do not move. Area around balloons is air – not correct in the body.</td></tr>
</table>

Starter	Support/Extension	Resources
Take a deep breath (5 min) Ask students to work in pairs. They count how many breaths they take in one minute, recording the values for use later in the lesson.		
How we breathe (10 min) Interactive resource where students complete a paragraph on what happens to different parts of the body when we breathe in.	**Support**: Students can discuss the possible answers in groups. **Extension**: Students can rewrite this paragraph for when we breathe out.	**Interactive**: How we breathe
Main	**Support/Extension**	**Resources**
Measuring the volume of the lungs (40 min) Demonstrate a bell jar and relate this to the different parts of the lungs. Explain to students that they will be finding out their lung volumes during the following experiment. Students follow the instructions on the practical sheet to calibrate a large plastic drinks bottle at half-litre intervals. They then use this calibrated apparatus to measure their own lung volume. Students continue to answer the questions on the practical sheet and carry out simple calculations as instructed.	**Support**: The access sheet details a method with a pre-calibrated bottle. It also has a simpler table and questions.	**Practical**: Measuring the volume of the lungs **Skill sheet**: Accuracy and precision
Plenary	**Support/Extension**	**Resources**
The effect of exercise (10 min) Ask one student from each pair to exercise on the spot. Measure their breathing rate. Discuss how increased activity affects the results.	**Support**: Compare breathing rates from earlier and describe effects of exercise.	
Peak flow meters (5 min) Introduce peak flow meters. Discuss what this records (rate of air flow during forced breath out). Compare the students' results. Introduce the idea of an asthmatic's reduced airway diameter and reduced peak flow readings.	**Support**: To help students visualise the difference, ask them to roll a piece of paper into a tube (normal airway) and roll the tube tighter (asthmatic).	
Homework		
Write three test questions on 'Structure of the gas exchange system and breathing'. Produce a mark scheme, with each question having 3–5 marks.		

2.4 Skeleton

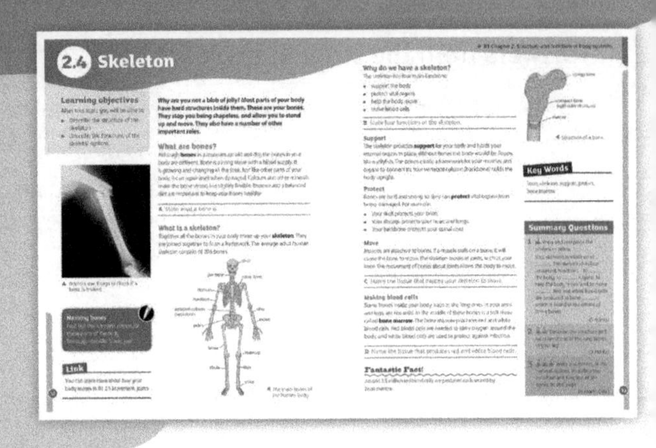

Biology NC link:

- the structure and functions of the human skeleton, to include support, protection, movement, and making blood cells.

Band	Outcome	Checkpoint	
		Question	**Activity**
Developing ↓	Name the main parts in the skeleton (Level 3).	D, 1	Main
	List the functions of the skeletal system (Level 4).	B, D, 1	Main
Secure ↓	Describe the structure of the skeleton (Level 5).	A, D, 1–3	Main
	Describe the functions of the skeletal system (Level 5).	B, D, 1–3	Main
Extending ↓	Explain the relationship between the bones and joints in the skeleton (Level 7).		Main
	Explain the link between structure and functions in the skeletal system (Level 7).	D, 2, 3	Main

Literacy
Students use scientific terminology correctly when linking skeletal structures to their functions.

They will also be required to communicate ideas, retrieving and collating information from a range of different sources when building a model of the skeleton.

APP
Students will use models of the skeleton to aid their understanding of the skeletal structure and associated functions (AF1).

Key Words
bone, skeleton, support, protect, bone marrow

Answers from the student book

In-text questions	**A** A living tissue with a blood supply, which is strong but slightly flexible. **B** To support the body, protect vital organs, help the body to move, and make blood cells. **C** muscle tissue **D** bone marrow
Activity	**Naming bones** patella, scapula, mandible
Summary questions	**1** bones, support, protect, blood, marrow (5 marks) **2** Any three from: hollow, contains bone marrow, produces blood cells, provides support, enables movement. **3** 6 mark question. Example answers: Bones/bone marrow produce blood cells. Red blood cells carry oxygen around the animal. White blood cells protect against infection. Bones are strong. They protect organs from being crushed. Provide structure to the organism. In conjunction with muscles, bones allow the animal to move.

Starter	Support/Extension	Resources
An alternative question-led lesson is also available.		**Question-led lesson**: Skeleton
What's in a skeleton? (10 min) Present student groups with large flip chart paper and board markers and ask the question 'What is your skeleton, and why do you need it?'. Allow them a few minutes to write down key words to answer the question, grouping key words into structural ideas or function. Discuss their answers, and correct any misconceptions.	**Support**: Students may be provided with an image of the skeleton as a visual prompt.	
Name those bones! (5 min) An interactive resource that asks students to label a diagram of the skeleton, using the names of some of the major bones in the body provided.		**Interactive**: Name those bones!
Main	**Support/Extension**	**Resources**
Build your own skeleton (40 min) Students use the activity sheet and photocopied images of bones to build a skeleton. Students then use the model skeleton and the information in the student book as a resource to label the bones on their own activity sheet. Students then answer the questions that follow.	**Support**: Students should work in mixed-ability groups.	**Activity**: Build your own skeleton
Plenary	**Support/Extension**	**Resources**
What's the skeleton for? (5 min) Present images of the skeleton on the board and point to different regions of the skeleton. Ask students to suggest what the bones in these areas do. The regions should include the skull, the ribcage, and the long bones of the arm and leg.	**Support**: Students may be provided with a list of possible skeletal regions and functions to choose from.	
Table of functions (10 min) Students draw a table that lists several regions of the skeleton (skull, ribcage, long bones in the arm and leg) in the first column. Students then fill in the second column with the functions of the bones in these regions.	**Support**: Provide students with a pre-drawn table to fill in. **Extension**: Students should include in their functions an explanation of how the function is achieved.	
Homework	**Support/Extension**	
Provide each student with an image of a different animal and ask them to add annotations around the picture to describe how the animal achieves support, movement, and protection. Independent research will be required to complete this task.	**Extension**: Students can be given more unusual animals, (e.g., fish or arthropods) to test their understanding and application of knowledge. Students should also provide an explanation for how these animals achieve their skeletal functions in their annotations, linking functions to structures.	

2.5 Movement: joints

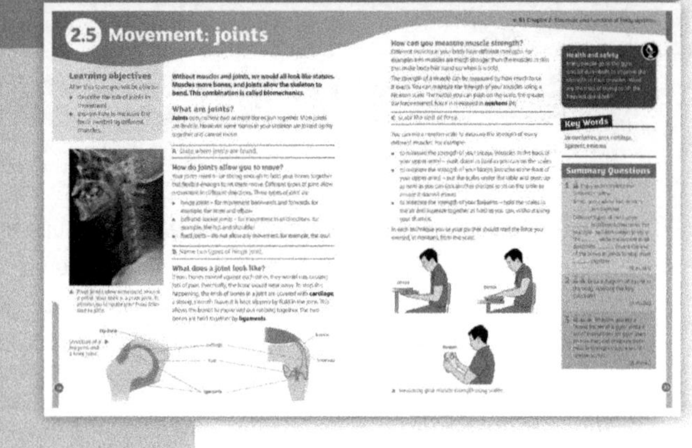

Biology NC link:

- biomechanics – the interaction between skeleton and muscles, including the measurement of force exerted by different muscles.

Working Scientifically NC link:

- make and record observations and measurements using a range of methods for different investigations; and evaluate the reliability of methods and suggest possible improvements.

Band	Outcome	Checkpoint	
		Question	**Activity**
Developing	State where joints are found in the body (Level 3).	A, B, 1	Homework
	State how a muscle exerts force during movement (Level 4).	C	Main
	Carry out an experiment to make simple observations (Level 4).		Main
Secure	Describe the role of joints (Level 5).	1	Main, Homework
	Explain how to measure the force exerted by different muscles (Level 5).	3	Main
	Carry out an experiment to make and record measurements of forces using the correct units (Level 5).		Main
Extending	Explain how the parts of a joint allow it to function (Level 7).	1, 2	Homework
	Explain the relationship between the forces required to move different masses (Level 7).		Main
	Carry out an experiment to record measurements of forces in newtons, evaluating the accuracy and precision of the method chosen (Level 7).		Main, Plenary 2

Maths
Students calculate means of their experimental results and plot a suitable graph to display their observations.

Literacy
Students extract information from text in order to carry out the practical, and must organise their ideas concisely when using scientific terms to explain their findings in the experiment.

APP
Students carry out an experiment, recording observations (AF4) and displaying these appropriately using a graph (AF3).

They will then comment on the suitability of their experimental method and propose improvements in their evaluation (AF5).

Key Words
biomechanics, joint, cartilage, ligament, newtons

Answers from the student book

In-text questions	**A** Where bones two or more join together. **B** knee and elbow **C** newton
Activity	**Health and safety** There is a high risk of causing injury to yourself, straining/spraining a muscle, and tearing a ligament if you drop the dumbbell on yourself.

Summary questions	1 bones, movement, hip, cartilage, rubbing (5 marks) 2 Diagram showing (any three from): two bones, ligament(s) joining the bones together, cartilage on ends of bones, fluid surrounding joint. 3 Example answers (6 marks): measuring equipment – newton (bathroom) scale; muscle force measured from reading on newton scale; select named muscle (e.g. biceps); push onto newton scale; record reading on scale; repeat reading to check for errors; calculate average force exerted on scale; repeat for second or subsequent muscle group(s)

Starter	Support/Extension	Resources
Walking skeletons (10 min) Show animations from the Internet, or from a film clip, which show a skeleton walking. Ask students why is it impossible for the skeleton to walk and the bones to move even though we know bones to be strong structures that are only slightly flexible. Discuss student ideas leading onto the need for joints, muscles, ligaments, cartilage, and tendons for movement.	**Support**: Focus on muscles and joints in the discussion. **Extension**: Students should explain the roles of different tissues used in movement.	
Arm movements (5 min) Using their own arms, ask students to identify where joints are and what range of movements they can achieve with these joints.	**Support**: Students should ignore the joints in the wrist and hand to avoid confusion. **Extension**: Students should consider if other types of joints are present around the body.	
Main	**Support/Extension**	**Resources**
Forces for lifting (40 min) Introduce the different parts of the arm needed for movement. Use scientific terminology such as biceps, triceps, and the different parts of a joint. Students then carry out an experiment investigating the forces required by the arm to lift different masses. Students will use a model of an arm with a hinge joint for the elbow to collect data in accordance with the method on the practical sheet. They will then display results on a graph to find a relationship between the two factors under investigation and answer the questions that follow.	**Support**: A support sheet is available with a suggested table of results and a graph grid with pre-labelled axes.	**Practical**: Forces for lifting **Skill sheet**: Calculating means **Skill sheet**: Choosing scales **Skill sheet**: Recording results
Plenary	**Support/Extension**	**Resources**
The role of joints in movement (5 min) The interactive resource requires students to use the definitions provided to fill in a crossword using key words in this topic.		**Interactive**: The role of joints in movement
Where, how, and why? (10 min) Evaluate the experiment as a discussion with students. Questions to consider include: Where in the experiment did you do something to make it fair? State the type of variable this is. How did you increase the accuracy in the experiment?	**Extension**: Students should offer detailed answers with explanations.	
Homework	**Support/Extension**	
Students apply their knowledge by writing a short paragraph about how a different joint elsewhere in the body works.	**Support**: Students should apply their ideas to another hinge joint, for example, the knee. **Extension**: Students should apply their knowledge to another type of joint, for example, a pivot or a ball and socket joint.	
An alternative WebQuest homework activity is also available on Kerboodle where students research hip replacements.		**WebQuest:** Hip replacement

2.6 Movement: muscles

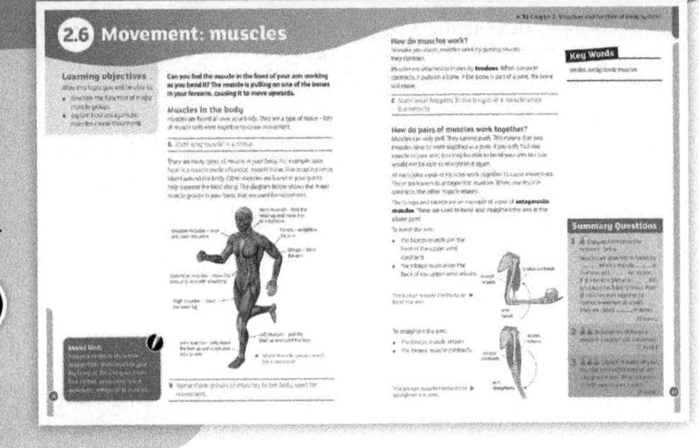

Biology NC link:

- the function of muscles and examples of antagonistic muscles.

Working Scientifically NC link:

- interpret observations and data, including identifying patterns and using observations, measurements and data to draw conclusions.

Band	Outcome	Checkpoint	
		Question	**Activity**
Developing	State the function of major muscle groups (Level 4).	B, 1	Starter 1, Plenary 2, Homework
	State the definition of antagonistic muscles (Level 4).	1	Lit, Starter 1, Plenary 1, Homework
	Carry out an experiment and interpret observations about the muscles involved in the movement of the elbow (Level 4).		Main
Secure	Describe the function of major muscle groups (Level 5).	C, 1	Starter 1, Plenary 2, Homework
	Explain how antagonistic muscles cause movement (Level 6).	3	Lit, Starter 1, Plenary 1, Homework
	Interpret data collected in an experiment, to identify a pattern between muscle fatigue and repetitive muscle contraction (Level 5).		Main
Extending	Explain how the muscle groups interact with other tissues to cause movement (Level 7).	2	Plenary 2, Homework
	Explain why it is necessary to have both muscles in an antagonistic pair to cause movement (Level 7).	3	Lit, Starter 1, Main, Plenary 1, Plenary 2, Homework
	Interpret data from the muscle contraction experiment, identifying patterns between the levels of fatigue during muscle contraction given different periods of rest (Level 7).		Main

Literacy

Students apply their scientific knowledge and understanding, using the key words learnt during the lesson, when explaining how antagonistic muscles are used in kicking a football (for their homework).

APP

In the student-book activity, students must design a model of an antagonistic muscle pair to explain how they work (AF1).

Students present muscle fatigue data from their experiments in appropriate tables and graphs (AF3).

They will then use this data to draw a reasoned conclusion relating muscle fatigue and periods of rest (AF5).

Key Words

tendon, antagonistic muscles

Answers from the student book

In-text questions	**A** Many muscle cells need to work together to cause movement. **B** Any three from: neck muscles, shoulder muscles, biceps and triceps, abdominal muscles, thigh muscles, calf muscles, shin muscles. **C** The muscle gets shorter.

Activity	**Model limb** The model should include a pair of antagonistic muscles on either side of a joint. Muscles should not be able to push, they can only contract. When one muscle contracts, the other relaxes.
Summary questions	**1** tendons, contracts, pulls, joint, antagonistic (5 marks) **2** Tendons join muscle to bone, ligaments join bone to bone. (2 marks) **3** Example answers (6 marks): Muscles can only pull. One muscle is required to bend the joint. A second muscle is required to straighten the joint. The muscles act on opposite sides of the joint. As one muscle contracts, the other relaxes. The muscle pair is antagonistic. Diagrams depicting the bending and straightening of a joint.

Starter	Support/Extension	Resources
Antagonistic muscles (10 min) Ask students what they understand by the word antagonist. Students may have met this word before in English lessons. Introduce the meaning of antagonistic muscles in science and ask students to find different antagonistic muscle pairs in the body by carrying out different actions, for example, by bending and straightening the arm at the elbow joint or the leg at the knee joint.		
Flexing your muscles (5 min) Ask students to lift a sizeable textbook. They need to observe any changes in the muscles of the upper arm and describe their observations to the class.	**Extension**: Students should be encouraged to offer their thoughts on why these changes occur.	
Main	**Support/Extension**	**Resources**
Investigating muscle fatigue (45 min) Students carry out a simple practical to investigate the action of muscles in the arm and how muscle fatigue links to the repetitive contraction of muscles. Students record their observations, identifying patterns and analysing the results obtained in the questions that follow.	**Support**: An access sheet is available where students are only required to repeat the experiment once, and the questions are of lower demand.	**Practical**: Investigating muscle fatigue
Plenary	**Support/Extension**	**Resources**
Revisiting antagonistic muscles (5 min) Students are presented with a summary of antagonistic muscles, where they must choose the correct words to fill individual gaps, using key words provided on the interactive resource.		**Interactive**: Revisiting antagonistic muscles
Other muscle pairs (10 min) Students apply their knowledge of antagonistic pairs to other parts of the body. They must find another antagonistic pair in the body (no names required) and explain how the muscle pair works in order to move the bones about the joint. Students pair-share their ideas, before offering these in a class discussion.	**Support**: Students concentrate on finding other antagonistic pairs of muscles around the body.	
Homework		
Provide students with a diagram of the leg with the hamstrings and quadriceps labelled. Students must write an account to explain how these muscles are used as an antagonistic pair during the kicking of a football.		

B1 Chapter 2 Checkpoint

Checkpoint lesson routes

The route through this lesson can be determined using the Checkpoint assessment.
Percentage pass marks are supplied in the Checkpoint teacher notes.

Route A (support)
Resource: B1 Chapter 2 Checkpoint: Revision

Students will work in groups moving through a carousel activity. Each card should take approximately 10 minutes to provide answers for. Suggestions for support are given in the table below. Four questions are also provided.

Route B (extension)
Resource: B1 Chapter 2 Checkpoint: Extension

Students will work through a carousel activity, and then attempt a few short extension questions.

Following this task, provide the students with paper, card, string, paper fasteners, sandwich bags (and any other materials you might think suitable). Ask them to either design a working arm, or working thorax, with as many components as possible.

Progression to *secure*

No.	Developing outcome	Secure outcome	Making progress
1	State what is meant by a tissue, an organ, and an organ system.	Define and state examples of tissues, organs, and organ systems.	Students need to gain a secure grasp of the vocabulary. To help this, take some time in the groups to ask them the meanings of the words, or to use the word in a sentence. They can use this vocabulary in Card 1 and Question 1.
2	State the hierarchy of organisation in a multicellular organism.	Explain the hierarchy of organisation in a multicellular organism.	Prepare four cards with one word (cell, tissue, organ, and organ system) and present them to the group, asking them to put them in an order explaining their reasoning. Students could also illustrate each of the words to check their understanding. They can then complete Card 1 and Question 1.
3	Name the parts of the gas exchange system.	Describe the structure of the gas exchange system.	Have an outline of the human torso and ask students to draw on the main structures of the gas exchange system, describing them as they draw. Clear up misconceptions about location and structure of organs, add any missing organs. Students can then start to work through Card 2 and Question 2.
4	State that the parts of the gas exchange system are adapted to their function.	Describe how the parts of the gas exchange system are adapted to their function.	Students should describe the adaptations as part of their work on Card 2.
5	State what happens to the ribcage and diaphragm during inhaling and exhaling.	Describe the processes of inhaling and exhaling.	Ask students to place their hands on their chest and take deep breaths in and out. They can describe what they feel. Start to link this to the movement of the ribs and muscles. Repeat with hands on abdomen, and link to action of diaphragm. This should help understanding of the breathing mechanism. They can then complete Question 2.
6	State a value of lung volume.	Explain how to measure lung volumes.	Ask students to breath into a paper bag. Ask the students what the air is a measure of? Then ask them to explain how they could measure this more accurately.
7	Name the main parts of the skeleton.	Describe the structure of the skeleton.	If possible, have a model skeleton available in the room for the completion of Card 3.
8	List the functions of the skeletal system.	Describe the functions of the skeletal system.	Students may need to use their book to help them work through Card 3.
9	State where joints are found in the body.	Describe the role of joints.	Students should include 'joints' in their answers to Question 3.
10	State that muscles exert a force during movement.	Explain how to measure the force exerted by different muscles.	Give the name of the correct piece of equipment (balance or newtonmeter) and ask students how to use them to measure the force exerted by a muscle.
11	State the function of major muscle groups.	Describe the function of major muscle groups.	Use a length of strong elastic in a stretched position to model a muscle, and ask students to use the example to explain how muscle groups work. Students can then complete Card 4 and Question 4.

Answers to end-of-chapter questions

1 reproductive system – produces new organisms, digestive system – breaks down food so it can be absorbed, respiratory system – takes in oxygen, removes carbon dioxide, circulatory system – transports materials around the body. (4 marks).

2a muscle cell (1 mark)

b contract/cause movement (1 mark)

c Group of similar cells working together to perform a function. (1 mark)

d organ system (1 mark)

e Two organs named with the correct function. One mark for the name, one mark for the function. (4 marks)

3a newton bathroom scale/forcemeter/newtonmeter (1 mark)

b newtons (1 mark)

c To make results more reliable/to check for an anomalies/to check for errors. (1 mark)

d Any three from the following:
Select first student. Push up against a bathroom scale, for example, against the bottom surface of a table. Repeat reading at least once to check for errors/anomalies. Repeat for other students in the group. Draw results as a bar chart.

4a ribs/ribcage (1 mark)

b diffusion (1 mark)

c muscle (1 mark)

d Any three from:
Diaphragm relaxes, rib cage lowers/moves in, chest cavity decreases in volume, pressure in chest increases, air/carbon dioxide force out of the lungs.

5 Students should be marked on the use of good English, organisation of information, spelling and grammar, and correct use of specialist terms. The best answers will be organised clearly in paragraphs, linking ideas, and reasoning correctly to compare the differences in exhaled and inhaled air (maximum of 6 marks).
Examples of correct scientific points:
Inhaled air contains more oxygen.
Oxygen is used in respiration.
Exhaled air contains more carbon dioxide.
Carbon dioxide is a waste product of respiration.
Exhaled air contains more water vapour.
Water vapour is a waste product of respiration.
Exhaled air is warmer.

Answer guide for Big Write

Developing	Secure	Extending
1–2 marks	3–4 marks	5–6 marks
The cartoon strip lacks detail. At least one bone or muscle used when tossing a pancake will have been labelled.	The cartoon strip is clearly presented. At least one muscle and one bone used when tossing a pancake will have been labelled. A simple explanation of how the body moves has been given.	The cartoon strip is well presented. The student has labelled at least one bone and two muscles used when tossing a pancake. A detailed explanation of how the body moves has been given, including the correct use of the term antagonistic muscles.

kerboodle

B1 Chapter 2 Checkpoint assessment (automarked)
B1 Chapter 2 Checkpoint: Revision
B1 Chapter 2 Checkpoint: Extension
B1 Chapter 2 Progress task (Investigation-planning)

3.1 Adolescence

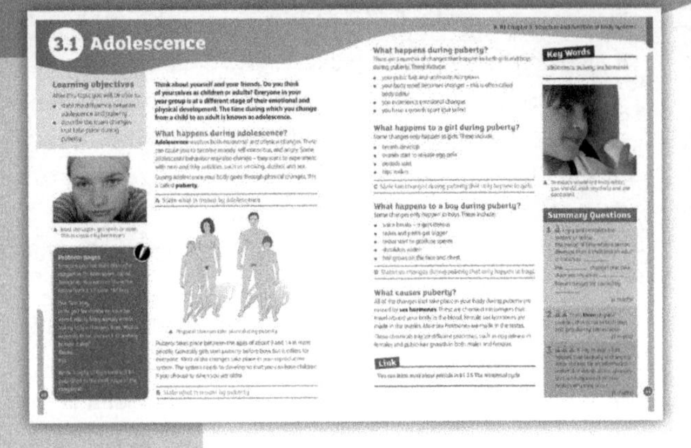

Biology NC link:

- reproduction in humans (as an example of a mammal), including the structure and function of the male and female reproductive systems.

Working Scientifically NC link:

- interpret observations and data, including identifying patterns and using observations, measurements, and data to draw conclusions.

Band	Outcome	Checkpoint	
		Question	Activity
Developing	State the definitions for adolescence and puberty (Level 4).	A, B, 1	
	State changes to the bodies of boys and girls during puberty (Level 4).	C, D, 2	Lit, Main, Plenary 1
↓	Interpret observations given, as changes that occur in boys or in girls (Level 4).		Main, Plenary 1
Secure	State the difference between adolescence and puberty (Level 5).	A, B, 1	Main
	Describe the main changes which take place during puberty (Level 5).	3	Lit, Main, Plenary 1
↓	Interpret observations given, to categorise the changes during adolescence (Level 5).		Main, Plenary 1
Extending	Explain the difference between adolescence and puberty (Level 7).	1	Main
	Explain the main changes that take place during puberty (Level 7).	3	Lit, Plenary 2, Homework
↓	Interpret observations given, to categorise and explain physical and emotional changes during adolescence (Level 7).		Main, Plenary 1

Literacy
Students pay attention to what others say in discussions, ask questions to develop ideas, and make contributions to discussions.

When writing answers to questions they need to use scientific terms confidently and correctly.

APP
Students identify differences, similarities or changes related to simple scientific ideas, processes or phenomena during their card sort (AF1).

Key Words
adolescence, puberty, sex hormones

Answers from the student book

In-text questions	**A** The period of time in which a person changes from a child into an adult. **B** The physical changes a person's body experiences when changing from a child to an adult. **C** Any two from: breasts develop, ovaries release eggs, periods start, hips widen. **D** Any two from: voice breaks, testes/penis get bigger, testes start to produce sperm, shoulders widen, growth of facial/chest hair.

Activity	**Problem pages** The reply should include the following points: Kyle is undergoing puberty, caused by male sex hormones. He is changing from a child into an adult. A number of changes will occur, including his voice deepening, getting taller, and his genitals growing. The whole process takes several years but the precise start and finish time is different for everyone. This is something that happens to everyone and we cannot stop puberty. It is nothing to worry about.
Summary questions	**1** adolescence, physical, puberty, hormones (4 marks) **2** pubic hair/underarm hair growth, body odour, growth spurt (3 marks) **3** Give two marks for general changes (pubic hair/underarm hair growth, body odour, emotional changes, and growth spurt). Give two marks for male-only changes (voice breaks, testes/penis get bigger, shoulders widen, facial/chest hair). Give two marks for reasons (hormones/ released from testes/ chemical messengers/ reproductive system needs to become fully functional).

Starter	Support/Extension	Resources
What's the difference? (10 min) Working in groups, students discuss what changes occur as we change from a child into an adult. They put their ideas or observations on a sheet of paper and present them to the class in a short opening discussion. For classes with very shy students, it may be easier for students to come up with their own ideas, write them onto sticky notes, and place these anonymously into a container for you to choose from.	**Support**: Students may find it easier to focus on physical changes, either observed in themselves or observed in their older siblings.	
Growing up (10 min) Pose the question: 'Why do we need to grow up?' Write suggested answers on the board, for example: • We grow up to be physically able to have children. • Growing up is just getting physically bigger. • Growing up is just getting more sensible. Discuss the statements and decide which statement is most accurate.	**Extension**: Students should offer their own suggestions for the definition of growing up.	
Main	**Support/Extension**	**Resources**
Changes during adolescence (40 min) Students are given a set of cards with statements about changes experienced during adolescence. Students must sort these cards according to changes that occur in girls and in boys, then answer the questions that follow.	**Support**: Take out cards relating to emotional changes, which are marked with a letter E, to allow students to solely focus on the physical changes that occur during adolescence.	**Activity**: Changes during adolescence
Plenary	**Support/Extension**	**Resources**
Changes in puberty (5 min) Interactive resource in which students sort a list of changes that occur during puberty into changes that happen to boys, girls, or both boys and girls.		**Interactive**: Changes in puberty
No worries! (5 min) Ask one student to suggest one typical problem a teenager might have about the changes that they experience during adolescence. Another student then gives advice to that student by explaining what is happening, and so on. (This is an opportunity to allay students' own concerns.)	**Support**: Students should concentrate on physical changes only.	
Homework	**Support/Extension**	
Produce an information leaflet with an outline of a human (gender neutral) in the middle. Put the heading 'Changes in a boy at adolescence' on one side, and 'Changes in a girl at adolescence' on the other side. Students then fill in this leaflet.	**Extension**: Students may wish to annotate the diagram in the centre of the page.	

3.2 Reproductive systems

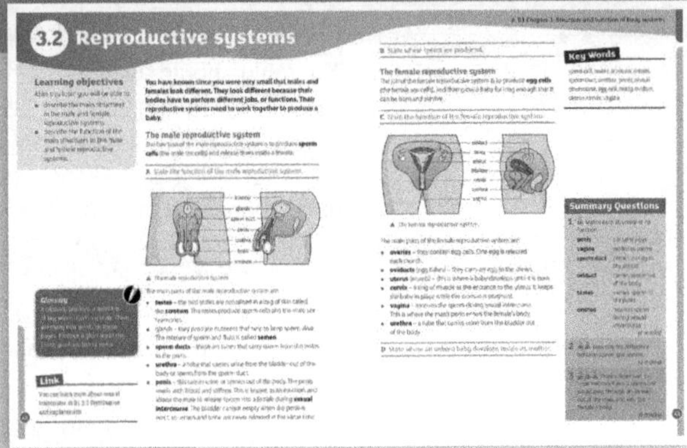

Biology NC link:

- reproduction in humans (as an example of a mammal), including the structure and function of the male and female reproductive systems.

Working Scientifically NC link:

- present observations and data using appropriate methods, including tables and graphs.

Band	Outcome	Checkpoint	
		Question	**Activity**
Developing	Name the main structures of the male and female reproductive system (Level 3).	D, 1	Lit, Starter 1, Starter 2, Main, Plenary 1, Plenary 2
	State a function of the main structures of the male and female reproductive system (Level 4).	A–C, 1	Lit, Starter 1, Main, Plenary 1, Plenary 2
	Extract information from text to state structures and functions of the key parts of the reproductive systems in a table (Level 4).		Main
Secure	Describe the main structures in the male and female reproductive systems (Level 5).	3	Starter 1, Starter 2, Main, Plenary 1, Plenary 2
	Describe the function of the main structures in the male and female reproductive systems (Level 6).	1	Starter 1, Main, Plenary 1, Plenary 2
	Extract information from text to describe structures and functions of the key parts of the reproductive systems in a table (Level 5).		Main
Extending	Explain how different parts of the male and female reproductive systems work together to achieve certain functions (Level 7).	3	Starter 1, Main, Homework
	Explain the adaptations of some of the main structures that help them function (Level 7).		Starter 1, Main, Homework
	Extract information from text to explain structures and functions of the key parts of the reproductive systems in a table (Level 8).		Main

Literacy
Students extract information from text in the student book, before summarising this material in tables using scientific terms.

APP
Students describe and explain biological processes logically and in detail (AF1).

Key Words
sperm cell, testes, scrotum, semen, sperm duct, urethra, penis, sexual intercourse, egg cell, ovary, oviduct, uterus, cervix, vagina

Answers from the student book

In-text questions	**A** Produce sperm and release them inside the female. **B** testes **C** Produce egg and allow a baby to grow until it is ready to be born. **D** uterus (womb)
Activity	**Glossary** The students' glossaries should contain key words from B1 Topics 3.1 and 3.2.

Summary questions	**1** 1 mark for each correct match. (6 marks) penis – carries sperm out of the body vagina – receives sperm during sexual intercourse sperm duct – carries sperm to the penis oviduct – carries an egg to the uterus testes – produce sperm ovaries – contain eggs **2** Sperm are the male sex cells; semen is a fluid containing both sperm and the nutrients to keep sperm alive. (2 marks) **3** 4 marks for identifying the correct structures, 1 mark for the correct order, and 1 mark for a well organised flow chart. testes → sperm duct → urethra/penis → vagina

Starter	Support/Extension	Resources
Reproductive structures (10 min) Introduce the structures of the male reproductive system. Outline the functions of each of the key structures. This would be best achieved using a model of the structures or an image on the board. Repeat for the structures of the female reproductive system.		
Label these parts! (10 min) Introduce the structures within the male and female reproductive systems. Students should then consolidate their knowledge using the interactive resource, which asks students to label the different parts of these systems.	**Support**: Limit the structures introduced only to those listed on the interactive.	**Interactive**: Label these parts!
Main	**Support/Extension**	**Resources**
Male and female reproductive systems (40 min) This activity requires students to extract information from the student book in order to label diagrams of both reproductive systems, fill in tables summarising structures and functions, and answer questions that follow.	**Support**: A support sheet is provided for students with partially filled-in tables, linking structures and functions of the two reproductive systems.	**Activity**: Male and female reproductive systems
Plenary	**Support/Extension**	**Resources**
Making connections (5 min) Produce a set of playing cards with the names of the main reproductive structures on half of them, and their functions on the other half. Issue the cards, one to each student. Then select one student to read their card. The student whose card matches must read theirs out. If correct, they get to pick the next student. Continue until all cards have been played out.	**Support**: Give students name cards rather than function cards, to test understanding rather than literacy skills.	
Word volleyball (5 min) Ask all the students to stand. Pass a soft sponge ball to a student who has to name a structure. That student then passes the ball to another standing player who has to state the function. They then name another structure, and the game continues. Once they get a correct answer they can sit down. The game ends when they have all sat down. (For every student to participate in this game, the set of key structures and functions may be repeated several times. This game is particularly useful for supporting students, due to the repetitive nature of recall.)		
Homework	**Support/Extension**	
Produce a crossword with as many names of the parts of the reproductive systems as possible. Students must also produce all of the clues.	**Support**: Students may write simple definitions of each structure as the clue. **Extension**: Students should be encouraged to give clues relating to different parts of the system, or how that part is adapted to its function.	

3.3 Fertilisation and implantation

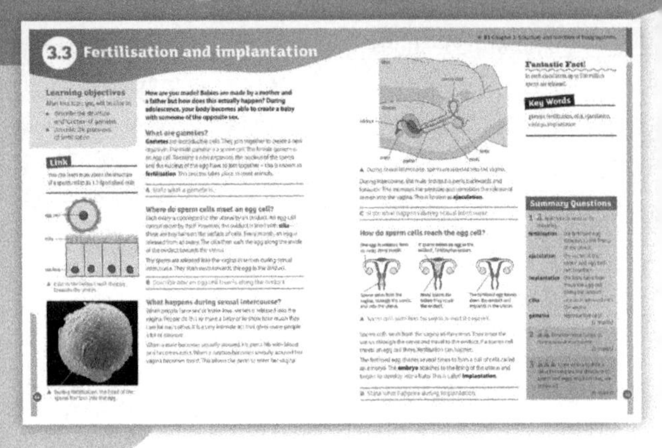
3.3 Fertilisation and implantation

Biology NC link:

- reproduction in humans (as an example of a mammal), gametes, and fertilisation.

Band	Outcome	Checkpoint	
		Question	**Activity**
Developing ↓	State the definition of gametes (Level 3).	A, 1	Starter 1, Main
	State what is meant by fertilisation (Level 4).	1	Lit, Main
Secure ↓	Describe the structure and function of gametes (Level 5).	3	Starter 1, Main, Plenary 2
	Describe the process of fertilisation (Level 5).	B, C, 1	Lit, Main, Plenary 1, Plenary 2
Extending ↓	Compare the male and female gametes (Level 7).	3	Main
	Explain the sequence of fertilisation and implantation (Level 7).		Lit, Main, Plenary 1, Homework

Maths
Students carry out simple calculations using magnification and scale to calculate the actual sizes of egg and sperm cells.

Literacy
The homework task requires students to use scientific terms correctly using a storyboard format to convey complex ideas to a KS3 audience.

APP
Students use a variety of different presentation skills to communicate scientific findings (AF3).

Key Words
gamete, fertilisation, cilia, ejaculation, embryo, implantation

Answers from the student book

In-text questions	**A** reproductive (sex) cells **B** moved along by cilia **C** Penis releases sperm/semen into the vagina. **D** Fertilised egg (or embryo) attaches to the lining of the uterus.
Activity	**Journey to the egg** The account of a sperm cell's journey should include the following. (Descriptions are included in parentheses.) testes (sperm made) → sperm duct (glands release fluid into duct to enable sperm to survive, mixture called semen) → urethra (→ penis) → vagina → cervix (ring of muscle prevents baby falling out) → uterus → oviduct → fertilises egg (sperm and egg nucleus join) → implantation in lining of uterus.
Summary questions	**1** fertilisation – the nuclei of the sperm and egg cell join together ejaculation – semen is released into the vagina implantation – the fertilised egg attaches to the lining of the uterus cilia – the little hairs that move the egg cell along the oviduct gametes – reproductive cells (5 marks) **2** Penis becomes erect and vagina becomes moist. Penis inserted into vagina. Sperm/semen released/ ejaculated into vagina. (3 marks) **3** Example answers (6 marks): Eggs are larger; sperm are smaller. Sperm can swim; eggs must be moved by cilia. Eggs are made before birth/only mature; sperm are made constantly. Only one egg released per month; millions of sperm released each ejaculation.

Starter	Support/Extension	Resources
Egg and sperm cells (5 min) Interactive resource in which students complete a paragraph on egg and sperm cells. **What we will learn today!** (10 min) List the three main key words from this lesson on the board: gametes, fertilisation, and implantation. Ask students to guess what these words mean, and then write their guesses in their books in pencil.		**Interactive**: Egg and sperm cells
Main	**Support/Extension**	**Resources**
Fertilisation and implantation (40 min) This activity sheet is split into two main sections plus one optional task. **Task 1 – The size of egg and sperm cells** Students use diagrams provided to carry out simple calculations using magnification size and scale to deduce the actual size of egg and sperm cells. **Task 2 – Sexual intercourse** Students connect phrases together to sequence events that occur during sexual intercourse. You may wish to discuss this topic first. **Task 3 – Fertilisation and implantation (optional)** Show the short film on fertilisation and cell cleavage, which shows the process of fertilisation and the splitting of the fertilised egg. The process of implantation is not covered in detail in this video. Discuss with the class the events shown on the film, and introduce the homework task (described below).	**Support**: An access sheet is available where questions of lower demand are given and students are not required to carry out calculations for Task 1. **Extension**: If the video is used, students should carry out an evaluation of the video shown for Task 3.	**Activity**: Fertilisation and implantation **Video**: Fertilisation and implantation
Plenary	**Support/Extension**	**Resources**
Sequencing (10 min) Write the words/phrases below on the board in any order. Students should then place the words in the correct order according to the sequence of events, defining each term. implantation, fertilisation, intercourse, gamete production, cell division **What we learnt today** (5 min) Revisit the definitions written in pencil at the beginning of the lesson. Students must use their pens to correct their initial thoughts ready for a short discussion.	**Support**: Students can be given the sequence on a sheet of paper, so they only need to focus on the definitions, or vice versa. **Extension**: Students should explain each term in detail.	
Homework	**Support/Extension**	
Students complete the storyboard of their own educational film to cover the entire topic. Students should indicate the images they would like to use, as well as the commentary, for each artwork. An alternative WebQuest homework activity is also available on Kerboodle where students research fertility treatment.	**Support**: The access sheet includes prompts for each frame of the video. **Extension**: Students should include explanations using scientific terminology.	**WebQuest**: Fertility treatment

3.4 Development of a fetus

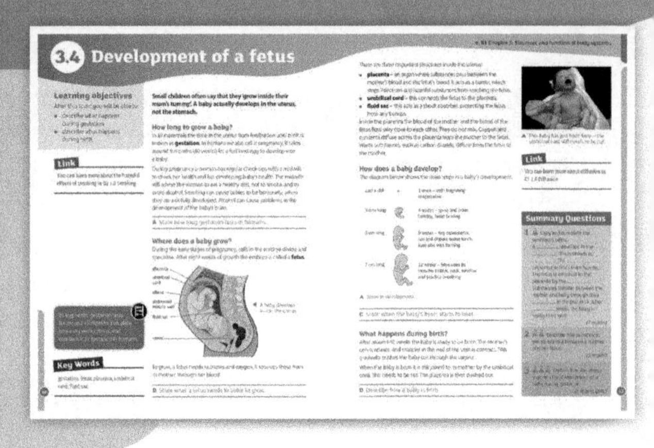
3.4 Development of a fetus

Biology NC link:

- reproduction in humans (as an example of a mammal), gestation and birth, and the effect of maternal lifestyle on the fetus through the placenta.

Band	Outcome	Checkpoint	
		Question	**Activity**
Developing ↓	State the definition of gestation (Level 3).	1	Plenary 2
	State how long a pregnancy lasts (Level 3).	A, 1, 2	Main, Plenary 2
Secure ↓	Describe what happens during gestation (Level 5).	C, 1, 2	Main, Plenary 2
	Describe what happens during birth (Level 5).	D	Main, Plenary 2
Extending ↓	Describe accurately the sequence of events during gestation (Level 7).	C, 2, 3	Main, Plenary 2
	Explain in detail how contractions bring about birth (Level 8).	D	Main, Plenary 2

Literacy
Students collate information from different sources, using scientific terms confidently to summarise their ideas.

APP
Students explain the processes involved in the development of a fetus (AF1), and present their ideas accordingly (AF3).

Key Words
gestation, fetus, placenta, umbilical cord, fluid sac

Answers from the student book

In-text questions	**A** about 9 months (40 weeks) **B** nutrients and oxygen **C** about 4 weeks **D** Cervix relaxes and uterus muscle contracts, pushing the baby out of the vagina.
Activity	**Elephant gestation** 22 × 4 = 88 weeks. This is more than twice the length of the gestation period in humans (40 weeks).
Summary questions	**1** fetus, uterus, gestation, fluid sac, umbilical cord, blood, 40 (7 marks) **2** Any three from: Substances transferred between maternal and fetal blood. Occurs in the placenta. Oxygen and nutrients diffuse from mother to baby. Waste substances, like carbon dioxide, diffuse from baby to mother. **3** 6 mark question. Example answers: Placenta is area where substances pass between the mother's and fetus's blood. It acts as a barrier, stopping infections and harmful substances reaching the fetus. Umbilical cord connects the fetus to the placenta. It carries the fetus's blood/oxygen/nutrients from the placenta to the baby and carries carbon dioxide from the fetus to the placenta. Fluid sac contains fluid THAT acts as a shock absorber/protects the fetus from bumps.

Starter	Support/Extension	Resources
Key word cascade (5 min) Write a key word on the board. Ask students to suggest another word which is connected to the key word. Add this to the board. Repeat the process until all the links are exhausted. Suggested key words include pregnancy, fetus, and placenta. **Egg to baby** (5 min) Ask students how an egg from the ovaries turns into a baby. Invite ideas and lead a short discussion about the ideas of development. This is a good opportunity to dispel possible misconceptions.	**Extension**: Students should justify why words are linked.	
Main	**Support/Extension**	**Resources**
Development and birth (45 min) This activity is split into three sections, and is run in the format of home and expert groups. Students should be split up into groups of three (mixed ability), called the home group, before the activity begins. Each section should take 15 minutes. **Task 1 – Becoming experts** Each member of the home group moves to a designated table to collect information from the resource card available. They must not remove the cards, although they can summarise the information as a diagram on a piece of paper. You may wish to introduce a word limit to prevent students from copying the resources. **Task 2 – Returning home** Students return to their home group and have five minutes to teach each topic to one another. **Task 3 – Answering questions** Students then attempt the questions on the activity sheet.	**Support**: The information cards are ramped, so give students the card on birth. **Extension**: Students should become experts on the card about the development of the baby.	**Activity**: Development and birth
Plenary	**Support/Extension**	**Resources**
Development links (5 min) Students link key words in this topic to their definitions using the interactive resource. **Egg to baby – revisited** (5 min) Students revisit their ideas from the beginning of the lesson, comparing what they thought originally to what they know now. Students should focus on the terms 'gestation' and 'birth' in particular.		**Interactive**: Development links
Homework	**Support/Extension**	
Write an account of the development of the baby using the notes obtained from the activity. The account should include scientific words used in a logical and coherent manner.	**Support**: Students should be provided with a different information card (one other than about birth) to summarise.	

3.5 The menstrual cycle

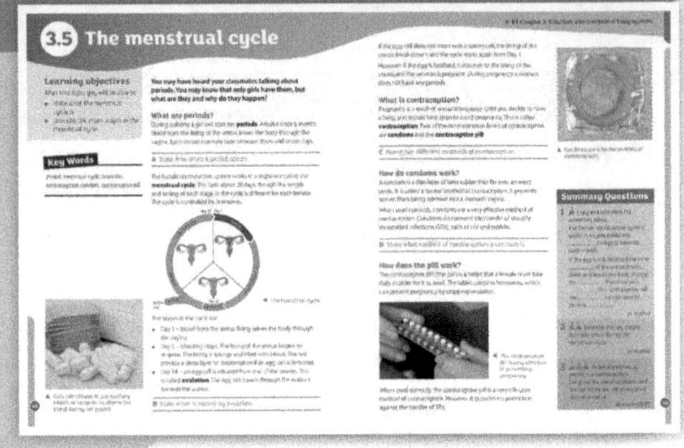

Biology NC link:

- reproduction in humans (as an example of a mammal), menstrual cycle (without details of hormones).

Working Scientifically NC link:

- present observations and data using appropriate methods, including tables and graphs.

Band	Outcome	Checkpoint	
		Question	Activity
Developing ↓	State a simple definition of the menstrual cycle (Level 4).	1	Starter 1, Main
	State the main stages in the menstrual cycle (Level 4).	1, 2	Starter 1, Main, Plenary 1, Plenary 2
	Present key pieces of information in a sequence (Level 4).		Main
Secure ↓	State what the menstrual cycle is (Level 5).		Starter 1, Main, Plenary 1
	Describe the main stages in the menstrual cycle (Level 5).	1, 2	Starter 1, Main, Plenary 1, Plenary 2
	Present information in the form of a graphical timeline (Level 6).		Main
Extending ↓	Explain the role of the menstrual cycle in reproduction (Level 7).		Main, Plenary 1, Plenary 2
	Describe the stages of the menstrual cycle as a timed sequence of events (Level 7).	2	Main, Plenary 1, Plenary 2
	Present information in the form of a scaled timeline or pie chart (Level 8).		Main

Literacy
Students are required to understand scientific terminology when interpreting information given, and to present this information using a different method.

APP
Students present information using a scaled timeline or as a pie chart (AF3).

Key Words
period, menstrual cycle, ovulation, contraception, condom, contraceptive pill

Answers from the student book

In-text questions	**A** once a month **B** The release of an egg cell from one of the ovaries. **C** condoms and the contraceptive pill **D** barrier method
Summary questions	**1** menstrual cycle, lining, vagina, period, condoms, pregnancy (6 marks) **2** period – lining is lost as blood through the vagina ovulation – egg is released Uterus lining thickens ready for a fertilised egg to implant. If egg is not fertilised, the lining breaks down and the cycle starts again. (4 marks) **3** 6 mark question. Example answers: Condoms are used by males during intercourse. They are an example of the barrier method of contraception. The barrier method protects against STIs and is highly effective at preventing pregnancy. The contraceptive pill is taken by females. It must be taken daily and gives no protection against STIs. It is highly effective at preventing pregnancy.

Starter	Support/Extension	Resources
An alternative question-led lesson is also available.		**Question-led lesson**: The menstrual cycle
Cycles in nature (5 min) Ask students to suggest as many events in nature as they can that occur in cycles. Ask them to feed their ideas back to the class. The aim is to introduce the idea of cycles and to produce a simple definition of a cycle in nature.		
Menstrual cycle facts (10 min) Interactive resource in which students complete a paragraph on the menstrual cycle. Students may copy the corrected summary into their books for future reference.		**Interactive:** Menstrual cycle facts
Main	**Support/Extension**	**Resources**
Timeline of the menstrual cycle (40 min) Students are presented with key events in the menstrual cycle as a series of text boxes that have been jumbled up. Students are required to read and interpret the information, sequence the boxes in the correct order, and answer the questions that follow.	**Support**: Students are simply required to sequence the text boxes in order. **Extension**: Students should arrange the timeline against a scaled axis of time, using graph paper or, as an extra challenge, students could present the sequence in a circle as a pie chart.	**Activity**: Timeline of the menstrual cycle
Plenary	**Support/Extension**	**Resources**
Loop game (5 min) Write down a list of events during the menstrual cycle as a pack of cards, with one event on each card. Students can then place the cards in the correct sequence to form a loop.	**Extension**: Students explain why each event is important while working on the loop game.	
Menstrual cycle in a minute (5 min) Write down a list of events during the menstrual cycle as a pack of cards, with one event on each card. Students are split into groups with one statement per group. Present the class with a clock and students must scale the events of the menstrual cycle to one minute. They will need to call out their key events in the cycle at the correct point in that minute. Give students a few minutes of thinking time before commencing the activity.	**Support**: Students should work on the scale of two seconds = one day.	
Homework	**Support/Extension**	
Students should prepare five questions on the reproduction topic so far, one for each lesson, together with a mark scheme.	**Support**: Students concentrate on short questions between 1–3 marks each. **Extension**: Students should write questions requiring higher-order-thinking skills, where each question is worth 3–5 marks.	

3.6 Flowers and pollination

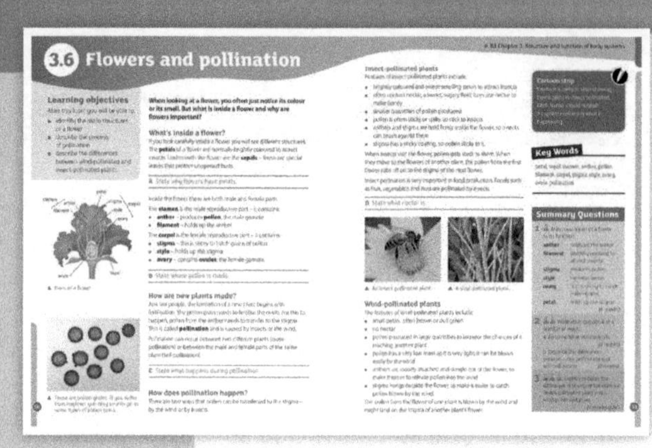
3.6 Flowers and pollination

Learning objectives

Key Words

Summary Questions

Biology NC link:

- reproduction in plants, including flower structure, wind and insect pollination, fertilisation, including quantitative investigation of some dispersal mechanisms
- the importance of plant reproduction through insect pollination in human food security.

Working Scientifically NC link:

- use appropriate techniques, apparatus, and materials during fieldwork and laboratory work, paying attention to health and safety.

Band	Outcome	Checkpoint	
		Question	**Activity**
Developing	Name the parts of a flower (Level 3).	B, 1	Starter 1, Main, Plenary 1
	State what is meant by pollination (Level 4).	2, C	Homework
	Name two methods of pollination (Level 3).	2, 3	
	Follow instructions to dissect a flower (Level 4).		Main
Secure	Identify the main structures in a flower (Level 5).	A, B, 1	Starter 1, Main, Plenary 1
	Describe the process of pollination (Level 6).	A–D, 2	Lit, Plenary 1, Homework
	Describe the differences between wind pollinated and insect pollinated plants (Level 6).	3	Main, Homework
	Use appropriate techniques to dissect a flower into its main parts (Level 5).		Main
Extending	Explain how the structures of the flower are adapted to their function (Level 7).	1	Starter 1, Main
	Explain the role of pollination in plant reproduction (Level 7).	2	Lit, Homework
	Explain the processes of wind and insect pollination, comparing the similarities and differences between the two (Level 7).	3	Lit, Main, Plenary 1, Homework
	Use appropriate techniques to dissect a flower and record detailed observations (Level 7).		Main

Literacy

Students must use scientific terminology correctly when naming key parts of the flower and describing their function.

APP

Students collect data and record their observations from experiment (AF4), and present this accordingly in a table (AF4).

Key Words

petal, sepal, stamen, anther, pollen, filament, carpel, stigma, style, ovary, ovule, pollination

Answers from the student book

In-text questions	**A** attract insects **B** anther **C** Pollen is transferred from anther to stigma. **D** Sweet, sugary fluid (that bees use to make honey).

Activity	**Cartoon strip** The cartoon strip should include the following steps: brightly coloured petals to attract insects; an insect visiting the flower; pollen transferred from the anther to the insect; insect moves to another plant; pollen is transferred from insect to stigma
Summary questions	**1** anther – produces pollen filament – holds up the anther stigma – this is sticky to 'catch' pollen grains style – holds up the stigma ovary – contains ovules petal – brightly coloured to attract insects (6 marks) **2** **a** transfer of pollen from anther to stigma. (2 marks) **b** cross-pollination is when pollen from one flower is transferred to stigma of another flower. Self-pollination is when pollen is transferred to the stigma in the same flower. (2 marks) **3** 6 mark question. Example answers: Insect pollinated (maximum of 3 marks) large, brightly coloured petals and sweetly scented; usually contain nectar, a sweet sugary fluid; smaller quantities of pollen produced; pollen is often sticky or spiky, to stick to insects; anthers and stigma held firm inside the flower, so insects can brush against them; stigma has a sticky coating, so pollen sticks to it Wind pollinated (maximum of 3 marks) small petals, often brown or dull green; no nectar; pollen produced in large quantities as lots never reach another flower; pollen is very light, so it can be blown easily by the wind; anthers are loosely attached and dangle out of the flower, to release pollen into the wind; stigma hangs outside the flower to catch the drifting pollen

Starter	Support/Extension	Resources
Parts of a flower (5 min) Students must link the key parts of a flower to their function using the interactive resource. **Beginning of life** (10 min) Hold a discussion based on the question. 'How do plants reproduce?'. This will then lead on to the main parts of a flower, what they do, where the gametes come from, and how are they are fertilised.		**Interactive**: Parts of a flower
Main	**Support/Extension**	**Resources**
Flower dissection (40 min) Each student should be presented with a simple flower such as a buttercup or single geranium flower. They need to use forceps to dissect out the four key parts of the flower carefully. These parts should then be drawn onto the practical sheet and labelled. Students then answer the questions that follow.	**Support**: Demonstrate flower dissection in small groups and use larger flowers that are easier to dissect, for example, fuchsias or freesias.	**Practical**: Flower dissection
Plenary	**Support/Extension**	**Resources**
Pollination role play (10 min) Divide the class into groups of 6–8 and ask them to design a role play where they take on the roles of insects and the parts of the flower required for pollination. Give groups two minutes to prepare and ask for volunteers to perform their role play. Students should consider the importance of insect pollination in terms of producing crops for humans. **Pollen grains** (5 min) Show students images of pollen grains or samples in a sealed container. Ask students to decide on the type of pollination they represent based on their adaptations, such as the presence of air sacs or hooks.	**Support**: Students should be told which roles to play in their groups, to limit the role play to its essentials. **Support**: Students should focus on physical features of the pollen observed.	
Homework	**Support/Extension**	
Write an account that describes the process of insect or wind pollination. If Plenary 1 was chosen the account should be of wind pollination to test for understanding across both types. Accounts of insect pollination should include the importance of insect pollination in human food security.	**Extension**: Students should write an account that compares the two types of pollination.	

3.7 Fertilisation and germination

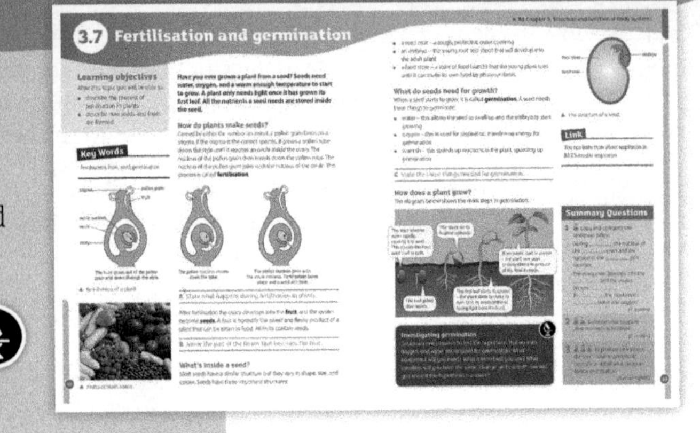

Biology NC link:
- reproduction in plants, including flower structure, seed, and fruit formation.

Working Scientifically NC link:
- make and record observations and measurements using a range of methods for different investigations; and evaluate the reliability of methods and suggest possible improvements.

Band	Outcome	Checkpoint	
		Question	**Activity**
Developing	State what is meant by fertilisation in plants (Level 3).	A, 1	Main
	State what seeds and fruit are (Level 3).	B, 1	Main
↓	Make and record observations of germination (Level 4).		Main
Secure	Describe the process of fertilisation in plants (Level 6).	A, 1	Main, Homework
	Describe how seeds and fruits are formed (Level 6).	B, 1, 2	Main
↓	Make and record observations in a table with clear headings and units, using data to calculate percentage germination (Level 5).		Main
Extending	Explain the process of fertilisation in plants, explaining the role of each of the parts involved in the process (Level 7).	1, 2	Homework
	Explain how the germination of seeds occurs (Level 7).	3	Starter 1, Main, Homework
↓	Make and record observations in a table, using data to calculate percentage germination, evaluating experimental procedure (Level 7).		Main

Maths
Students carry out simple calculations when working out the percentage of successful germination from experimental data, and draw graphs using this data by selecting appropriate scales for the axes on the graphs.

Literacy
Students discuss the conclusions of their experiment using scientific terminology, and evaluate the validity of the experiment using key terms such as accuracy and precision.

APP
Students decide on the best graph to present their results (AF3), using the data recorded from their observations (AF4).

Students will then evaluate the experimental procedure (AF5).

Key Words
fertilisation, fruit, seed, germination

Answers from the student book

In-text questions	**A** The pollen grain and ovule nuclei fuse. **B** ovary **C** water, oxygen, warmth
Activity	**Investigating germination** Experimental procedure should include placing the same number of seeds in the same apparatus set-up, placed in different conditions, changing one factor at a time. The experiment can be based on the practical provided with this lesson.

Summary questions	1 fertilisation, pollen, ovule, fruit, seeds, germinate, warmth (7 marks) 2 Ovule develops into a seed. Ovary develops into the fruit. (2 marks) 3 6 mark question. Example answers: Seed absorbs water and swells. Hard seed coat starts to split. Root grows downwards transferring energy from food store in seed. shoot starts to grow upwards first leaf starts to emerge plant starts to photosynthesise to produce its own food using light from the Sun.

Starter	Support/Extension	Resources
Germination (10 min) Introduce the idea of the germination of seeds. Students then complete a fill-in-the-gap activity using the interactive resource to consolidate their knowledge and understanding. **Seed-packet detective** (5 min) Students look at the instructions on a packet of seeds. They discuss the weather conditions indicated on the packet that are required for seed germination and growth.	**Support**: Use seed packets designed for children and recap on MRS GREN.	**Interactive**: Germination
Main	**Support/Extension**	**Resources**
Successful seeds (40 min) Students carry out a practical to investigate germination with different amounts of water. Students analyse the results by calculating percentage of successful germination and plotting a graph of their results. They then answer the questions that follow, relating to the experiment itself and the content learnt this lesson. Students will require the use of the student book in order to answer questions. For this practical to be successful, a demo of this experiment could be set up three to four days in advance so that students may use the sample set of results for their analysis.	**Support**: A support sheet is available with a suggested table of results and a pre-labelled graph grid.	**Practical**: Successful seeds **Skill sheet**: Recording results **Skill sheet**: Calculating percentages **Skill sheet**: Choosing scales **Skill sheet**: Drawing graphs
Plenary	**Support/Extension**	**Resources**
Accuracy and precision (5 min) Write the two words on the board and give students a few minutes in groups to discuss the two words. What do they mean? How did they make their results both accurate and precise? **Why graph?** (10 min) Ask why the ability to plot and interpret graphs is important in science. Lead a short discussion, culminating in the conclusion that visual presentation is easier to interpret than tables of numerical data.	**Extension**: Students should offer their ideas for an evaluation of this experiment. **Extension**: Show a range of graphs depicting experimental data and ask students to explain what the graphs show, justifying the choice of graphs drawn.	**Skill sheet**: Accuracy and precision
Homework	**Support/Extension**	
Students produce labelled diagrams of fertilisation of a plant and germination of a seed.	**Extension**: Students should explain the role of each part of a plant in fertilisation.	

3.8 Seed dispersal

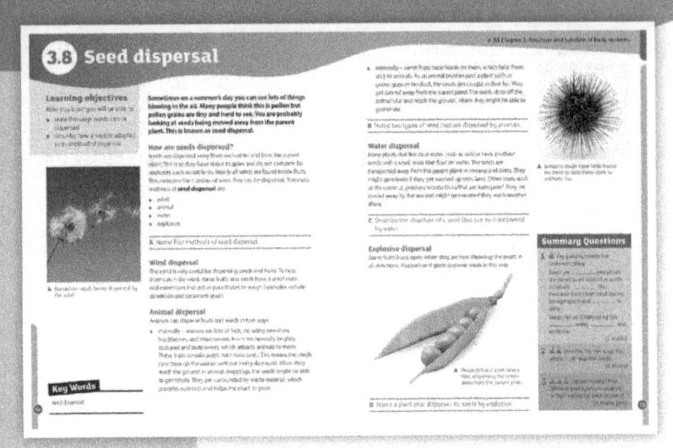

Biology NC link:

- reproduction in plants, including seed and fruit formation and dispersal, including quantitative investigation of some dispersal mechanisms.

Working Scientifically NC link:

- select, plan, and carry out the most appropriate types of scientific enquiries to test predictions, including identifying independent, dependent, and control variables, where appropriate.

Band	Outcome	Checkpoint	
		Question	**Activity**
Developing	State what is meant by seed dispersal (Level 4).	1	Starter 1, Starter 2
	Name the methods of seed dispersal (Level 4).	A, 1	Starter 1
	Plan a simple experiment, stating the variables, when given a hypothesis (Level 4).		Main
Secure	State the ways seeds can be dispersed (Level 5).	B, 1, 2	Starter 1
	Describe how a seed is adapted to its method of dispersal (Level 6).	C, 3	Plenary 1
	Plan a simple experiment to test one hypothesis about seed dispersal, identifying a range of variables (Level 6).		Main
Extending	Explain why seeds are dispersed (Level 7).	1	Starter 1, Main, Homework
	Explain how the adaptations of seeds aid dispersal (Level 7).	C, 3	Starter 2, Plenary 1
	Plan and design an experiment to test a hypothesis about seed dispersal, clearly explaining all the variables involved (Level 8).		Main

Maths
Students collect data from which they can calculate arithmetic means using simple calculations.

They will also plot a graph of their results, deciding on the most appropriate graph to draw given the nature of their variables, as well as choosing the appropriate scales for the axes.

Literacy
Students will use scientific terminology correctly when writing a concise experimental procedure from their plan.

APP
Students plan an experiment by choosing suitable variables and ranges, recording their observations (AF4).

They will then present this data in tables and graphs (AF3), drawing a conclusion and providing a simple evaluation (AF5).

Key Words
seed dispersal

Answers from the student book

In-text questions	
	A wind, animal, water, explosive
	B Any two from: blackberries, strawberries, tomatoes, goose grass, burdock.
	C light/able to float/waterproof
	D pea/gorse

Summary questions	**1** dispersed, competition, nutrients, wind, animals (5 marks) **2** Internally – seeds contains within fruit that animals eat. The seed passes through the animal without getting damaged, reaching the ground in animal droppings. Externally – seeds may have hooks on them which stick to animals as they walk past. The seeds eventually drop off onto the ground. **3** 6 mark question. Example answers: Wind dispersion: seeds are light, seeds have parachutes/wings. Dispersion by being eaten by animals: sweet/brightly coloured fruit. Dispersion by being stuck on animal's fur: have hooks. Dispersion by water: light, float, waterproof. Dispersion by explosion: fruits burst open.

kerboodle

Starter	Support/Extension	Resources
Seed dispersal (10 min) Show photographs or a short film clip about seed dispersal. Discuss why plants go to such lengths to move away from the parent plant. Students suggest a definition of seed dispersal.		
Sycamore seeds (5 min) Drop a few sycamore seeds from head-height as a demonstration. Ask students to describe what they have observed. Discuss why the seeds spin, and where the seeds land in relation to the parent plant (you). This demonstration can be adapted for other seeds.	**Extension**: Students should suggest how this particular seed is adapted to aid its dispersal.	
Main	**Support/Extension**	**Resources**
Investigating seed dispersal (40 min) This practical requires students to consolidate all their ideas about what makes a good practical. Students should be shown a range of apparatus available to them, before deciding on their own hypothesis to investigate, and the apparatus that will be needed in their experimental procedure. Students must describe their method on the worksheet in terms of the independent, dependent, and control variables. For safety reasons, it is important that students are aware that they must not begin their experiment until you have signed off their procedure. This is a long planning and practical session, so students will be required to analyse their results, and answer the questions that follow for homework.	**Support**: An access sheet is available that guides students through the planning process using a given hypothesis. The access sheet also includes a suggested table of results.	**Practical**: Investigating seed dispersal **Skill sheet**: Planning investigations **Skill sheet**: Recording results **Skill sheet**: Calculating means **Skill sheet**: Drawing graphs **Skill sheet**: Choosing scales
Plenary	**Support/Extension**	**Resources**
Wind and animal dispersal (5 min) A range of characteristics of seeds belonging to either wind or animal dispersal methods are shown on the interactive resource. Students must group these characteristics accordingly. **Experimental conclusions** (5 min) Discuss students' findings from their experiments. Did their experiments work according to plan? What were their conclusions with respect to their hypotheses? This plenary serves as a lead-in to their homework task, and is an opportunity for you to offer students extra hints and tips towards their task.		**Interactive**: Wind and animal dispersal
Homework	**Support/Extension**	**Resources**
Students should complete the questions on the practical sheet, analysing their data, and drawing a graph of their results. They should also write a conclusion for their experiment.	**Extension**: Students should offer a basic evaluation, offering one way to improve their experimental procedure.	

B1 Chapter 3 Checkpoint

Checkpoint lesson routes

The route through this lesson can be determined using the Checkpoint assessment.

Percentage pass marks are supplied in the Checkpoint teacher notes.

Route A (support)
Resource: B1 Chapter 3 Checkpoint: Revision

The revision activity is a crossword already completed with key words, but without clues. Students need to produce the clues for the crossword answers.

Route B (extension)
Resource: B1 Chapter 3 Checkpoint: Extension

For extension, students can also do the crossword activity but should be encouraged to create clues which move from simple functions to involved explanations for the words.

Following the crossword, students should work to design two questions on reproduction with mark schemes. Guidance is given in the extension sheet.

Progression to *secure*

No.	Developing outcome	Secure outcome	Making progress
1	State the definitions for adolescence and puberty.	State the difference between adolescence and puberty.	Check the clues the students have produced for these two words, these are terms they find difficult to differentiate. Clear any confusion as they work. Crossword task clues Across: 14, 22
2	State changes of the bodies of boys and girls during puberty.	Describe the main changes which take place during puberty.	Most students find little difficulty with these body changes. They may be embarrassed as they discuss the terms, so address the terms as any other scientific term. Crossword task clues Across: 14, 22
3	Name the main structures of the male and female reproductive systems.	Describe the main structures in the male and female reproductive systems.	Students may not remember the scientific name for the parts, preferring common names. They may struggle with correct spellings. Crossword task clues Across: 12, 18, 20, Down: 2, 5, 14
4	State a function of the main structures of the male and female reproductive system.	Describe the function of the main structures in the male and female reproductive systems.	Students often struggle with functions of the various parts. Have simple, clear, prepared diagrams of male and female systems, and talk them through the key parts in sequence, e.g. eggs made in ovary; travel down the oviduct; develop into the baby in the uterus. Crossword task clues Across: 12, 18, 20, Down: 2, 5, 14
5	State the definition of gametes.	Describe the structure and function of gametes.	You may need to provide help with correct spelling. Crossword task clues Across: 7, 10, Down: 1
6	State what is meant by fertilisation.	Describe the process of fertilisation.	Stress this is the joining of the gametes. This will help for here, and for flower fertilisation. Crossword task clues Across: 7, 10, Down: 1, 6
7	State the definition of gestation.	Describe what happens during gestation.	Students may struggle with sequences. Have two prepared discussions of the idea. The lower level focuses on pregnancy as the development of a baby, and refers to placenta and umbilical cord. The higher explanation refers to a sequence of development of structures. One aid is 'embryo' followed by 'fetus' ('E' followed by 'F'). Crossword task clues Across: 3, Down: 15, 9, 11, 12
8	State how long a pregnancy lasts.	Describe what happens during birth.	Crossword task clues Down: 11, 17
9	State a simple definition of the menstrual cycle.	Describe the main stages of the menstrual cycle.	This is a difficult concept. For help break it down to three simple stages: 1 – uterus wall thickens; 2 – egg is released; 3 – uterus lining is shed and the woman returns to the beginning. Crossword task clues Across: 4, 23
10	Name the parts of a flower.	Identify the main structures in a flower.	Crossword task clues Across: 9, 16, Down: 3, 21
11	State what is meant by pollination.	Describe the process of pollination.	This concept is often confused with fertilisation in the flower. Stress that this is the transfer of the male gamete, and the equivalent to intercourse in humans. Use a flower drawing to talk through the sequence of events. Crossword task clues Across: 16, 24, Down: 3

12	Name two methods of pollination.	Describe the differences between wind pollinated and insect pollinated plants.	Students may need reminding about wind pollination. Crossword task clues Across: 16, 24, Down: 3
13	State what is meant by fertilisation in plants.	Describe the process of fertilisation in plants.	Crossword task clues Down: 6
14	State what seeds and fruit are.	Describe how seeds and fruits are formed.	Using a halved apple, describe how the seed has been formed in the centre, and the fruit around the seed. Crossword task clues Across: 8, Down: 19
15	State what is meant by seed dispersal.	State the ways seeds can be dispersed.	Students may confuse pollination and dispersal. They need to separate the ideas. Crossword task clues Across: 1, 8, Down: 19
16	Name some methods of seed dispersal.	Describe how a seed is adapted to its method of dispersal.	Crossword task clues Across: 1, 8, Down: 19

Answers to end-of-chapter questions

1a Girls – breasts develop, periods start. Boys – testes produce sperm, voice deepens. Both – pubic hair grows, growth spurt. (6 marks) **b** puberty (1 mark)

2a A – oviduct, B – ovary, C – uterus, D – cervix (2 marks)

b vagina (1 mark) **c** uterus (1 mark) **d** An egg is released from an ovary. (2 marks)

3a umbilical cord (1 mark) **b** surrounded by (shock absorbing) fluid (1 mark)

c Cervix relaxes, muscles in uterus wall contract, baby pushed through vagina. (3 marks)

d Any three from the following:
Allows maternal and fetal blood to flow close together. Supplies oxygen/nutrients. Removes waster/carbon dioxide. Prevents infections/harmful substances passing to the fetus.

4a Any two from:
pollen produced in large quantities, pollen is very light, anthers are loosely attached and dangle out of the flower, stigma hangs outside the flower.

b Any two from:
large, brightly coloured petals, sweetly scented, contain nectar, smaller quantities of pollen produced, anthers and stigma held firmly inside the flower.

c Pollen is transferred from the anther to the stigma. (2 marks)

d Any four from:
Pollen tube grows. Pollen tube grows down the style into the ovary. Nucleus of the pollen grain travels down the pollen tube. Joins with the nucleus of the ovule/fertilisation (1 mark). Ovary becomes a fruit. Ovules turn into seeds.

5 Students should be marked on the use of good English, organisation of information, spelling and grammar, and correct use of specialist terms. The best answers will be organised clearly in paragraphs, describing the main structures, and linking these ideas to their functions (maximum of 6 marks). Examples of correct scientific points:

petals – brightly coloured to attract insects
sepals – special leaves which protect unopened buds
stamen – male reproductive part
anther – produces pollen
filament – holds up the anther
carpel – female reproductive part
stigma – sticky to 'catch' grains of pollen
style – holds up the stigma
ovary – contains ovules

Answer guide for Case Study

Developing	Secure	Extending
1–2 marks	3–4 marks	5–6 marks
The control of key variables is not considered. A plan is evident, but may lack detail or be poorly sequenced. Few scientific words are used correctly.	Most key variables are identified. A plan has been produced which uses some appropriate equipment. Some key scientific terms have been used correctly.	Key variables are identified. A logical plan has been produced which would lead to a valid investigation. A range of key scientific terms are used correctly.

kerboodle

B1 Chapter 3 Checkpoint: assessment (automarked)	B1 Chapter 3 Checkpoint: Extension
B1 Chapter 3 Checkpoint: Revision	B1 Chapter 3 Progress task (Information-handling and problem-solving)

Chemistry 1

National curriculum links for this unit	
Chapter	**National Curriculum topic**
Chapter 1: Particles and their behaviour	The particulate nature of matter
Chapter 2: Elements, atoms, and compounds	Atoms, elements, and compounds Pure and impure substances
Chapter 3: Reactions	Chemical reactions
Chapter 4: Acids and alkalis	Chemical reactions

Preparing for Key Stage 4 success

Knowledge

Underpinning knowledge is covered in this unit for KS4 study of:

- The particulate nature of matter
- Atoms, elements, and compounds
- Chemical reactions
- Energetics
- Acids, alkalis, and neutralisation

Maths

Skills developed in this unit (Topic number).

- Understand number size and scale and the quantitative relationship between units (1.2, 1.4, 1.6, 2.2).
- Use of, calculations with, and conversion between fractions, percentages, and ratios (2.1, 2.4).
- Plot and draw graphs (line graphs, bar charts, pie charts, scatter graphs, histograms) selecting appropriate scales for the axes (1.3).
- Extract and interpret information from charts, graphs, and tables (1.3, 2.3, 3.6, 4.2, 4.3).
- Understand when and how to use estimation (1.2, 1.5).
- Understand and use direct proportion and simple ratios (1.1, 3.2).
- Carry out calculations involving $+, -, \times, \div$, either singly or in combination (3.1, 3.2, 3.5, 3.6, 4.1, 4.4).
- Understand and use the symbols $=, <, >, \sim$ (3.4).

Literacy

Skills developed in this unit (Topic number).

- Predicting, making inferences, describing relationships (1.4, 3.3, 3.4, 3.5, 4.3).
- Accessing information to ascertain meaning, using word skills and comprehension strategies, particularly in a scientific context (1.5, 1.7, 3.1, 4.3).
- Communicating ideas and information to a wide range of audiences and a variety of situations, adapting writing style to suit audience and purpose (1.3, 1.7, 2.2, 2.4, 3.5).
- Making connections within/across a range of texts/themes and from personal experience (1.5).
- Use of scientific terms correctly (1.1, 4.1, 4.2, 4.4).
- Organisation of ideas and information (1.1, 1.2, 1.3, 1.4, 1.5, 2.1, 2.2, 2.3, 2.4, 3.3, 3.4, 3.5, 4.3, 4.4).
- Collaboration and exploratory talk (1.2).
- Attention to the 'rules' of the particular form of writing (e.g., news article, scientific report) (3.2, 3.4, 3.6).
- Legibility, SPAG, and sentence structure (1.6, 2.1, 3.6).

Assessment Skills

- Quantitative problem solving (1.3, 2.2, 2.4, 3.5, 3.6, 4.1, 4.2, 4.3) (end-of-chapter 3 Q3)
- Application of Working Scientifically (1.1, 1.3, 1.4, 1.6, 3.2, 3.3, 3.4, 3.6, 4.1, 4.3, 4.4) (end-of-chapter 3 Q2)

KS2 Link	Check before:	Checkpoint	Catch-up
Many materials can exist in the solid, liquid, and gas states.	C1 1.1 The particle model	Ask students to name two materials they know for each of solids, liquids, and gases.	Give simple materials to hold and classify, such as chocolate and water. This can be linked to the properties below.
Different materials have different properties.	C1 1.2 Solids, liquids, and gases	Ask students to write a list of different properties materials can possess.	Card sort activity where students need to match the correct definition to property keywords, such as 'hardness'.
The different properties of different materials make them suitable for different uses.	C1 1.2 Solids, liquids, and gases	Ask students to suggest suitable materials for making a saucepan and a tent. Ask them to explain their choices.	Provide a selection of materials, with descriptions of their properties and uses, for students to observe.
The state of a material depends on the temperature.	C1 1.3 Melting and freezing	Ask students what will happen to a snowman when the temperature increases.	Allow students to observe an ice cube placed in a warm location.
Changes of state are reversible.	C1 1.3 Melting and freezing	Ask students what will happen to water in an ice cube tray when it is placed in a freezer.	Place an ice cube tray filled with water into a freezer – allow students to observe before and after.
Melting, freezing, evaporating, boiling, and condensing are changes of state.	C1 1.3 Melting and freezing	Ask students to label a diagram of water boiling in a kettle to show their understanding of the key terms.	Demonstrate a kettle boiling, with discussion of what is happening. Include what happens when you place a cold surface in the path of steam.
Some changes result in the formation of new materials.	C1 2.3 Elements, atoms, and compounds	Ask students to describe what happens when a cake is baked, in terms of the starting materials and the end product.	Use students to represent the individual ingredients. Model them reacting. Discuss what has happened to the ingredients and that the new product has different properties to the original.
Changes that form new materials are not reversible.	C1 2.3 Elements, atoms, and compounds	Ask students to describe the differences between bread and toast, and raw and cooked eggs, and to decide if the original material can be obtained from the product.	Demonstrate cooking an egg in a tin lid over a Bunsen burner. Allow students to make observations on the egg that will allow them to conclude that the original material has been changed irreversibly.
Changes that are not reversible include burning, oxidation, and reactions of acid.	C1 3.3 Burning fuels	Ask students to draw a diagram showing what happens when a candle burns and where the wax goes.	Provide a cloze passage and diagram for students to label with cards containing keywords and descriptions.

kerboodle

C1 Unit pre-test
C1 Big practical project (foundation)
C1 Big practical project (higher)
C1 Big practical project teacher notes
C1 Practical project hints: graph plotting
C1 Practical project hints: planning
C1 Practical project hints: writing frame
C1 End-of-unit test (foundation)
C1 End-of-unit test (foundation) mark scheme
C1 End-of-unit test (higher)
C1 End-of-unit test (higher) mark scheme

Answers to Picture Puzzler

Key Words

acid, thermometer, oxygen, melting

The key word is **atom**.

Close Up

frost on a window

1.1 The particle model

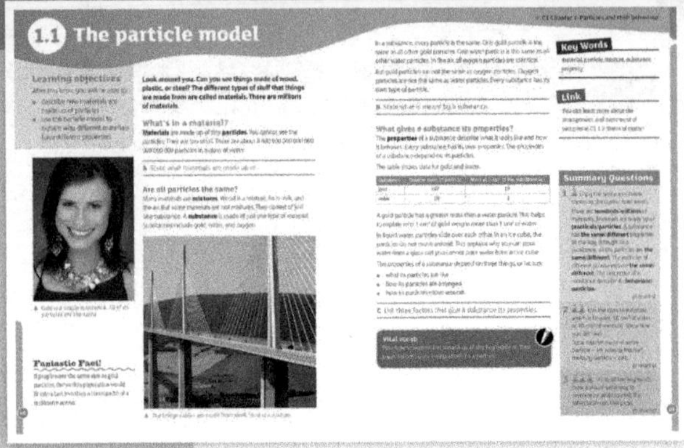

Chemistry NC link:

- the properties of different states of matter (solid, liquid, and, gas) in terms of the particle model, including gas pressure.

Working Scientifically NC link:

- present reasoned explanations, including explaining data in relation to predictions and hypotheses.

Band	Outcome	Checkpoint	
		Question	Activity
Developing	State that materials are made up of particles (Level 4).	A, 1	Main 1
	Match particle models to the properties of a material (Level 4).	C, 1	Plenary 1, Plenary 2
	State what toy building bricks are representing when used to model substances (Level 4).		Main 2
Secure	Describe how materials are made up of particles (Level 5).	A, B, 1	
	Use the particle model to explain why different materials have different properties (Level 6).	C, 1	Plenary 1, Plenary 2
	Use the particle model to explain how building brick models are representing common substances (Level 6).		Main 2
Extending	Explain how a range of materials are made up of particles (Level 7).	A, B, 1	
	Evaluate particle models that explain why different materials have different properties (Level 7).	C, 1	Plenary 1, Plenary 2
	Design and explain a new representation of the particle model (Level 8).		Main 2

Maths
In Summary Question 2 students use the idea of direct proportion to make predictions about the relative mass of elements.

Literacy
The Vital Vocab activity in the student book asks students to use scientific terms, and attempt to use them correctly in discussions and in writing.

APP
Students can use particle models (abstract ideas) to explain the properties of substances (AF1).

Key Words
material, particle, mixture, substance, property

Answers from the student book

In-text questions	**A** tiny particles **B** A material that has the same properties all the way through. **C** What its particles are like, how its particles are arranged, and how its particles move.
Activity	**Vital vocab** Students should offer explanations of the key words on this spread to a partner. Their definitions should be scientifically correct.
Summary questions	**1** millions, particles, same, same, different, behaviour (6 marks) **2** 10 cm^3 of mercury is heavier because its particles are heavier. (2 marks) **3** Visual summary should include key words, meanings of key words, examples to illustrate key words. Visual summary should be logically organised. (6 marks)

Starter	Support/Extension	Resources
What do these key words mean? (5 min) Ask students to decide what each of the key words displayed in the corresponding student-book spread mean. Asking students to explain keywords will gauge prior knowledge students have from KS2, and provide indications of which terms need revisiting.		
Who can identify the most materials? (10 min) Ask students to make a list of all the different materials they can see in the classroom – see who has the longest list. Can students group the materials in their lists at all?	**Extension**: Students could be asked to see if there are any similarities or differences in the materials they identify.	
Main	**Support/Extension**	**Resources**
Building bricks as particles (5 min) Use toy building bricks to demonstrate individual particles within a larger amount of substance – start with a large group all connected and then break them down into the individual particles. It is important to stress that each building brick is the same if you have a pure substance. Use different coloured bricks to demonstrate different substances and discuss how these would have different properties.	**Extension**: Students will be able to suggest their own models to describe particles within materials and suggest weaknesses of any models suggested.	
Introducing the particle model (20 min) Students complete the activity sheet, introducing them to the particle model. Students will need to complete a written section about particles and discuss the particle model.		**Activity**: Introducing the particle model
Particle summary (10 min) Students should complete the questions provided in the corresponding student-book spread to check their understanding of how the properties of materials depend on the type of particle present, and the way these particles are arranged.		
Plenary	**Support/Extension**	**Resources**
Considering models (10 min) Students will see a picture that represents particles within a material. Students need to think about how this model is representing particles. They must then decide if the reasons given in the resource make the model a good or a bad one.	**Extension**: Ask students to describe how they could improve the model given.	**Interactive**: Considering models
Particle sentences (5 min) Ask students to use the key words from the student book to write sentences that summarise what they have learnt about materials and particles.	**Support**: Display the key words during the activity.	
Homework		
Research a material of your choice and write a summary of its properties and uses.		

1.2 States of matter

Chemistry NC link:

- the properties of the different states of matter (solid, liquid, and gas) in terms of the particle model, including gas pressure.

Physics NC link:

- similarities and differences, including density differences, between solids, liquids, and gases
- the differences in arrangements, in motion, and in closeness of particles explaining shape and density.

Working Scientifically NC link:

- interpret observations and data, including identifying patterns and using observations, measurements, and data to draw conclusions.

Band	Outcome	Checkpoint	
		Question	**Activity**
Developing	Identify a substance in its three states (Level 3).	Starter 1	Main 3
	Match properties of the three states of matter to the name of the state (Level 4).		Plenary 1
	Make relevant observations in order to decide if something is a solid, liquid, or gas (Level 4).		Main 3
Secure	Describe the properties of a substance in its three states (Level 5).	B, 1, 2	
	Use ideas about particles to explain the properties of a substance in its three states (Level 6).		Main 3
	Use observations to decide if substances are solids, liquids, or gases (Level 6).		Main 3
Extending	Discuss the properties of a range of substances in their three states (Level 7).	B, C, 1–3	
	Use ideas about how fast particles are moving to explain the properties of a substance in its three states (Level 7).	3	Main 3
	Identify how the observations made would differ if the substances had been at different temperatures (Level 8).		Main 3

Maths

Express particle? Activity asks students to use number size and scale to convert between km/s and m/s to apply these to real-life situations.

Ask students to estimate how many particles are in tiny objects such as a pin head and then find out the answer.

Literacy

Students pay close attention to what others say in discussions. Ask questions to develop ideas and make contributions that take account of others' views, by discussing and planning a flow chart of questions to help them decide if a substance is solid, liquid, or gas.

APP

Use a particle model (abstract ideas) when describing processes or phenomena (AF1).

Students will use the observations they make during the practical activity to decide on a substance's state (AF5).

Key Words

solid, liquid, gas, states of matter

Answers from the student book

In-text questions	**A** solid, liquid, gas **B** Solids cannot flow, liquids can flow. A Solids' shape is fixed, a liquid takes the shape of its container. Solids exist at colder temperatures than liquids. **C** You cannot compress a liquid because its particles touch their neighbours.
Activity	**Express particle?** The train travels at 0.135 km/s. This is (0.135 × 1000) = 135 m/s. So the oxygen particles travel faster.

Summary questions	1 There are **three** states of matter. You **cannot** compress a substance in the solid state because the particles touch each other. In the liquid and gas states, a substance flows because the particles **can** move from place to place. You **can** compress a gas because the particles are spread out. (4 marks) 2 A substance flows in the liquid state and in the gas state. You cannot compress a substance in the liquid state but you can compress it in the gas state. In the liquid state a substance takes the shape of the bottom of its container but in the gas state a substance takes the shape of the whole container. (3 marks) 3 6 mark question. Example answers: In the solid and liquid states the particles touch their neighbours so you cannot compress water in the solid and liquid states. In the gas state the particles do not touch their neighbours so you can compress water in the gas state. In the solid state the particles are in fixed positions so the shape of a solid is fixed. In the liquid and gas states particles move from place to place so the shape in the liquid and gas states is not fixed. In the liquid and gas states water can flow.

Starter	Support/Extension	Resources
An alternative question-led lesson is also available.		**Question-led lesson**: States of matter
Solid, liquid, or gas? (5 min) Display interactive activity of various objects which students can drag into the correct columns for solids, liquids, or gases. Discussion should take place of how small particles are. For example, there are over 300 000 000 000 000 000 000 000 particles in a teaspoon of water. The ability of students can be gauged through the ease with which they categorise objects and the reasoning behind their choices.		**Interactive**: Solid, liquid, or gas?
What state is this? (10 min) Provide students with an array of simple objects and substances to classify as solids, liquids, or gases.	**Support**: Students will often prefer to touch/see objects to aid their decision making.	
Main	**Support/Extension**	**Resources**
Defining states of matter (10 min) Display interactive particle model animations (found on the Internet) for solids, liquids, and gases. Draw up a table of properties for each state, including particle arrangement, density, particle motion, and shape (an example is available on the corresponding student-book spread).	**Support**: The support sheet contains an observation table with questions to help students identify the state of matter.	
Students as particles (5 min) Use a group of students to model particles. Arrange them as a solid, liquid, and gas. Discuss how fast the particles are moving in each state, and their relative positions.		
Properties of solids, liquids, and gases (20 min) Students complete the practical allowing them to make observations on the properties of substances and materials, and conclude whether they are solids, liquids, or gases.	**Extension**: Give students substances that are harder to define (e.g., sand, hair gel, jelly).	**Practical**: Properties of solids, liquids, and gases **Skill sheet**: Recording results
Plenary	**Support/Extension**	**Resources**
Quick-fire identification (5 min) Call out properties of solids, liquids, and gases. Students should correctly identify solid, liquid, or gas, displaying their answer on mini-whiteboards.	**Extension**: Ask students to explain their choices.	
States of matter taboo (10 min) Students are chosen to describe a material in terms of its properties, without identifying its state. A student has to try and identify what it is and its state of matter.		
Homework		
Design a detailed poster with explanatory notes on the three states of matter, discussing the properties of each and giving examples for each along with examples of materials that are harder to classify.		

1.3 Melting and freezing

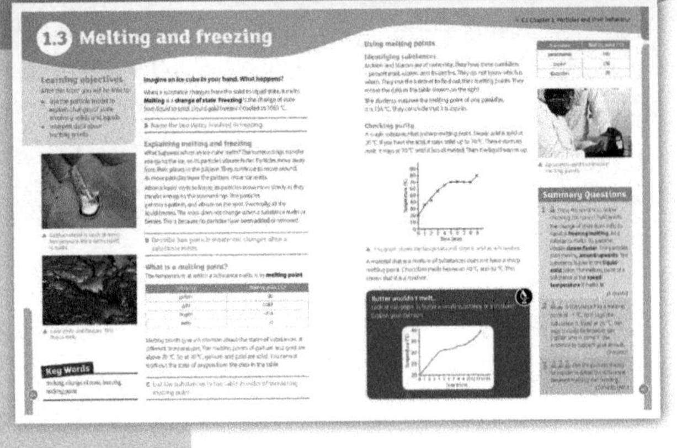

Chemistry NC link:
- changes of state in terms of the particle model
- energy changes on changes of state (qualitative).

Physics NC link:
- reversibility in melting, freezing, evaporation, sublimation, condensation, and dissolving
- the differences in arrangements, in motion, and in closeness of particles explaining changes of state.

Working Scientifically NC link:
- interpret observations and data, including identifying patterns and using observations, measurements, and data to draw conclusions.

Band	Outcome	Checkpoint	
		Question,	**Activity**
Developing	Describe how substances change as the temperature changes (Level 3).		Starter 1, Starter 2, Main 1
	State the meaning of the term melting point (Level 3).	1	
	Describe the observations seen as stearic acid cools in terms of the states of matter it is in (Level 4).		Main 1
Secure	Discuss the change in particle movement during melting and freezing, using particle diagrams to help (Level 5).	B, 1, 2	Starter 2
	Interpret melting point data to decide the state of a substance at a given temperature (Level 5).	3	
	Use cooling data to decide the melting point of stearic acid (Level 6).		Main 1
Extending	Explain why there is a period of constant temperature during melting and freezing (the latent phase) (Level 7).		Main 1, Main 2
	Interpret melting point data to explain the particle movement of different substances at given temperatures (Level 7).		Main 1, Main 2
	Locate the melting point of stearic acid on a graph of data plotted from observations (Level 8).		Main 1

Maths
The maths task in the student book requires students to interpret a graph showing the melting of butter, and explain whether butter is a pure substance or a mixture.

Record temperatures of stearic acid as it cools, using this to plot a cooling curve and to identify the melting point.

Literacy
Students can present and explain their results to the rest of the class.

APP
Students apply their knowledge of the particle model to explain observations in their experiment (AF1).

During the practical students must collect data, choosing appropriate time periods to record observations for the stearic acid (AF4).

Key Words
melting, change of state, freezing, melting point

Answers from the student book

In-text questions	**A** liquid and solid **B** The particles first start to move more slowly. The particles arrange themselves in a pattern and vibrate on the spot. **C** oxygen, water, gallium, gold
Activity	**Butter wouldn't melt...** Butter is a mixture of substances. The graph shows this because it does not show a sharp melting point.
Summary questions	**1** melting, faster, around, liquid, temperature (5 marks) **2** Ben is correct. If the melting point is -7 °C then the substance must be in either the liquid or gas state at 20 °C. You cannot know which of these two states it is in unless you know its boiling point. (3 marks) **3** 6 mark question. Example answers: Melting is the change from the solid to the liquid state. On melting, the particles vibrate faster and move away from their places in the pattern. More and more particles start moving around. When all the particles are moving around from place to place, the substance has melted. Freezing is the change from the liquid to the solid state. On freezing, the particles start to move more slowly. They get into a pattern, and vibrate on the spot.

Starter	Support/Extension	Resources
How does water become ice? (5 min) Ask students to name the processes that occur when water is placed into an ice cube tray and placed into the freezer, and then when an ice cube is left in a warm place. Introduce the terms reversible and irreversible. **What happens as water freezes?** (10 min) Students reorder the descriptions of freezing on the interactive resource to check their understanding.	**Extension**: To extend the starter activities, students should be asked to consider the energy transfers involved in the processes.	**Interactive**: What happens as water freezes?
Main	**Support/Extension**	**Resources**
Observing the cooling of stearic acid (20 min) Students observe the temperature of stearic acid over time as it cools and then plot their data to produce a cooling curve for stearic acid.	**Support**: Students should be provided with pre-drawn axes. **Extension**: Students will be able to choose their own scales for each axis.	**Practical**: Observing the cooling of stearic acid **Skill sheet**: Choosing scales
Presentation and discussion of results (20 min) Introduce students to cooling curves and how these can be interpreted to find the melting point, and to show whether a substance is pure or impure. Students may require extra guidance on the meanings of these keywords. In groups, students should plan a two-minute presentation to the class to explain their results. Students should describe the energy transfers during this phase change. As a class, discuss where the melting point would be found on the graph. Discuss how melting points are not sharp for mixtures and how melting points can be used to identify substances.	**Extension**: Students should explain why the graph 'levels off' and has a period with no temperature change.	**Skill sheet**: Recording results **Skill sheet**: Drawing graphs
Plenary	**Support/Extension**	**Resources**
What is happening to the particles in the stearic acid? (5 min) Ask students to sketch the cooling curve for stearic acid on a mini-whiteboard. Then ask students to draw particle diagrams for each stage in the curve and name the state for each significant section of the graph. **Melting points** (5 min) Ask students to refer to the table of melting points on the corresponding student-book spread. Name a temperature and ask students which state each substance would be in.	**Support**: Developing students could be placed in groups to enable peer support and aid recall of the particle behaviour at different stages.	
Homework		
Give students the melting point of iron (1538 °C) and ask students to suggest why steel does not have one specific melting temperature. An alternative WebQuest homework activity is also available on Kerboodle where students research how roads are made safer in adverse weather conditions.		**WebQuest**: Safer roads

1.4 Boiling

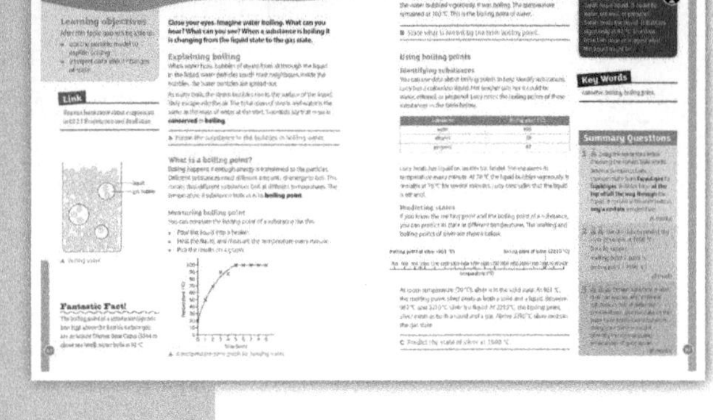

Chemistry NC link:
- changes of state in terms of the particle model
- energy changes on changes of state (qualitative).

Physics NC link:
- reversibility in melting, freezing, evaporation, sublimation, condensation, and dissolving
- the differences in arrangements, in motion, and in closeness of particles explaining changes of state.

Working Scientifically NC link:
- interpret observations and data, including identifying patterns and using observations, measurements, and data to draw conclusions.

Band	Outcome	Checkpoint	
		Question	**Activity**
Developing	Describe boiling as a change of state (Level 4).	1	Starter 1
	Recognise that different substances boil at different temperatures (Level 4).	2	
	Draw straightforward conclusions from boiling point data presented in tables and graphs (Level 4).		Main 1
Secure	Use the particle model to explain boiling (Level 5).		Starter 2
	Explain why different substances boil at different temperatures (Level 6).	2	Main 1, Plenary 1, Plenary 2
	Select data and information about boiling points and use them to contribute to conclusions (Level 5).		Main 1
Extending	Use the particle model and latent heat to explain boiling (Level 7).	3	Main 1
	Explain why different substances boil at different temperatures using particle diagrams and latent heat (Level 8).	3	Main 1
	Assess the strength of evidence from boiling point data, deciding whether it is sufficient to support a conclusion (Level 7).		Main 1

Maths
Order, add, and subtract negative numbers in the context of boiling and melting point data.

Literacy
From the activity students construct clear and coherent sentences, and synthesise alternative ways of presenting ideas and information (tables, lists) when explaining boiling points.

APP
Students can use abstract models to explain melting points (AF1).

Students can interpret graphs and tables from the student book questions and from the practical (AF5).

Key Words
boiling, boiling point

Answers from the student book

In-text questions	**A** steam/water in the gas state/water vapour **B** The temperature at which a substance boils. **C** Silver is in the liquid state at 1000 °C.

Activity	**Mystery liquid** The substance is likely to be propanol.
Summary questions	**1** liquid, gas, all the way through, a certain (4 marks) **2** Copper is in the liquid state at 2000 °C. (1 mark) **3** Example answers (6 marks): Any model that has identical particles that can move around relative to each other. Diagrams to be included. Table or similar to compare how the model is like, and not like, reality.

Starter	Support/Extension	Resources
Describing boiling (5 min) Boil a beaker of water. Ask students to describe why they start to see bubbles forming, and where this energy is transferred from.	**Support**: Students could be asked to focus on observations only.	
What happens when water boils? (10 min) Students use the interactive resource to reorder descriptions of boiling to check their understanding of the sequence of events.	**Extension**: Students could be asked to suggest explanations for what is happening.	**Interactive**: What happens when water boils?
Main	**Support/Extension**	**Resources**
Heating water (25 min) Students use the supplied data to plot a heating curve for water. Students then need to consider what is happening to the particles at each stage of the process, together with the energy transfers that occur during this process. Discuss where the boiling point is found on the curve, and why there are periods with constant temperatures (the latent phase). Students should discuss the reversibility of boiling at this stage. **Consolidating states** (15 min) Students should complete the questions provided on the corresponding student-book spread to check their understanding of boiling and to gain practice at predicting the state a substance is found in at certain temperatures, given its boiling point.	**Support**: A support sheet is available with pre-drawn axes for drawing the graph. **Extension**: Students will be able to apply the particle models to aid their descriptions.	**Activity**: Heating water **Skill sheet**: Choosing scales **Skill sheet**: Drawing graphs
Plenary	**Support/Extension**	**Resources**
Which boiling point is which? (5 min) Display a list of substances on the board (e.g., oxygen, water, iron, mercury) with a jumbled up list of their boiling points. Ask students to guess which boiling point belongs to which substance using their everyday knowledge of them. (Substances selected will need to have boiling points that are not close to one another and will need to have well known properties.) **How can substances be identified using boiling points?** (5 min) Students write a paragraph, explaining how you would go about setting up an experiment to identify a substance if you knew its boiling point.	**Support**: Extra information can be added about the chosen substances such as the state it is in at room temperature.	
Homework	**Support/Extension**	
Prepare a fact sheet on different ways the boiling point of water can be changed. Explain why being able to change the boiling point of water may be useful.	**Support**: This can be given in the form of hints. For example, ask students to answer questions such as 'Why do we add salt to icy roads?'	

1.5 More changes of state

1.5 More changes of state

C1 Chapter 1 Particles and their behaviour

Learning objectives

What happens to the water when you use a hairdryer to dry your hair? It changes state from liquid to gas without boiling. This is called evaporation.

Explaining evaporation

Key Words

How is evaporation useful?

What is condensation?

What is sublimation?

Summary Questions

Chemistry NC link:
- changes of state in terms of the particle model
- energy changes on changes of state (qualitative).

Physics NC link:
- reversibility in melting, freezing, evaporation, sublimation, condensation, and dissolving
- the differences in arrangements, in motion, and in closeness of particles explaining changes of state.

Working Scientifically NC link:
- ask questions and develop a line of enquiry based on observations of the real world, alongside prior knowledge and experience.

Band	Outcome	Checkpoint	
		Question	**Activity**
Developing	Recall changes of state involving gases (Level 3).	D, 1	
	Describe how particles change in their arrangements during evaporation, condensation, and sublimation (Level 4).	A, 1, 2	
	Carry out a practical on evaporation, carrying out experimental procedures carefully, and recording results accurately (Level 4).		Main 1, Main 2
Secure	Describe changes of state involving gases (Level 5).	A–D, 1–3	Main 1, Main 2
	Use a particle model to explain evaporating, condensing, and subliming (Level 6).	1–3	
	Explain how the practical procedure can be kept fair to ensure valid results (Level 6).		Main 1, Main 2
Extending	Explain what occurs during sublimation and condensation using particle models (Level 7).	1–3	
	Explain, using particle models, the differences between evaporation and boiling (Level 7).	A, 1–3	
	Justify and evaluate the practical procedure chosen based on students' understanding of changes of state, and given the results obtained (Level 7).		Main 1, Main 2

Maths
Students will need to use estimation to gauge the size of crystals grown given the unusual shapes that will be produced.

Literacy
Students can answer extended questions describing the differences in the crystals they have produced and why these have arisen, applying their knowledge to the answers.

APP
Students apply their understanding of evaporation in planning their experiment to grow the biggest copper sulfate crystals (AF4).

Key Words
evaporation, condensation, sublimation

Answers from the student book

In-text questions	**A** In evaporation, particles escape from the surface of the liquid, but in boiling, bubbles of the substance in the gas state form throughout the liquid, rise to the surface, and escape. Evaporation happens at any temperature, but boiling happens only at the boiling point. **B** A hairdryer heats the substance in its liquid state, and supplies moving air to move just evaporated particles away. **C** On condensing, a substance in the liquid state is formed. **D** subliming

Activity	**Evaluating evaporation** Make the test fair by soaking the same type of material in water and having equal-sized pieces of this material. It is not possible to know whether the evidence supports the conclusion because the investigation is not fair.
Summary questionss	**1** In boiling substances change from the liquid to the gas state. In boiling particles leave from all parts of the liquid. In condensing substances change from the gas state to the liquid state. In evaporating particles leave from the surface of the liquid. In evaporating substances change from the liquid to the gas state. (5 marks) **2** On condensing, particles in the gas state move closer together until they touch each other. The particles stop moving around throughout the whole container, and instead they move around each other in the bottom part of the container. (2 marks) **3** 6 mark question. Example answers: Condensation is the change of state from gas to liquid, but evaporation and boiling involve a substance changing from its liquid to its gas state. In condensation, particles get closer together, but in boiling and evaporation the particles get further apart. In condensation, particles move more slowly, but in boiling and evaporation they start to move faster. In evaporation particles leave the surface of the liquid, but in boiling, bubbles of the substance in its gas state form throughout the liquid. They rise to the surface and escape. Evaporation can happen at any temperature, but boiling only happens at the boiling point. Condensation can happen at any temperature below the boiling point, but boiling can only happen at the boiling point.

Starter	Support/Extension	Resources
Iodine sublimation (10 min) Demonstrate the sublimation of iodine in a fume cupboard. If available, solid carbon dioxide ('dry ice') could also be shown. Demonstrate how the solid that has sublimed can be recollected (see RSC Practical Chemistry) as a solid again without the liquid being seen. As with the previous changes of states, students should consider the energy transfers involved in sublimation and condensation, and discuss the reversibility of this change. **Observing condensation** (5 min) Ask students to breathe on a cold surface such as a mirror. Discuss what is happening to the particles to turn them from a gas into a liquid. Ask students to explain whether this change is reversible or irreversible.	**Support**: Evaporation and condensation will need to be revisited. **Extension**: Students can be told that the process of gases being collected back as a solid is called deposition.	
Main	**Support/Extension**	**Resources**
Who can make the biggest crystals? (40 min) Explain to students that copper sulfate crystals will form from copper sulfate solution as the solution evaporates, and that the slower the evaporation, the bigger the crystals will be. Students then need to predict how they can obtain the biggest crystals by considering the factors affecting evaporation. Students should read the corresponding student-book spread and answer the summary questions to check their understanding of the processes met. Crystals will need to be revisited in another lesson.	**Support**: Students issued with the access sheet, where they make copper sulfate crystals using a given method. **Extension**: Students should try and explain why slower evaporation may result in larger crystals.	**Practical**: Who can make the biggest crystals?
Plenary	**Support/Extension**	**Resources**
Identifying evaporation, condensation, and sublimation (5 min) An interactive resource where students match state changes to pictures of evaporation, condensation, and sublimation. **What's the difference between evaporation and boiling?** (5 min) Ask students to recall the differences between evaporation and boiling.	**Extension**: Ask students to draw particle diagrams to illustrate the processes.	**Interactive**: Identifying evaporation, condensation, and sublimation
Homework		
Students use their knowledge of evaporation to prepare a leaflet for householders on how they can dry their washing most efficiently.		

1.6 Diffusion

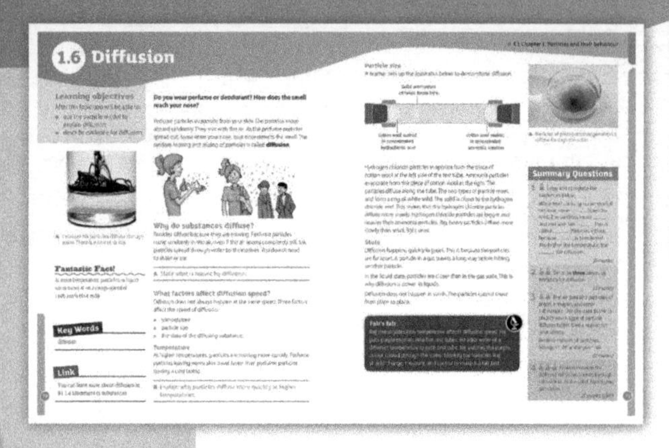

Chemistry NC link:

- diffusion in terms of the particle model.

Physics NC link:

- diffusion in liquids and gases driven by differences in concentration.

Working Scientifically NC link:

- identify independent, dependent, and control variables where appropriate.

Band	Outcome	Checkpoint	
		Question	**Activity**
Developing	Describe examples of diffusion (Level 4).		Starter 1, Starter 2
	Describe the movement of particles in diffusion (Level 4).	A, B, 1	Plenary 1
	Identify the dependent and independent variable when investigating the rates of diffusion (Level 4).	WS	Main 1
Secure	Use the particle model to explain diffusion (Level 6).	3	Main 1
	Describe evidence for diffusion (Level 5).	2	Main 1
	Identify variables that need to be kept constant when investigating the rates of diffusion of $KMnO_4$ (Level 6).	WS	Main 1
Extending	Use particle diagrams to explain how diffusion occurs and the factors that affect it (Level 7).	4	Main 1
	Describe why diffusion is faster at higher temperatures, using the concept of how fast particles are moving. (Level 8).		Main 1, Plenary 1
	Identify key variables in complex contexts, explaining why some cannot be readily controlled, and planning appropriate approaches to investigating the rates of diffusion of $KMnO_4$ (Level 7).		Main 1, Plenary 1

Maths
In the practical activity students use the quantitative relationship between units to convert the times they record between the units of seconds and minutes.

Literacy
Students pay attention to legibility, spelling, punctuation, grammar, and sentence structure when they write a leaflet on diffusion.

APP
Students identify significant variables and recognise those which are independent and those which are dependent when answering the student-book activity (AF4).

Key Words
diffusion

Answers from the student book

In-text questions	**A** The random moving and mixing of particles. **B** The particles are moving more quickly.
Activity	**Fair's fair** Variable to change – temperature; variable to measure – time for purple colour to be evenly spread throughout the water; variables to control – size and number of crystals, volume of water.

Summary questions	**1** particles, randomly, air, diffusion, energy, faster (6 marks) **2** You might be able to smell particles of a substance diffusing in the air. You might be able to see particles of a coloured substance moving through the air. You might be able to see particles of a coloured substance moving through a liquid. (3 marks) **3** Nitrogen particles diffuse faster because their particles have a smaller mass. (2 marks) **4** 6 mark question. Example answers: Diffusion happens quickly in gases because the particles are far apart. A particle can travel a relatively long way before colliding with another particle. Diffusion happens slower in liquids because the particles are closer together. A particle is likely to travel only a short distance before it collides with another particle. Diffusion does not happen in solids because the particles are packed tightly together. The gaps between the particles are small, so the particles cannot move form place to place.

Starter	Support/Extension	Resources
Perfume diffusion (5 min) Spray perfume or air freshener in one corner of the room. Ask students to put their hand up when they are able to smell it. Discuss how the particles have moved around the room. Be aware of students with respiratory problems. **Modelling diffusion** (10 min) Have five students acting as diffusing particles. Ask them to make their way across the room. Put more and more other students in their way to demonstrate diffusion through the different states, and hence the relative speeds. Asking students to travel in pairs with arms interlinked will allow modelling of how greater particle mass affects diffusion speed.	**Support**: Students can be asked to concentrate on why students who are closer can smell the perfume first.	
Main	**Support/Extension**	**Resources**
What affects the rate of diffusion? (30 min) Students will consider how temperature affects the rate of diffusion of $KMnO_4$ in water, and identify the variables within the investigation. Students should be aware of other factors affecting diffusion, for example, surface area (met in B1) and concentration.	**Support**: The support sheet contains a table of results for students to fill in. Support students in order to make their investigations as fair as possible, for example, by discussing the size of particles chosen or how they are placed in the water to minimise early diffusion. **Extension**: Students should discuss how quickly particles are moving and how it plays a part in diffusion in their explanations.	**Practical**: What affects the rate of diffusion? **Skill sheet**: Choosing scales **Skill sheet**: Recording results **Skill sheet**: Drawing graphs
Checking understanding of diffusion (10 min) Students should complete the questions provided in the corresponding student-book spread to check their understanding of diffusion.		
Plenary	**Support/Extension**	**Resources**
Describing diffusion (5 min) Students complete a passage on diffusion from the interactive resource.		**Interactive**: Describing diffusion
Diffusion true or false statements (5 min) Assign one corner of the room to 'true' and one to 'false'. Call out statements about diffusion, for example, 'it is faster when the temperature is colder'. Students decide if the statement is true or false and move to the appropriate corner of the room.	**Extension**: Ask students to explain their decisions.	
Homework		
Write a short paragraph explaining why hot water is best for making cups of tea.		

1.7 Gas pressure

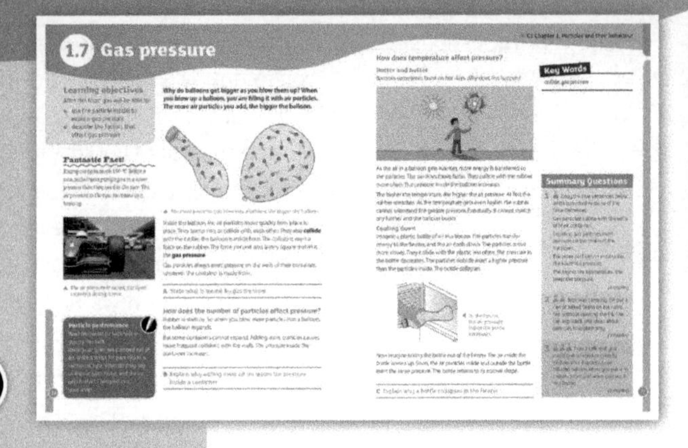

Chemistry NC link:
- the properties of the different states of matter (solid, liquid, and gas) in terms of the particle model, including gas pressure.

Working Scientifically NC link:
- interpret observations and data, including identifying patterns and using observations, measurements, and data to draw conclusions.

Band	Outcome	Checkpoint	
		Question	**Activity**
Developing	Describe simply what gas pressure is (Level 4).	A	Plenary 1, Plenary 2
	State examples of gas pressure in everyday situations (Level 4).		Literacy, Starter 1, Starter 2, Plenary 1, Plenary 2
	Collect and interpret simple primary data to provide evidence for gas pressure (Level 4).		Main 1
Secure	Use the particle model to explain gas pressure (Level 6).	C, 2	Main 1, Plenary 1
	Describe the factors that affect gas pressure (Level 6).		Main 1
	Collect, analyse, and interpret primary data to provide evidence for gas pressure (Level 6).		Main 1
Extending	Use particle diagrams to explain how gas pressure is created (Level 7).	3	
	Explain, using particle diagrams, what happens to gas pressure as the temperature increases (Level 8).	3	
	Process data, including using multi-step calculations and compound measures, to identify complex relationships between variables (Level 8).		Main 1

Literacy
In the student book students identify main ideas, events, and supporting details when writing and performing a script.

APP
Using models to aid explanations of gas pressure (AF1).

Using data as evidence from experiments with gas pressure (AF4).

Key Words
collide, gas pressure

Answers from the student book

In-text questions	**A** The force per unit area caused by particles colliding with the walls of their container. **B** There are more particles causing more frequent collisions with the walls inside the container. **C** The particles transfer energy to the freezer and the air cools down. The particles move more slowly. They collide with the plastic less often, so the pressure in the bottle decreases.
Activity	**Particle performance** Script to indicate that particles move faster as the air gets hotter, leading to more frequent collisions with the rubber tyres, and so increased pressure.

Summary questions	
Summary questions	**1** Gas particles collide with the walls of their container. Colliding gas particles exert pressure on the inside of their container. The more particles in a container, the **higher** the pressure. The higher the temperature, the **higher** the pressure. (4 marks) **2** There are air particles in the closed can, above the baked beans. On heating, the gas particles move faster. They collide with the walls of the container more frequently, so the pressure increases. Eventually the pressure is so high that the container isn't strong enough to withstand this pressure, and the container explodes. (3 marks) **3** Example points (6 marks): In a warm room, the particles are moving more quickly. The particles collide with the walls of the rubber more often. The air pressure inside the balloon increases. The rubber will stretch and the balloon expand. In the freezer the particles transfer energy to the freezer, and the air cools down. The particles move more slowly and collide with the rubber less often. The pressure inside the balloon decreases. The rubber stretches out less and the balloon shrinks.

kerboodle

Starter	Support/Extension	Resources
What happens when gas pressure builds up? (5 min) Demonstrate gas pressure by placing a small amount of water in an empty camera film cartridge case along with an indigestion tablet, placing the lid on and turning it upside down. (Ensure there is plenty of space around the experiment and that there is something to mop up the resulting puddle afterwards). Alternatively, drop a mint sweet into a bottle of diet cola, leaving the lid off and observe the resulting fountain caused by the gas being able to escape more quickly from the bottle due to the reaction with the mint. **What are gases like?** (10 min) Discuss the statements with students to ensure that they all have a good recall of the behaviour of gases from previous lessons and from KS2. The interactive resource will allow you to find out how confident students are with the behaviour of gases. Any weaknesses will need to be revisited before the concept of gas pressure can be taught.	**Support**: Students can also be given a blown-up balloon in order to feel the pressure inside. Alternatively, this can be done over the end of a plastic gas syringe and trying to compress it. This will help them to visualise what is happening to the particles within a gas.	**Interactive**: What are gases like?
Main	**Support/Extension**	**Resources**
What affects gas pressure? (25 min) Students will consider the factors that affect how much gas pressure is generated. A recap at the end of the practical can make use of animations that are readily available on the Internet. **Drawing particle diagrams** (15 min) Ask students to draw a storyboard of particle diagrams to show what happens as you blow a balloon up, giving in-depth explanations for each picture on their storyboard.	**Support**: Provide key words and phrases on which to base drawings. **Extension**: Students should explain why solids, liquids, and gases exert pressure differently.	**Practical**: What affects gas pressure?
Plenary	**Support/Extension**	**Resources**
Gas pressure explanations (5 min) Without referring to their books or class notes, students should explain to a partner how gas pressure is created. **When do we need pressure?** (5 min) Ask students to come up with three situations where pressure is helpful or essential, and three situations where it is unhelpful or even dangerous.	**Extension**: Students should use particle diagrams when discussing how pressure builds up.	
Homework		
Explain, using your knowledge on gas pressure, why fizzy drinks sometimes spray out when they are opened.		

C1 Chapter 1 Checkpoint

Checkpoint lesson routes

The route through this lesson can be determined using the Checkpoint assessment. Percentage pass marks are supplied in the Checkpoint teacher notes.

Route A (support)
Resource: C1 Chapter 1 Checkpoint: Revision

Students will work through a revision activity that allows them to gradually revisit and consolidate their understanding of the particle model and the three states of matter.

Route B (extension)
Resource: C1 Chapter 1 Checkpoint: Extension

Students will be asked to draw a cartoon strip showing what happens to particles of water when a bowl of water is left in a room for a period of time and the temperature changes. They will need to use particle diagrams to complete their cartoon strip.

Progression to *secure*

No.	Developing outcome	Secure outcome	Making progress
1	State that materials are made up of particles.	Describe how materials are made up of particles.	In Task 1 students divide a lump of modelling clay into smaller and smaller portions until they have a very small quantity. The tiny piece they have left still has many thousands, if not millions of particles in it.
2	Match particle models to the properties of a material.	Use the particle model to explain why different materials have different properties.	In Task 2 students fill in boxes to create a particle model for the three states of matter. They can then complete descriptions for each state and its behaviour (cloze activity).
4	Match properties of the three states of matter to the name of the state.	Use ideas about particles to explain the properties of a substance in its three states.	In Task 3 students select statements that best describe how the properties change as an ice cube melts to water and then boils.
5	Describe how substances change as the temperature changes.	Use the particle model to explain changes of state involving solids and liquids.	In Task 3 students annotate a diagram to explain what is happening as water moves between its three states.
6	State the meaning of the term melting point.	Explain changes of state using particle kinetics and temperature.	In Task 4 students will use data on water to discuss how temperature influences the state of water.
7	Describe boiling as a change of state.	Use the particle model to explain boiling.	Students will need to add further annotation to their diagrams in Task 3. Time should be spent with students explaining the difference between evaporation and boiling. This is often an area of confusion.
8	Recognise that different substances boil at different temperatures.	Interpret data about changes of state.	In Task 4 students need to interpret melting point and boiling point data for an unfamiliar substance. You can provide a temperature scale for students to visualise where temperatures are in relation to each other.
9	Recall changes of state involving gases.	Describe changes of state involving gases.	Students need to name all the state changes to complete their annotated diagrams in Task 3.
10	Describe how particles change in their arrangements during evaporation, condensation, and sublimation.	Use the particle model to explain evaporating, condensing, and subliming.	Students need to use particle diagrams to show the changes in arrangements of particles during all state changes.
11	Describe examples of diffusion.	Use the particle model to explain diffusion.	In Task 5 students can answer some simple questions that will allow them to gather all the information they need for an explanation. They can then work together to write the best explanation.

12	Describe the movement of particles in diffusion.	Describe evidence for diffusion.	Students are guided to give examples, and link them with their explanations in Task 5.
13	Describe simply what gas pressure is.	Use the particle model to explain gas pressure.	Task 6 is in a similar format to Task 5. Students identify the key information and then form their explanations.
14	State examples of gas pressure in everyday situations.	Describe the factors that affect gas pressure.	Recap on the conclusions from the practical in Topic C1 1.7.

Answers to end-of-chapter questions

1 The particles in the diagram are identical, separate from each other, and randomly arranged. (2 marks)
2 The particles are touching each other and randomly arranged. They move around, in and out of each other. (2 marks)
3a platinum (1 mark)
b neon, krypton, mercury, bromine, silver, platinum (5 marks)
c neon or krypton (1 mark)
d bromine and mercury (2 marks)
e mercury (1 mark)
4a C (1 mark)
b Credit a sensible explanation of why the statements A, B, or D do not explain why solids cannot be poured. (1 mark)
5 Olivia is incorrect. Gas pressure is the result of gas particles colliding with the inside of their container, not with each other. (2 marks)
6 Students should be marked on the use of good English, organisation of information, spelling and grammar, and correct use of specialist scientific terms. The best answers will be organised in a way that allows easy comparison between boiling and evaporation, showing clear similarities and difference (maximum of 6 marks).
Examples of correct scientific points:
In both evaporating and boiling, a substance changes from the liquid to the gas state.
In evaporating, particles leave from the surface of the liquid.
In boiling, bubbles of gas form throughout the liquid, move up to the surface, and leave the liquid.
Evaporation can happen at any temperature.
Boiling can happen only at the boiling point.
In both evaporating and boiling, the particles start off by touching their neighbours, but then move apart from each other.

Answer guide for the Maths challenge

Developing	Secure	Extending
1–2 marks	3–4 marks	5–6 marks
• The student has drawn one of the three charts/graphs correctly, with suitable scales and correctly labelled axes and segments **OR** the student has drawn all three charts/graphs but the scales are unsuitable and/or the axes or segments are incorrectly or incompletely labelled. • Some points, bars, and angles are plotted correctly but there are many mistakes. • The student has not stated which type of chart or graph is most suitable.	• The bar chart, scatter graph, and pie chart are all drawn but their scales may not be suitable, and some of the axes or segments may be incorrectly or incompletely labelled. • Most points, bars, and angles are plotted correctly but there are some mistakes. • The student has stated that the bar chart or the pie chart are suitable ways of displaying the data but has not given a convincing reason.	• The bar chart, scatter graph, and pie chart have suitable scales, and all axes and segments are labelled. • Points, bars, and angles are plotted correctly. • The student has explained that the pie chart is the best way to display the data because it shows the different proportions of each gas that are in the air.

kerboodle

P1 Chapter 1 Checkpoint assessment (automarked)
P1 Chapter 1 Checkpoint: Revision
P1 Chapter 1 Checkpoint: Extension
P1 Chapter 1 Progress task (Handling information)

2.1 Elements

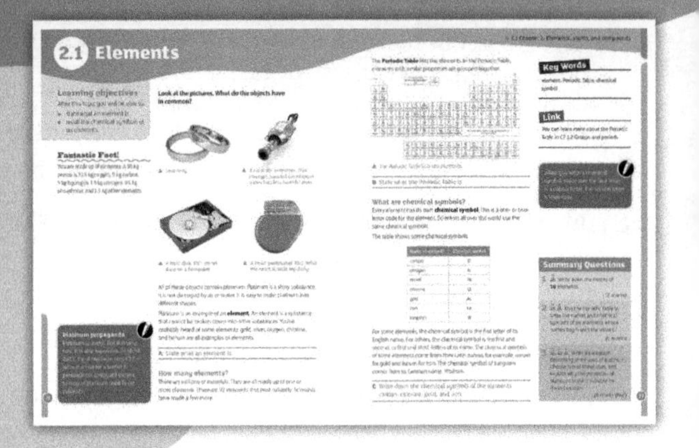

Chemistry NC link:

- differences between atoms, elements, and compounds
- chemical symbols and formulae for elements and compounds.

Working Scientifically NC link:

- present observations and data using appropriate methods, including tables and graphs.

Band	Outcome	Checkpoint	
		Question	Activity
Developing	Match the term element to its definition (Level 3).	A	Starter 2, Plenary 1
	State examples of elements (Level 4).	C, 1	Starter 1, Main 1, Plenary 2
	Present some simple facts about an element (Level 3).	3	Lit, Main 1, Main 2
Secure	State what an element is (Level 4).	A	Main 1, Plenary 1
	Recall the chemical symbols of six elements (Level 5).	C, 2	Main 1, Plenary 2
	Record observations and data on elements (Level 5).		Main 1
Extending	Explain why certain elements are used for given roles, in terms of the properties of the elements (Level 7).	3	Lit, Main 1
	Compare the properties and uses of different elements (Level 7).	3	Main 1
	Use observations and data obtained to form conclusions about given elements (Level 7).		Main 1

Maths

In the research activity students can use the data from the Fantastic Fact! box to calculate simple percentages of different elements found in the human body.

Literacy

In the student-book activity students write a leaflet to persuade car scrapyard owners to recycle platinum.

Students summarise ideas about elements into a leaflet during the activity, and as a dating profile for homework.

APP

Students communicate their ideas using appropriate methods for the selected audience. For example, by writing a persuasive leaflet for platinum recycling (AF3).

Students summarise information from data given to draw conclusions about elements (AF5).

Key Words

element, Periodic Table, chemical symbol

Answers from the student book

In-text questions	**A** A substance that cannot be broken down into simpler substances. **B** The Periodic Table lists the elements. In the Periodic Table, elements with similar properties are grouped together. **C** C; Cl; Au; Fe
Activity	**Platinum propaganda** Points to include: Platinum has many uses. Platinum is rare. For these reasons, platinum is expensive. Recycling platinum can make money for car scrapyard owners. Recycling platinum increases the likelihood of there being enough platinum to meet future demand for important uses, such as heart pacemakers and catalytic converters.

Summary questions	**1** Credit any ten elements found in the periodic table. (10 marks) **2** Carbon (C), chlorine (Cl), copper (Cu), calcium (Ca), caesium (Cs), chromium (Cr) (6 marks) **3** 6 mark question. Example answers: Uses of platinum include jewellery, catalytic converters, hard disks, making heart pacemakers. Jewellery – platinum suitable because it is shiny, not damaged by air or water, can be made into different shapes. Heart pacemaker – platinum suitable because it is not damaged by air and water and can be made into different shapes.

Starter	Support/Extension	Resources
Elements wordsearch (5 min) Students locate names of different elements from the interactive resource using the list provided. **Looking at elements** (5 min) Display samples of several different elements. Ask students to consider how they are the same. Discuss that each substance they are looking at is an element, even though they may look very different. The link is that all elements are made of identical particles.		**Interactive**: Elements wordsearch
Main	**Support/Extension**	**Resources**
The elements (40 min) Students work in small groups to research several elements assigned to them, and then produce information leaflets that can be placed together to produce a large scale, class Periodic Table. If elements found in the human body are chosen, the Fantastic Fact! box will allow students to calculate percentages of some elements found there.	**Support**: Students should be given elements that are familiar and easy to find information on. **Extension**: Students should be encouraged to research more obscure or reactive elements, considering why some elements are known about but can be isolated only briefly.	**Activity**: The elements **Skill sheet**: Calculating percentages
Interesting facts (5 min) Quiz students on the facts that have been discovered during their research for the previous task.		
Plenary	**Support/Extension**	**Resources**
What is an element? (5 min) Ask students to work in pairs to decide on a definition of an element. They should compare this with another pair and then refine their definition. **Break the code** (5 min) Give students lists of elements and their chemical symbols. Students spell out words with the chemical symbols within a certain category. For example, bear can be spelt using beryllium (Be) and argon (Ar).	**Support**: Give students a subset of the list, where they will only need to concentrate on the first 30 elements.	
Homework		
Prepare a 'dating profile' for a particular element, imagining it were a person. The dating profile should outline all the element's wonderful qualities, where it is useful, and how it can be found. If students do not have access to text books or the Internet, they can rewrite the element they have researched during the lesson into a dating profile.		

2.2 Atoms

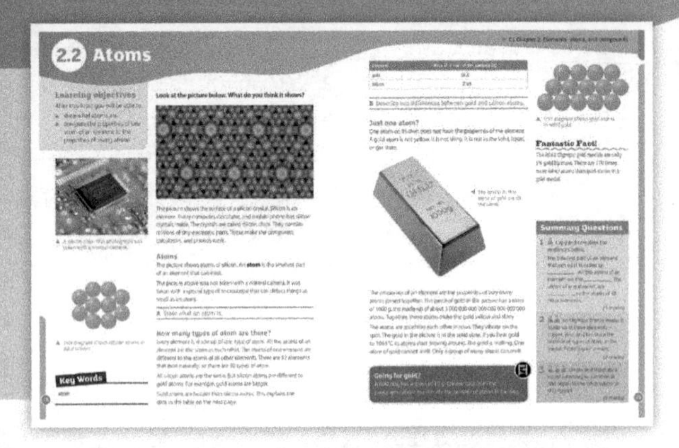

Chemistry NC link:

- differences between atoms, elements, and compounds
- a simple (Dalton) atomic model.

Band	Outcome	Checkpoint	
		Question	**Activity**
Developing ↓	Identify substances that are elements, giving a simple reason for their answer (Level 4).	B, 1, 2	Starter 1, Main 1, Main 2, Plenary 1
	List the properties of some elements (Level 3).	A, 1, 2	Starter 1, Main 1, Plenary 1, Plenary 2
Secure ↓	State what atoms are (Level 5).	A, 1, 3	Starter 1, Main 1, Plenary 1, Plenary 2
	Compare the properties of one atom of an element to the properties of many atoms (Level 6).	3	Starter 2, Main 1, Main 2, Plenary 1, Plenary 2
Extending ↓	Link the behaviour of atoms within substances to why elements, but not lone atoms, exhibit properties (Level 7).	3	Starter 2, Main 1, Main 2, Plenary 1
	Use information given to draw conclusions about how the properties of atoms contribute to the properties of elements (Level 8).	3	Starter 2, Main 1, Main 2, Plenary 1, Plenary 2

Maths

Students use information given in the student book to estimate the number of gold atoms in a ring of 10 g, and the information supplied for the homework to work out percentage mass of different elements in a coin.

APP

Students describe and model how atoms are the component parts of elements (AF1).

Students use and evaluate models to explain the difference between properties of atoms and properties of elements (AF5).

Key Words

atom

Answers from the student book

In-text questions	**A** An atom is the smallest part of an element that can exist. **B** Gold atoms are bigger and heavier than silicon atoms.
Activity	**Going for gold** In 1000 g of gold there are about 3×10^{24} atoms. So in 10 g there are about $3 \times 10^{24} \div 100 = 3 \times 10^{22}$ atoms.
Summary questions	**1** atom, same, different (3 marks) **2** There are three types of atoms in the medal, since there are three different elements, and each element has a different type of atom from every other element. (2 marks) **3** Credit sensible visual summaries. Key points to include – key words, meanings of key words, examples to illustrate key words. Visual summary should be logically organised. (6 marks)

Starter	Support/Extension	Resources
What is an atom? (5 min) Use the picture of silicon atoms in the student book to illustrate individual atoms within a substance. Discuss atoms in elements being unique to that element.		
Do atoms have the same properties as elements? (10 min) Ask students to stand in a group and act as a new, hypothetical element called 'human being'. Place a ball with one student and ask them to pass it around; this is modelling electricity conduction. Drape a large coloured cloth across them and explain this is the colour of the element. Now ask one student to leave the group and stand far away – discuss that this student no longer shares the same properties as they are not under the coloured cloth anymore or able to pass the ball.	**Extension**: Ask students to think of other properties and how they could model these. Alternatively, students can offer an evaluation for the model used, justifying their answer.	
Main	**Support/Extension**	**Resources**
Properties of atoms and elements (15 min) Students work through the questions on the activity sheet. At this stage, it is important to explain how an element transfers energy and conducts electricity if the second starter was not chosen. Students may not be able to attempt Question 4 otherwise.	**Extension**: Students should use particle models or diagrams to aid their explanations.	**Activity**: Properties of atoms and elements
Creative writing (10 min) Students write a story about an atom that gets separated from its 'element family', and the changes in properties it experiences because of this.		
Summarising learning (15 min) Students complete the questions and activities from the student book.		
Plenary	**Support/Extension**	**Resources**
Atom statements (5 min) Students need to select correct statements about atoms when given a choice of six statements on the interactive resource.		**Interactive**: Atom statements
Moving traffic lights (10 min) Ask different questions based on the lesson. Students move between different 'stations' in the classroom (red, amber, and green) depending on their confidence level for that question. 'Green' students can explain the concept to 'amber', then 'amber' can explain to 'red'. You can then reveal the answer afterwards with help from a group of your choosing.		
Homework	**Support/Extension**	
The two-pence-coin used to be made from a mixture of copper, tin, and zinc. It is currently made from copper-plated steel. Students write a short paragraph to explain why the new composition of coins is better, using properties of the different metals to explain their answers.	**Extension**: Students can justify which method of coin making is better. They can also be given the following maths problem. A two-pence coin has a mass of 7.12 g, and is made from 97% copper, 2.5% zinc, 0.5% tin. What are the masses of each of the elements?	
An alternative WebQuest homework activity is also available on Kerboodle where students research chemical elements.		**WebQuest**: Elements on Earth

2.3 Compounds

Chemistry NC link:
- differences between atoms, elements, and compounds
- chemical symbols and formulae for elements and compounds.

Physics NC link:
- atoms and molecules as particles.

Working Scientifically NC link:
- interpret observations and data, including identifying patterns and using observations, measurements, and data to draw conclusions.

Band	Outcome	Checkpoint	
		Question	**Activity**
Developing	State that elements and compounds are different (Level 3).	B, C, 1, 2	Lit, Starter 2, Plenary 1
	Identify elements within compounds (Level 4).	B, C, 2	Lit, Starter 2
	State one difference between iron and sulfur compared with iron sulfide (Level 4).		Main 1
Secure	State what a compound is (Level 5).	A, 1	Lit, Starter 2, Plenary 1
	Explain why a compound has different properties to the elements in it (Level 6).	B, C, 2, 3	Lit, Starter 2, Main 1, Main 3
	Describe similarities and differences between iron, sulfur, and iron sulfide (Level 5).		Main 1
Extending	Differentiate elements from compounds when given names and properties (Level 7).	B, C, 2, 3	Lit, Plenary 2
	Use particle diagrams to explain why a compound has different properties to the elements in it (Level 7).		Starter, Mains 1–3
	Apply existing knowledge to suggest reasons for the differences between iron, sulfur, and iron sulfide (Level 7).		Main 1

Maths
Students consider temperature scales when answering Summary Question 2.

Literacy
In the student-book activity students must organise ideas and information into a table, before writing a paragraph comparing the properties of a compound and its constituent elements.

APP
Students use the appropriate scientific terminology correctly when describing properties of compounds and elements (AF3).

Key Words
compound, molecule

Answers from the student book

In-text questions

A A substance made up of atoms of two or more elements.
B The boiling point of water is higher than the boiling point of hydrogen.
C For example, sodium is silver-coloured and shiny; sodium chloride is white and not shiny.

Activity

Organising ideas

Name of substance	State at room temperature	Colour	Other properties
sodium	solid	silver	fizzes in water
chlorine	gas	green	poisonous and smelly
sodium chloride	solid	white	no smell, not poisonous, does not fizz in water

This is an example of the table. The paragraph should be organised in a similar way.

Summary questions	**1** two, different to, two, strongly (4 marks) **2** The boiling point of water is higher than the boiling point of oxygen. This is because weak forces hold molecules close to each other in liquid oxygen. Stronger forces hold molecules close together in liquid water. You need to transfer more energy to water to separate the molecules from each other than to oxygen to separate oxygen molecules from each other. **3** 6 mark question. Example answers: Water is liquid at room temperature but hydrogen and oxygen are gases. There are weaker forces holding molecules close to each other in liquid hydrogen and liquid oxygen than there are in liquid water. You need to transfer more energy to water to separate the molecules from each other than to hydrogen to separate hydrogen molecules from each other. You cannot see oxygen and hydrogen at room temperature but you can see water. Oxygen and hydrogen are bonded differently to water. Oxygen is only oxygen atoms bonded together, hydrogen is only hydrogen atoms bonded together, but water is made from oxygen and hydrogen bonded to each other. Oxygen and hydrogen are elements, water is a compound.

Starter	Support/Extension	Resources
An alternative question-led lesson is also available. **What are these made from?** (5 min) Display pictures of common compounds such as water and salt. Ask students if they know what they are made from. Link back to the idea that everything is made of atoms. **Magnesium and oxygen demonstration** (10 min) Show students an unreacted piece of magnesium ribbon. React it with oxygen by placing it in a Bunsen flame. Discuss with students that the two elements have combined to form a compound and that this will have different properties, for example, in its appearance. It is important to tell students NOT to look directly at the bright, white light produced in this reaction.	**Support**: Reactions have been met in simple detail at KS2 but may need to be briefly revisited. **Extension**: Students use particle diagrams to explain the changes in arrangement of atoms in reactions.	**Question-led lesson**: Compounds
Main	**Support/Extension**	**Resources**
Introducing compounds (20 min) Demonstrate the reaction between sodium metal and chlorine gas in a fume cupboard. Students will also carry out two short experiments and record all their observations in a table. There are also questions that follow, requiring students to apply their knowledge and understanding on this subject. **Consolidation** (15 min) Students should work through questions in the student book to consolidate their understanding. **Summary paragraph** (5 min) Students should write a short paragraph explaining the differences between compounds and their constituent elements, and why these differences exist.	**Support**: A support sheet is available with a suggested table for observations. **Extension**: Students should use particle diagrams to explain the reactions observed. **Support**: Students can be provided with a number scale for negative numbers to clarify possible confusion regarding negative boiling points.	**Practical**: Introducing compounds **Skill sheet**: Recording results
Plenary	**Support/Extension**	**Resources**
Matching definitions (5 min) Students need to link the key words element, compound, and molecule to its correct definition on the interactive resource. **Choose the correct term** (5 min) Display names and chemical formulae for elements and compounds, one at a time. Ask students to write either 'compound' or 'element' on a mini-whiteboard to correctly identify each one.	**Extension**: Students should be asked to explain their choices.	**Interactive**: Matching definitions
Homework	**Support/Extension**	
Write a short paragraph to explain why our bones are not grey in colour and do not react with water, even though they contain calcium.	**Extension**: Students can use particle diagrams in their explanation.	

2.4 Chemical formulae

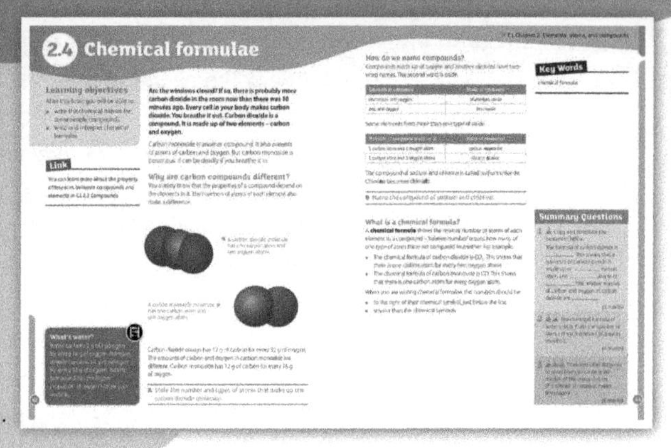

Chemistry NC link:

- differences between atoms, elements, and compounds
- chemical symbols and formulae for elements and compounds.

Working Scientifically NC link:

- understand and use SI units and IUPAC (International Union of Pure and Applied Chemistry) chemical nomenclature.

Band	Outcome	Checkpoint	
		Question	**Activity**
Developing ↓	State how many different elements are in a compound by looking at a chemical formula (Level 3).	A, B, 1–3	Main 1, Main 2, Plenary 1
	Name the elements in a compound (Level 4).	2, 3	Main 1, Main 2
	Match elements to their symbols (Level 4).	1	Main 1, Plenary 1
Secure ↓	Write the chemical names for some simple compounds (Level 5).	B, 3	Main 2
	Write and interpret chemical formulae (Level 6).	A, 1, 2	Main 1, Main 2, Plenary 1
	Describe elements and compounds using familiar symbols and formulae (Level 6).	A, B, 1, 2	Main 1, Plenary 1, Homework
Extending ↓	Calculate the percentage of a given element within a compound (Level 7).		Maths, Main 2
	Use data provided to calculate formula masses for compounds (Level 8).		Main 2
	Explain what chemical formulae show (Level 7).	3	Main 1, Main 2, Plenary 1, Homework

Maths
Carry out calculations involving +, −, ×, ÷, in order to decide which compound contains a greater proportion of oxygen in the student-book activity and for homework.

Literacy
Students work in groups to re-organise phrases into a well-developed paragraph using their scientific knowledge and understanding.

APP
Students use models to demonstrate the differences between compounds (AF1).

Key Words
chemical formula

Answers from the student book

In-text questions	**A** 1 carbon atom and 2 oxygen atoms **B** carbon monoxide
Activity	**What's water?** Water has 2 g of hydrogen to every 16 g of oxygen. The ratio is mass of hydrogen : mass of oxygen 2 g : 16 g The ratio in nitrogen dioxide is mass of nitrogen : mass of oxygen 14 g : 32 g This is 7 g : 16 g So water has the higher proportion of oxygen.

Summary questions	**1** CO_2, one, two, oxygen, different (5 marks) **2** two atoms of hydrogen and one atom of oxygen (2 marks) **3** Diagrams of models to be clearly labelled. Models to show the relative number of atoms of each element in the molecules, with clearly differentiated elements. Compounds to include: CO, CO_2, SO_3, H_2O, NO_2 (6 marks)

Starter	Support/Extension	Resources
Student role play (10 min) In small groups, students plan and deliver a short role play that shows what happens when elements combine to form a compound.	**Support**: Students can discuss in groups the key steps in a reaction. **Extension**: Students should discuss the differences in properties between elements and compounds in their role plays.	
Recalling definitions (5 min) Students should recall and write down the definitions for atom, element, and compound.	**Extension**: Students should be asked to recall the definition for molecule.	
Main	**Support/Extension**	**Resources**
Modelling compounds (20 min) Provide students with molecular modelling kits (or different coloured building bricks: you will need several different colours). Ask them to build models for CO, CO_2, CH_4, and H_2O. Discuss with students how each model represents one molecule, and that the proportion of each element is fixed so the mass each element contributes is fixed. Ask students to build several models of the same molecule and to explain why the proportion of each element does not change when more molecules are present.		
What does a chemical formula tell us? (20 min) Students work through questions on the activity sheet to consolidate their knowledge and understanding of chemical formulae.	**Extension**: Students to calculate some simple formula masses for compounds.	**Activity**: What does a chemical formula tell us?
Plenary	**Support/Extension**	**Resources**
Linking formulae to compounds (5 min) Interactive resource in which students match compound names to chemical formulae. **Story domino** (10 min) Arrange students in groups. Each group has one scribe (who remains seated) and several 'runners'. Give students the starting phrase on the board, and the runners have five minutes to find the rest of the phrases hidden around the classroom to summarise their learning. Runners must not remove the phrases they find but relay the information back to the scribe. The group then has 2 minutes to rearrange the phrases found to form the 'story'.		**Interactive**: Linking formulae to compounds
Homework	**Support/Extension**	
Give students the formulae of three compounds (e.g., Na_2O, FeO, and Al_2O_3). Students list the number of atoms for each element and name the compounds.	**Extension**: Students are given the relative masses of elements and asked to find the element that contributes more mass per compound.	

C1 Chapter 2 Checkpoint

Checkpoint lesson routes

The route through this lesson can be determined using the Checkpoint assessment. Percentage pass marks are supplied in the Checkpoint teacher notes.

Route A (support)
Resource: C1 Chapter 2 Checkpoint: Revision

Students will produce a revision poster about atoms, elements, compounds, and formulae, using the prompts shown on the revision activity.

Route B (extension)
Resource: C1 Chapter 2 Checkpoint: Extension

Students will produce a revision poster about atoms, elements, compounds, and formulae. The extension sheet will contain questions to consider when producing their posters to allow them to extend the skills.

Progression to *secure*

No.	Developing outcome	Secure outcome	Making progress
1	Match the term 'element' to its definition.	State what an element is.	The revision activity asks students to create a poster. Prompts are provided to lead students to writing a full definition for an element. Once students have created each section of their poster, work with them to check against each prompt.
2	State examples of elements.	Recall the chemical symbols of six elements.	Students will add examples of chemical symbols to their poster. Some students may confuse an element's chemical symbol with the first letter of the element's name (e.g., thinking 'C' is the symbol for copper).
3	Identify substances that are elements, giving a simple reason for their answer.	State what atoms are.	Students should define an atom, explaining its relationship to elements, in their poster. Prompts are provided.
4	List the properties of some elements.	Compare the properties of one atom of an element to the properties of many atoms.	Students should include a particle diagram in their poster that shows the individual atoms within an element and use additional notes to explain the properties seen in a group of atoms.
5	State that elements and compounds are different.	State what a compound is.	Students should define a compound and use particle diagrams to illustrate the concept.
6	Identify elements within compounds.	Explain why a compound has different properties to the elements in it.	Prompts are provided in the revision activity to help students discuss an example they have seen that illustrates the different properties of elements and compounds.
7	State how many different elements are in a compound by looking at a chemical formula.	Write the chemical formulae for some simple compounds.	After looking at the examples given on the revision activity, students will add additional examples of compound formulae to their poster.
8	Name the elements in a compound.	Write and interpret formulae.	Students should explain what a chemical formula shows on their poster.

Answers to end-of-chapter questions

1a A substance that cannot be broken down into simpler substances. (1 mark)
b one (1 mark)
c oxygen (1 mark)
d two (1 mark)
e one, oxygen (2 marks)
2a three (1 mark)
b two (1 mark)
c Compound because it includes atoms of two elements. (2 marks)
d sulfur – 1, oxygen – 2 (2 marks)
e SO_2 (2 marks)
3 Elements have only one type of atom, compounds have more than one type of atom. The properties of compounds are different to the properties of the elements that make a compound. (2 marks)
4 Students should be marked on the use of good English, organisation of information, spelling and grammar, and correct use of specialist terms. The best answers will present observations in clear, detailed paragraphs (maximum of 6 marks).
Examples of correct scientific points:
The Group 1 elements include lithium, sodium, and potassium.
The melting point decreases from top to bottom of Group 1.
The Group 0 elements include neon, argon, and krypton.
The melting point increases from top to bottom of Group 0.
The pattern is different for the two groups – in one group, melting point increases, in the other it decreases.

Answer guide for Big Write

Developing	Secure	Extending
1–2 marks	3–4 marks	5–6 marks
• The web pages include explanations of the meanings of the terms atoms, elements, compounds, and formulae, but the explanations lack clarity and detail. • There are few, if any, diagrams. • There are few, if any, examples. • The content of pages is not logically organised.	• The web pages include explanations of the meanings of the terms atoms, elements, compounds, and formulae, but some of the explanations may lack clarity or detail. • Diagrams are included, but they may be inaccurate or unclear. • Examples are included, but they are inadequate or incorrect. • The content of pages shows some attempt at organisation.	• The web pages include clear and detailed explanations of the meanings of the terms atoms, elements, compounds, and formulae. • Clear and accurate diagrams and suitable examples are included. • The content of the pages is logically organised.

kerboodle

C1 Chapter 2 Checkpoint assessment (automarked)
C1 Chapter 2 Checkpoint: Revision
C1 Chapter 2 Checkpoint: Extension
C1 Chapter 2 Progress task (Investigation planning)

3.1 Chemical reactions

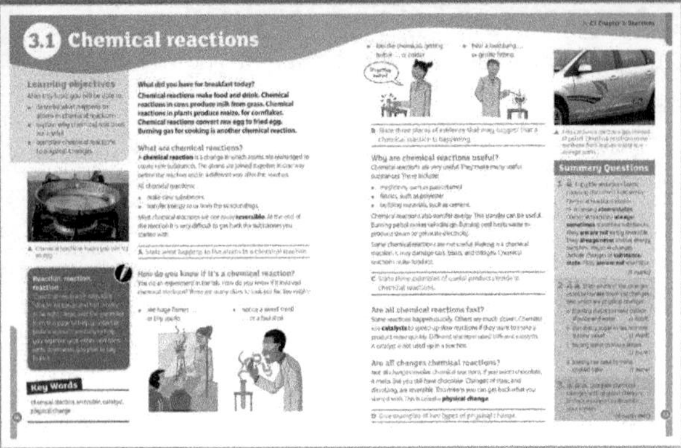

Chemistry NC link:
- chemical reactions as the rearrangement of atoms
- what catalysts do.

Physics NC link:
- the difference between chemical and physical changes.

Working Scientifically NC link:
- make and record observations and measurements using a range of methods for different investigations; and evaluate the reliability of methods and suggest possible improvements.

Band	Outcome	Checkpoint	
		Question	**Activity**
Developing	State what a chemical reaction is (Level 3).	1	Starter 1, Main 2, Plenary 1, Plenary 2
	State what happens to the reactants in a chemical reaction (Level 4).	A, C, 1	Main 2, Plenary 1, Plenary 2
	State some signs of a chemical reaction (Level 3).	B	Main 2, Plenary 1
	Record basic observations from practical work (Level 4).		Main 1
Secure	Describe what happens to atoms in chemical reactions (Level 5).	A, 1	Main 1, Main 2, Plenary 1
	Explain why chemical reactions are useful (Level 6).	C	Main 1, Main 2
	Compare chemical reactions to physical changes (Level 6).	B, 1–3	Main 2
	Identify chemical and physical reactions from practical observations (Level 5).		Main 1
Extending	Describe in detail what happens to particles in a chemical reaction (Level 7).		Main 2, Plenary 2
	Compare and contrast physical and chemical reactions (Level 7).	2, 3	Main 1, Main 2, Plenary 1
	Explain the differences in physical and chemical changes (Level 8).	3	Main 1, Main 2
	Categorise observations in terms of chemical reactions or physical changes, and suggest reasons why these observations occur (Level 7).		Main 1

Maths
Students use ideas of the number scale when measuring different quantities of reactants in the practical, as well as measuring temperature changes using a thermometer.

Literacy
Students will use scientific terminology, apply their understanding, and organise ideas and information when completing the student-book activity.

APP
Students use their observations and data from the practical to draw valid conclusions to decide whether a reaction is a chemical or physical change (AF5).

Key Words
chemical reaction, reversible, catalyst, physical change

Answers from the student book

In-text questions	**A** Atoms are rearranged. **B** Any three from: flames/sparks, smells, chemicals getting hotter or colder, fizzing. **C** paracetamol, polyester, cement **D** dissolving and changes of state

Activity	**Reaction, reaction, reaction** Possible points include: • Some reactions cause bangs. • Some reactions produce gases with bad smells. • Many reactions do not cause bangs or produce gases with bad smells, for example, cooking foods, reactions in humans, burning gas in cooking.
Summary questions	**1** atoms, always, are, always, state, are (6 marks) **2 a** chemical (1 mark) **b** physical (1 mark) **c** physical (1 mark) **d** chemical (1 mark) **3** 6 mark question. Example answers: Chemical changes make new substances. Physical changes do not make new substances. Chemical changes are not reversible. Physical changes are reversible. Chemical changes include burning reactions. Physical changes include changes of state, dissolving, and mixing.

Starter	Support/Extension	Resources
An alternative question-led lesson is also available. These starter activities are designed to gauge preconceptions within students. **What is a reaction?** (5 min) Ask students to discuss what they think a reaction is, and to give some examples of reactions they know about, for example, from burning of methane in a Bunsen burner to frying an egg.		**Question-led lesson**: Chemical reactions
Greedy teacher! (10 min) Set up a Bunsen burner and use this to boil a beaker of water, then add a teabag and then, using tongs, toast a piece of bread. Ask students to guess why you may be doing this, and how it relates to the lesson.	**Extension:** Some students may be able to spot a difference between the physical and chemical changes taking place.	
Main	**Support/Extension**	**Resources**
Finding out about reactions (25 min) Students carry out a series of reactions to observe what happens and find the signs that can be used to show reactions are occurring. Students then use their observations to answer questions based on chemical reactions and physical changes.	**Support**: The support sheet allows students to record their observations in a suggested table of results.	**Practical**: Finding out about reactions **Skill sheet**: Recording results
Consolidation (10 min) Ask groups of students to feed back what they observed during the practical. Discuss the key differences between chemical and physical reactions. Students can complete questions in the student book to check their understanding.		
Plenary	**Support/Extension**	**Resources**
Signs of reactions (5 min) Ask students to write down on a mini-whiteboard the signs of a chemical reaction, and explain the differences between a physical and a chemical change.	**Extension**: Students should be asked to describe how physical reactions can be seen to be occurring.	
Reactions crossword (10 min) Students use the clues given on the interactive resource to complete a crossword of key words in this topic.		**Interactive**: Reactions crossword
Homework	**Support/Extension**	
Produce a poster showing the signs of a chemical reaction. Students should include the action of catalysts in chemical reactions, giving examples where appropriate.	**Extension**: Students can dedicate a section on their poster to the differences between physical changes and chemical reactions.	
An alternative WebQuest homework activity is also available on Kerboodle where students research how chemicals and chemical reactions are involved in cooking.		**WebQuest**: Kitchen chemistry

3.2 Word equations

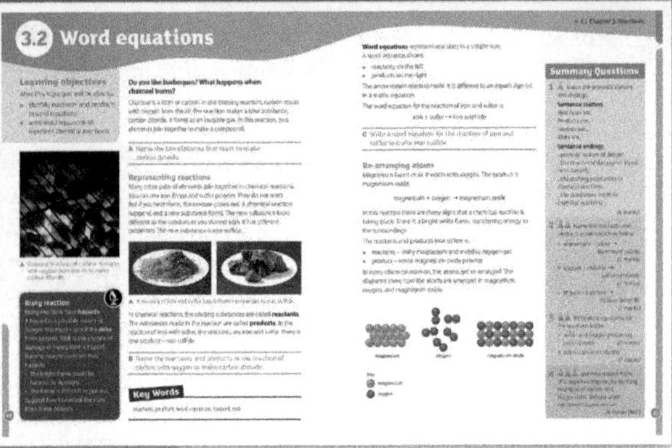

Chemistry NC link:

- chemical symbols and formulae for elements and compounds
- chemical reactions as the rearrangement of atoms
- representing chemical reactions using formulae and using equations.

Working Scientifically NC link:

- present observations and data using appropriate methods, including tables and graphs.

Band	Outcome	Checkpoint	
		Question	Activity
Developing ↓	Identify reactants and products for a given reaction (Level 4).	B, 2	Main 1
	State the elements that have formed a compound (Level 3).	A	
	Write observations seen when two elements react (Level 4).		Main 1
Secure ↓	Identify reactants and products in word equations (Level 5).	A, B, 2	Main 1
	Write word equations to represent chemical reactions (Level 6).	C, 3	Main 1
	Represent practical observations using word equations (Level 5).		Main 1
Extending ↓	Convert word equations into formula equations (Level 7).		Main 1, Plenary 1
	Construct a formula equation for a reaction without the use of word equations (Level 8).		Main 1, Plenary 1
	Represent practical observations as a formula equation (Level 7).		Main 1

Maths
In balancing equations, students will show their understanding of direct proportions and simple ratios in quantitative problem solving.

Literacy
Students will use the rules of scientific writing in order to construct word and formula equations.

Students must also take care with the spelling of element or compound names when using out the interactive resource.

APP
Students will use equations to correctly represent and communicate what happens to the elements during chemical reactions (AF3).

Key Words
reactant, product, word equation, hazard, risk

Answers from the student book

In-text questions	**A** carbon and oxygen **B** Reactants: carbon and oxygen; Product: carbon dioxide **C** iron + sulfur → iron sulfide
Activity	**Risky reaction** Control risk from hazard of bright flame damaging eyesight by not staring directly at the flame. Control risk from hazard of flame being difficult to put out by burning only small quantities of magnesium.

Summary questions	1 Reactants are the starting substances in chemical reactions. Products are the substances made in chemical reactions. Hazards are possible sources of danger. Risks are the chances of damage or injury from hazards. (4 marks) **2a** Reactants: aluminium and iodine; Product: aluminium iodide (2 marks) **b** Reactants: sodium and chlorine; Product: sodium chloride (2 marks) **c** Reactants: lithium and bromine; Product: lithium bromide (2 marks) **3a** sulfur + oxygen → sulfur dioxide (2 marks) **b** potassium + chlorine → potassium chloride (2 marks) **4** 6 mark question. Example answers: Both react with oxygen in the air. carbon + oxygen → carbon dioxide magnesium + oxygen → magnesium oxide Magnesium burns with a bright white light and produces a white powder that remains in the container. Carbon glows red as it burns, and the product is carbon dioxide gas, which escapes into the atmosphere.

kerboodle

Starter	Support/Extension	Resources
Describing reactions (5 min) Light a Bunsen burner or match in front of students and ask them to describe what they see in their own words. Go on to discuss how equations can be used to simplify the process of describing reactions, and make the process uniform between scientists.		
What happens during reactions? (10 min) Using different coloured vests or sashes, some students will model magnesium metal and several pairs of students will model oxygen molecules. Model the reaction between the two by rearranging the students into new, mixed colour pairings representing magnesium oxide.	**Extension**: Have some 'spare' students – this can lead to a discussion on why some material may remain unreacted at the end.	
Main	**Support/Extension**	**Resources**
Reacting elements (30 min) Demonstrate three or four different elements undergoing reactions. Students draw a results table. They note down the reactants as they observe the reactions, and decide on the product each time. Students can then use the information to produce word equations. Risks and hazards should be discussed throughout.	**Support**: The accompanying support sheet includes a suggested table of results and extra hints for students on writing the word equation. **Extension**: Encourage students to write balanced formula equations for each reaction. Provide the Periodic Table and relevant formulae for reactants and products, from which to choose.	**Practical**: Reacting elements **Skill sheet**: Recording results
Risky reaction (10 min) Snowball activity in which students discuss ideas for the activity 'Risky reaction' in the student book, first in pairs, then in groups of four, and eventually as a whole-class discussion.		
Plenary	**Support/Extension**	**Resources**
Completing equations (10 min) Interactive resource in which students complete word equations, paying particular attention to correct spelling. **Defining key words** (5 min) Students use their mini-whiteboards to write the key word when you give them a definition based on the work in this lesson.	**Extension**: Students write corresponding formula equations for the reaction.	**Interactive**: Completing equations
Homework	**Support/Extension**	
Research how different elements produce different coloured flames when burned in oxygen, and how this is useful for making fireworks.	**Support**: Guide students to the fact that it is the metal element in a compound that affects the colour of the flame.	

3.3 Burning fuels

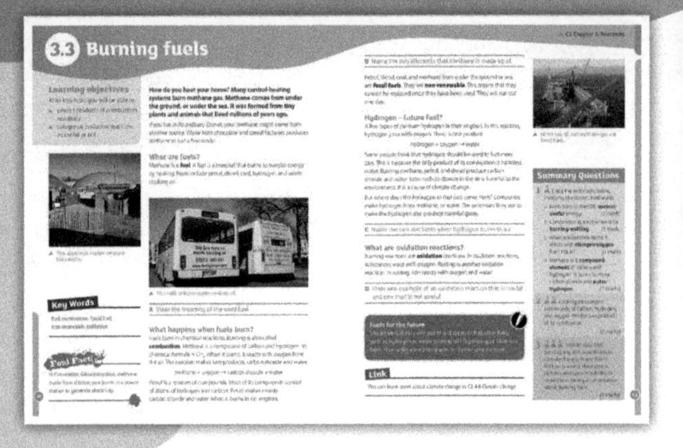

Chemistry NC link:

- combustion, thermal decomposition, oxidation, and displacement reactions.

Working Scientifically NC link:

- evaluate data, showing awareness of potential sources of random and systematic error.

Band	Outcome	Checkpoint	
		Question	Activity
Developing	State what a fuel is (Level 3).	A, 1	Plenary 1
	State what fuels react with when they burn (Level 4).	C, 1	Plenary 1
	Identify one point about a practical procedure that contributed to inaccuracies in results (Level 4).		Main 1
Secure	Predict products of combustion reactions (Level 5).	B, 2	Plenary 1
	Categorise oxidation reactions as useful or not (Level 6).	D, 2	
	Suggest one improvement to the practical procedure to improve on the accuracy of the results obtained (Level 5).		Main 1
Extending	Construct formula equations for some combustion reactions (Level 7).	3	Plenary 1
	Explain the benefits and disadvantages of some oxidation reactions (Level 8).	D, 3	Lit, Plenary 1
	Explain why it is important to know how much of a fuel is burnt when determining the amount of heat released (Level 7).		Main 1

Maths
Students must demonstrate an appreciation of the number scale when reading temperatures from thermometers and masses from mass balances.

Students will carry out calculations involving +, −, ×, ÷, either singly or in combination, to determine temperature and mass changes. In the extension, simple calculations will also be carried out relating to energy per gram of fuel.

Literacy
Students will organise ideas in a table, before summarising this information in a coherent manner when arguing their viewpoint in the student-book activity.

APP
Students note down observations, using suitable intervals of independent variables (AF4).

Students offer suggestions towards the validity of results obtained (AF5).

Key Words
fuel, combustion, fossil fuel, non-renewable, oxidation

Answers from the student book

In-text questions	**A** A fuel is a material that burns to transfer energy by heating. **B** carbon and hydrogen **C** hydrogen and oxygen **D** burning fuel; rusting iron

Activity	**Fuels for the future** Possible points to include: • Petrol and diesel produce carbon dioxide on burning. This is a greenhouse gas. • Burning cooking oil also produces carbon dioxide on burning, but the plants from which the oil was produced removed carbon dioxide from the atmosphere while they were growing. • Burning hydrogen produces just one harmless product, water. • Petrol and diesel are non-renewable. • Used cooking oil and hydrogen are renewable.
Summary questions	**1** useful, burning, oxygen, compound, water (5 marks) **2** carbon dioxide and water (2 marks) **3** Suggested comments (Nathan) – burning fuels such as petrol and methane produces carbon dioxide gas, which contributes to climate change. Suggested comments (Riana) – burning hydrogen produces one product, water, which does not contribute to climate change. (6 marks)

Starter	Support/Extension	Resources
What have these got in common? (5 min) Display pictures of coal, chocolate, bread, and petrol on the board. Ask students to come up with ideas on what they have in common. Students should conclude they all 'provide energy', that is, they are fuels.		
Burning fuels demonstration (10 min) Set up the classic experiment for the combustion of fuels (using an inverted funnel, delivery tubes, cobalt chloride paper in a U-tube, and limewater with reduced pressure provided by a running tap). Demonstrate the burning of ethanol and a candle as students will go on to consider the values of each fuel. Additional explanation will be required for water turning cobalt chloride paper from blue to pink, and how limewater goes from colourless to cloudy due to carbon dioxide.	**Support**: Students can focus on physical observations from this demonstration.	
Main	**Support/Extension**	**Resources**
Energy transfers in different fuels (25 min) Students will carry out a simple calorimetric experiment to compare the effectiveness of a candle and a spirit burner as fuels for heating water.	**Support**: A support sheet is available with a suggested table of results. **Extension**: Students should consider if the method they used can give conclusive data on which fuel transfers energy the quickest and suggest how it can be improved.	**Practical**: Energy transfers in different fuels **Skill sheet**: Recording results
Fuels for the future (15 min) Depending on your class, students may carry out the student-book activity or question 3 of the summary questions to discuss different types of fuels for the future.		
Plenary	**Support/Extension**	**Resources**
What happens when a fuel burns? (5 min) Interactive resource in which students complete a paragraph by choosing the correct word to summarise the key points of the lesson.	**Extension**: Students should write formula equations for the oxidation of carbon and iron, to consolidate knowledge from the previous lesson.	**Interactive**: What happens when a fuel burns?
Pros and cons of fuels (5 min) Ask students to recall one benefit and one disadvantage of burning fossil fuels, and the same for a green fuel such as hydrogen. It is a common misconception that 'green alternatives' have no disadvantages so this is an important point to clarify, as many have inherent problems. For example, during their production fossil fuels may still be used.	**Extension**: Students should provide more benefits and disadvantages, focusing on scientific ideas.	
Homework	**Support/Extension**	
Produce an information leaflet on alternative fuels that can be used to fuel cars. Include word equations for the combustion of cooking fats and of hydrogen.	**Extension**: Students include formula equations for the combustion of fuels.	

3.4 Thermal decomposition

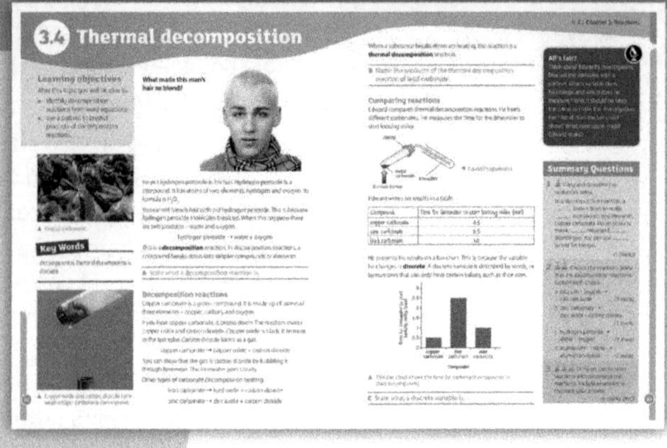

Chemistry NC link:

- combustion, thermal decomposition, oxidation and displacement reactions.

Working Scientifically NC link:

- interpret observations and data, including identifying patterns and using observations, measurements and data to draw conclusions.

Band	Outcome	Checkpoint	
		Question	**Activity**
Developing	State simply what a decomposition reaction is (Level 3).	A, 1	Main 1, Plenary 1
	Describe the products of a decomposition reaction (Level 4).	A, 1	Main 1, Plenary 1
	Compare results from a practical, relating this to different speeds of decomposition (Level 4).	1	Starter 2, Main 1
Secure	Identify decomposition reactions from word equations (Level 5).	2	Main 1, Plenary 1
	Use a pattern to predict products of decomposition reactions (Level 6).		Main 1
	Use practical results to decide which compound decomposes most readily (Level 5).		Main 1, Plenary 2
Extending	Write formula equations for decomposition reactions (Level 7).	2	Main 1, Main 2
	Compare decomposition reactions with combustion reactions (Level 8).	3	Plenary 1
	Use experimental observations to predict products of decomposition for other substances (Level 7).		Main 1

Maths
Students will extract and interpret information from graphs when completing the student-book activity.

Literacy
Students use scientific concepts and terminology when explaining the thermal decomposition of chemicals.

APP
In the student-book activity, students state the variables in a practical (AF4) and explain the relationship between variables (AF5).

Key Words
decomposition, thermal decomposition, discrete

Answers from the student book

In-text questions	**A** A decomposition reaction is a reaction in which a compound breaks down into simpler compounds or elements. **B** lead oxide and carbon dioxide **C** A discrete variable is described by words or by numbers that can only have certain values, for example, shoe sizes.
Activity	**All's fair?** Edward changes the compound he heats. He measures the time for the limewater to start to look milky. To make sure the investigation is fair he needs to keep the amount of compound he heats constant, as well as the size of the Bunsen flame, the amount that the Bunsen air hole is open, and the distance from the Bunsen flame to the test tube. The bar chart shows that copper carbonate is the fastest to decompose and zinc carbonate is the slowest.

Summary questions	1 compound, simpler, copper, carbon, limewater (5 marks) 2 Equations **b** and **c** are decomposition reactions because a compound (zinc carbonate and hydrogen peroxide) breaks down to make two simpler compounds. (4 marks) 3 6 mark question. Example answers: In combustion reactions an element or compound reacts with oxygen from the air. This means that there are two or more reactants in combustion reactions. A more complex product is made in a combustion reaction. In decomposition reactions a compound breaks down to form at least two products. In a decomposition reaction there is just one reactant. Simpler products are made in a decomposition reaction. In both combustion and decomposition reactions new substances are made. Both combustion and decomposition reactions are not reversible.

Starter	Support/Extension	Resources
What is in these substances? (5 min) Write the chemical formulae for copper carbonate ($CuCO_3$), zinc carbonate ($ZnCO_3$), magnesium carbonate ($MgCO_3$), and hydrogen peroxide (H_2O_2) on the board. Ask students to identify the elements present using a periodic table.	**Extension**: Students should be able to predict the names of the compounds given their chemical formulae.	
Testing for carbon dioxide (10 min) Ask students to blow gently through straws into test tubes containing approximately 1 cm^3 of limewater. Discuss that the carbon dioxide they are exhaling turns the limewater cloudy and that limewater can be used to test for carbon dioxide's presence.	**Extension**: Students should link this back to the U-tube experiment for the products of combustion.	
Main	**Support/Extension**	**Resources**
Decomposition word equations (10 min) Using the student-book examples, discuss what happens during decomposition and highlight the word equations showing these reactions. Ensure students realise that some substances only decompose when heated and this is called thermal decomposition. Students can then attempt question 2 in the summary questions, and pick out one example of spontaneous decomposition and one example of thermal decomposition.	**Extension**: Students can try and write accompanying formula equations for the word equations shown.	
Decomposition reactions (30 min) Students carry out the thermal decomposition reaction for three metal carbonates using their results to draw conclusions and answer the questions that follow on the practical sheet.	**Support**: A support sheet is available to students with a suggested table of results.	**Practical**: Decomposition reactions **Skill sheet**: Recording results
Plenary	**Support/Extension**	**Resources**
Defining decomposition (10 min) Ask students to write a definition for decomposition without using their lesson notes or student book. Then give students a range of different word equations for students to pick out the correct equations that demonstrate decomposition.	**Extension**: Students can include thermal decomposition in their definition and explain the similarities and differences between combustion and decomposition.	
Interpreting results (5 min) Interactive resource in which students highlight the correct terms in a paragraph describing a decomposition reaction.		**Interactive**: Interpreting results
Homework		
Research the uses of hydrogen peroxide and write a summary on how it is stored to minimise decomposition.		

3.5 Conservation of mass

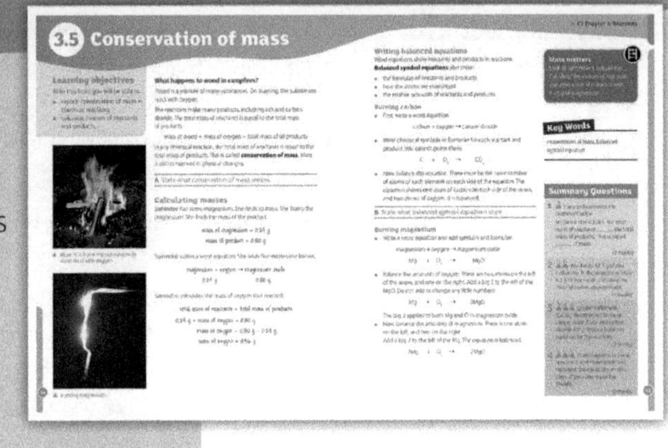

Chemistry NC link:
- conservation of mass, changes of state, and chemical reactions
- representing chemical reactions using formulae and using equations
- combustion, thermal decomposition, oxidation, and displacement reactions.

Physics NC link:
- conservation of material and of mass.

Working Scientifically NC link:

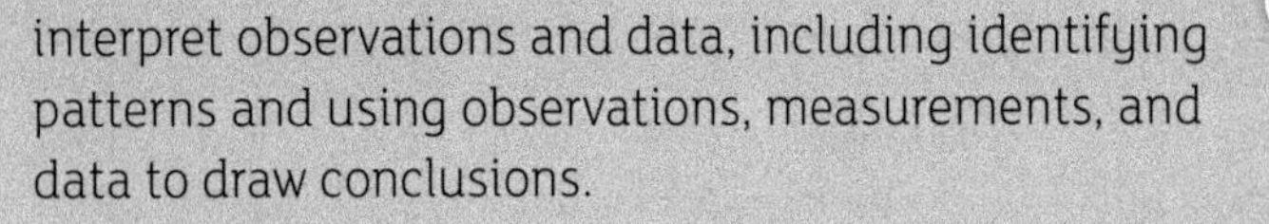

- interpret observations and data, including identifying patterns and using observations, measurements, and data to draw conclusions.

Band	Outcome	Checkpoint	
		Question	Activity
Developing	State what happens to the mass of the reactants and products in chemical reactions (Level 4).	A, 2	Starter 1, Starter 2, Main 1, Plenary 2
	Describe how to find out the mass of a reactant or product (Level 4).	1, 2	Maths, Main 1, Plenary 2
	Make a conclusion by comparing the masses of reactants and products (Level 4).		Main 1
Secure	Explain conservation of mass in chemical reactions (Level 6).	2	Maths, Main 1, Plenary 2
	Calculate masses of reactants and products (Level 6).	2	Maths, Main 1, Homework
	Make a conclusion from data based on the idea of conservation of mass (Level 6).		Main 1
Extending	Apply the conservation of mass in unfamiliar situations, giving a reasoned explanation (Level 7).	2	Maths, Main 1
	From word and formula equations, predict and explain whether the mass within a reaction vessel will stay the same (Level 8).		Main 1, Plenary 1, Homework
	Use the conservation of mass to deduce the type of reaction in unfamiliar situations based on experimental data given (Level 8).		Main 1, Plenary 1, Homework

Maths

Students carry out calculations involving +, −, ×, and ÷ to calculate masses of reactants or products based on the conservation of mass.

Students will also identify the mathematical aspects of chemical reactions using direct proportions and simple ratios to balance equations.

Literacy

Present reasoned explanations for observations in experiments based on the conservation of mass.

APP

Students must draw conclusions consistent with their observations in experimental procedures and explain these using scientific knowledge and understanding (AF5).

Key Words

conservation of mass, balanced symbol equation

Answers from the student book

In-text questions	**A** In a chemical reaction or physical change, the total mass of starting substances is the same as the total mass of substances at the end of the change. **B** Balanced symbol equations show the formulae of reactants and products, how the atoms are rearranged, and the relative amounts of reactants and products.
Activity	**Mass matters** Since the mass of magnesium has doubled, the masses of the other reactant and the product will also double. So the mass of oxygen = (0.56 g) × 2 = 1.12 g and the mass of magnesium oxide = (0.80 g) × 2 = 1.60 g
Summary questions	**1** is equal to, conservation (2 marks) **2** 12.5 g − 8.1 g = 4.4 g of carbon dioxide (2 marks) **3** $CuCO_3 \rightarrow CuO + CO_2$ (already balanced) (3 marks) **4** Credit labelled diagrams of suitable models. Ensure that the atoms of different elements are shown as different entities, and that atoms in molecules are joined to show they are chemically bonded. (6 marks)

Starter	Support/Extension	Resources
Where does the candle go? (5 min) Burn a candle (or show a candle that has burned down significantly) and ask the students where the wax has gone. Discuss the wax turning into new substances when it reacts with oxygen. **Thinking about mass** (5 min) Ask students to consider what would happen to their mass if they picked up a rucksack full of rocks. Ask them to offer ideas about how this relates to chemical reactions.	**Support**: Some students believe that the wax simply melts and so find it hard to visualise the wax turning into different products after burning. Consider using a burning log that has become smaller as an example in addition to the candle.	
Main	**Support/Extension**	**Resources**
Conservation of mass (40 min) Students carry out two experiments (burning magnesium in a crucible and the reaction between a carbonate and acid) and use their understanding of the conservation of mass to explain their observations. Students should answer related questions on the practical sheet while they wait for Experiment 1 to finish.	**Support**: A support sheet is available with a suggested table of results. **Extension**: Students should use the corresponding section in the student book to help them balance equations in the extension questions on the practical sheet.	**Practical**: Conservation of mass **Skill sheet**: Recording results
Summing it up! (10 min) Students work through summary questions 1 and 2 in the student book and copy these into their books for future reference.	**Extension**: Students should gain an appreciation of ratios in chemical reactions by working through the maths activity in the student book.	
Plenary	**Support/Extension**	**Resources**
Explaining mass changes (5 min) Students will link each of the observations given with the type of reaction that occurs in the interactive resource. **Moving traffic lights** (5 min) Ask students how confident they would be to describe the conservation of mass in their own words. Give them areas in the classroom for green (confident), amber (unsure), and red (no idea) to move to. The greens can then explain to the ambers, and ambers to reds. Hopefully, after five minutes, the students should be able to move up one level (if red or amber).		**Interactive**: Explaining mass changes
Homework	**Support/Extension**	
Provide a list of equations with one missing mass each time for students to practise their calculations. Masses can also be omitted altogether if you require students to predict mass changes in the reaction vessel.	**Extension**: Include some unbalanced equations near the end of the practical sheet.	

3.6 Exothermic and endothermic

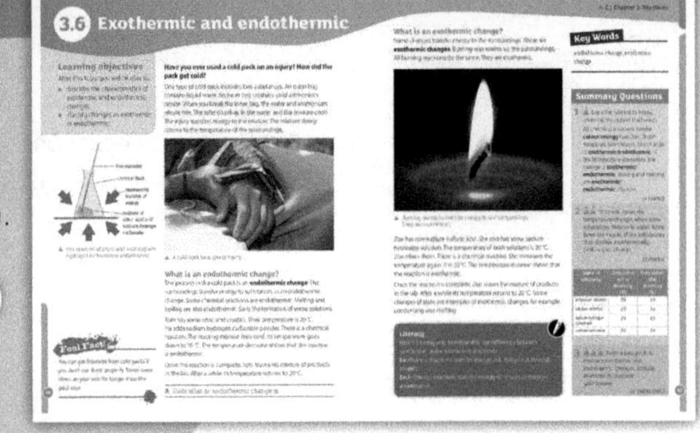

Chemistry NC link:

- exothermic and endothermic chemical reactions (qualitative).

Working Scientifically NC link:

- interpret observations and data, including identifying patterns and using observations, measurements, and data to draw conclusions.

Band	Outcome	Checkpoint	
		Question	**Activity**
Developing	State simply what happens in endothermic and exothermic changes (Level 4).	B, 1, 3	Main 1, Plenary 1, Homework
	Identify a reaction as endothermic or exothermic (Level 4).	A, 1	Main 1, Plenary 1, Homework
	Record temperature changes during an exothermic and an endothermic change (Level 4).		Main 1
Secure	Describe the characteristics of exothermic and endothermic changes (Level 5).	A, B, 1, 3	Main 1, Plenary 2, Homework
	Classify changes as exothermic or endothermic (Level 6).	2	Main 1, Plenary 2, Homework
	Calculate the temperature change and make a conclusion in a range of familiar exothermic and endothermic changes (Level 6).		Main 1
Extending	Apply temperature changes to exothermic and endothermic changes in unfamiliar situations (Level 7).	2	Main 1, Plenary 2, Homework
	Begin considering endothermic and exothermic changes in terms of energy transfers to and from the surroundings (Level 8).	3	Main 1, Homework
	Calculate the temperature change and make a conclusion in a range of unfamiliar exothermic and endothermic changes (Level 6).		Main 1

Maths
Students must show an appreciation of relative sizes on number scales to read temperatures from a thermometer, and carry out basic calculations to work out temperature differences during chemical reactions.

Literacy
Students compare the similarities and differences between exothermic and endothermic reactions. They summarise this information using scientific knowledge in question 3.

Students must present an innovative product by demonstrating their understanding and by using scientific terms for homework.

APP
Students draw conclusions based on observations in their experiments (AF5).

Key Words
endothermic change, exothermic change

Answers from the student book

In-text questions	**A** A change that transfers energy from the surroundings.

Summary questions	1 energy, exothermic, endothermic, endothermic (4 marks) 2 Calcium chloride and sodium carbonate dissolve exothermically. The data show this because the temperature increases during dissolving. (3 marks) 3 6 mark question. Example answers: Both endothermic and exothermic changes involve energy transfers between the reacting mixture and the surroundings. In an exothermic change energy is transferred to the surroundings. In an endothermic change energy is transferred from the surroundings to the reaction mixture. During an exothermic change the temperature of the reaction mixture increases. During an endothermic change the temperature of the reaction mixture decreases. Credit suitable examples taken from the spread or the practical sheet.

kerboodle

Starter	Support/Extension	Resources
How do we utilise energy transfers? (5 min) Pass a packaged hand warmer and injury cooler around the class, before activating them and passing them around again to allow students to feel exothermic and endothermic reactions occurring.	**Support**: Some students may need guiding towards the fact that a chemical reaction is taking place.	
When ice melts (5 min) Students select the correct words to fill in the gaps when describing the melting of ice in the interactive resource.	**Extension**: Discuss how these reactions are reversible, in order for the hand warmer to be reused.	**Interactive**: When ice melts
Main	**Support/Extension**	**Resources**
Energy transfers in chemistry (25 min) Students carry out four short practicals, monitoring temperature changes and recording their results in a results table. They will then decide if these reactions are endothermic or exothermic, and answer the questions that follow.	**Support**: The layout required for the results table is very similar to their previous practicals in this topic. Students should be steered towards these support sheets if they have trouble drawing out a results table.	**Practical**: Energy transfers in chemistry **Skill sheet**: Recording results
Designing products (20 min) Students design a novel invention that utilises endothermic and exothermic changes.	**Support**: Students may need an idea to get them started. Suggestions include drinks coolers, baby food warmers, and self-heating cans. **Extension**: Students should also consider the suitability of the reactions they choose for their inventions, in terms of hazards of the chemicals used.	
Plenary	**Support/Extension**	**Resources**
Remembering energy transfers (5 min) Ask students to make up a catchy phrase or mnemonic to help them remember that exothermic changes transfer energy to the surroundings and endothermic changes transfer energy from the surroundings.		
Sweet reaction (5 min) Ask students if they've ever had a sherbet sweet. Ask them to describe what they feel on their tongue when they eat this sweet, and what type of energy transfer it must be (it should feel cold as it is an endothermic change).		
Homework	**Support/Extension**	
Design an advertising campaign for the invention created in the lesson to explain how this novel product works.	**Extension**: Students should include an explanation of the chemical reaction, a balanced symbol equation, and the energy transfers involved.	

C1 Chapter 3 Checkpoint

Checkpoint lesson routes

The route through this lesson can be determined using the Checkpoint assessment. Percentage pass marks are supplied in the Checkpoint teacher notes.

Route A (support)
Resource: C1 Chapter 3 Checkpoint: Revision

Prompt headings are provided as a starting point from which to construct a visual summary. Students can then attempt some questions about reactions in order to assess their own learning and decide if they need to add more to their visual summaries. In addition, you may wish to give students an overview of the secure outcomes to check against after completing their visual summaries.

Route B (extension)
Resource: C1 Chapter 3 Checkpoint: Extension

Students can construct a visual summary on the topic of reactions, based on the broad headings from the chapter.

Students can attempt several questions to help them assess their own learning and the effectiveness of their visual summary.

Progression to *secure*

No.	Developing outcome	Secure outcome	Making progress
1	State what a chemical reaction is.	Describe what happens to atoms in chemical reactions.	Students can make relevant links on their visual summaries using appropriate keywords. They need to describe in their annotations that atoms are arranged differently after a reaction.
2	State that new products are formed and original reactants are no longer present.	Explain why chemical reactions are useful.	Students can make relevant links on their visual summaries and add examples of useful chemical reactions. Students may struggle thinking about chemical reactions outside of the lab. You may wish to remind students of examples previously given.
3	State what a physical change and a chemical reaction are.	Compare chemical reactions to physical changes.	Students can make relevant comparisons between physical changes and chemical reactions in their visual summary. They will need to identify signs of a chemical reaction in Question 1 of the revision activity.
4	State that elements can combine together to make new substances.	Identify reactants and products in word equations.	Students can make relevant links on their visual summaries using appropriate keywords and a word equation. They can identify reactants and products in their answer to Question 2 on the revision activity.
5	Complete simple word equations.	Write word equations to represent chemical reactions.	Students are asked in Question 2 on the revision activity to write a word equation for magnesium burning in oxygen.
6	State what a fuel is.	Predict products of combustion reactions.	Students can make relevant links between fuels and combustion reactions on their visual summaries using appropriate keywords.
7	State what fuels react with when they burn.	Categorise oxidation reactions as useful or not.	Students should identify links on their visual summaries of types of oxidation reactions using appropriate keywords.
8	State simply what a decomposition reaction is.	Identify decomposition reactions from word equations.	If students have not linked 'decomposition' and 'word equation' in their visual summary, ask them to. They will then need to think about why the two are linked.
9	Describe the products of a decomposition reaction.	Use a pattern to predict products of decomposition reactions.	Students should make reference to patterns in reactions on their mind maps using appropriate keywords and complete Question 4 on the revision activity.
10	State what happens to the mass of the reactants and products in chemical reactions.	Explain conservation of mass in chemical reactions.	Students should make links to examples of conservation of mass on their visual summaries using appropriate keywords. They should then answer the question on conservation of mass.

11	Describe how to find out the mass of a reactant or product.	Calculate masses of reactants and products.	Question 5 on the revision activity asks students to carry out a calculation. Step-by-step guidance is given but some students will need further support.
12	State simply what happens in endothermic and exothermic changes.	Describe the characteristics of exothermic and endothermic changes.	Students should make relevant links to exothermic and endothermic changes on their visual summaries using appropriate keywords and complete Question 3 on the revision activity.
13	Identify a change as endothermic or exothermic.	Classify changes as exothermic or endothermic.	Students should make relevant links to exothermic and endothermic changes on their visual summaries using appropriate keywords and complete Question 3 on the revision activity.

Answers to end-of-chapter questions

1a The appearance of the product is different from the appearance of the reactants (suggesting new materials are formed). There is a flame (showing energy is transferred to the surroundings). (2 marks)
b Atoms are rearranged. (1 mark)
2a Burning reactions are exothermic – they transfer energy to the surroundings. (2 marks)
b fuel type/ethanol or propanol (1 mark)
c amount of water and distance from flame to water (2 marks)
d ensure results are fair (1 mark)
3a thermal decomposition (1 mark)
b calcium oxide and carbon dioxide (2 marks)
c $100\ g - 56\ g = 44\ g$ (2 marks)
4a All the representations show a new substance is made. Diagram Z shows how atoms are rearranged. (2 marks)
b Students should be marked on the use of good English, organisation of information, spelling and grammar, and correct use of specialist terms. The best answers will be organised in a clear manner, presenting well-reasoned advantages and disadvantages of the different methods of representing the reaction (maximum of 6 marks).
Examples of correct scientific points:
All three representations show the reactants and products.
Equation X gives the names of the reactants and products.
Equation Y shows the formulae of the reactants and products, and partially indicates how the reactants and products are rearranged.
Equation Y and diagram Z show the relative amounts of each reactant and product.
Diagram Z shows how the atoms are rearranged.

Answer guide for Big Write

Developing	Secure	Extending
1–2 marks	3–4 marks	5–6 marks
• Students plan a talk in which they give one reason for the importance of chemistry. • The talk includes just one or two examples.	• Students plan a talk in which they explain why chemistry is important. • The talk includes a few examples. • The talk includes some persuasive elements.	• Students plan a talk in which they explain in detail why chemistry is important. • The talk includes a range of examples, including the use of chemical reactions to make new products and transfer energy. • The talk is persuasive and well organised.

kerboodle

C1 Chapter 3 Checkpoint assessment (automarked)
C1 Chapter 3 Checkpoint: Revision
C1 Chapter 3 Checkpoint: Extension
C1 Chapter 3 Progress task (Information-handling and problem-solving)

4.1 Acids and alkalis

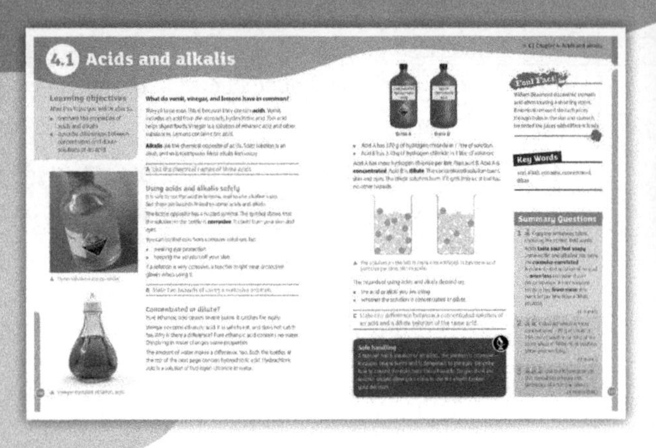
4.1 Acids and alkalis
Learning objectives
What do vomit, vinegar, and lemons have in common?
Using acids and alkalis safely
Concentrated or dilute?
Safe handling
Key Words
Summary Questions

Chemistry NC link:

- defining acids and alkalis in terms of neutralisation reactions.

Working Scientifically NC link:

- evaluate risks.

Band	Outcome	Checkpoint	
		Question	**Activity**
Developing	Name some common properties of acids and alkalis (Level 3).	1, 3	Main 1
	Describe, in simple terms, what the key words 'concentrated' and 'dilute' mean (Level 4).	C, 1	Main 1, Main 3
	Label hazard symbols and describe the hazards relating to them (Level 4).		Main 2
Secure	Compare the properties of acids and alkalis (Level 5).	1, 3	Main 1, Main 3
	Describe differences between concentrated and dilute solutions of an acid (Level 5).	C, 1, 2	Main 1, Main 3
	Identify and describe the meaning of hazard symbols and offer suitable safety precautions (Level 5).		Main 2
Extending	Compare the different particles found in acids and alkalis (Level 7).	1, 3	Main 1, Main 3
	Explain what 'concentrated' and 'dilute' mean, in terms of the numbers of particles present (Level 7).	C, 1, 2	Main 1, Main 3
	Offer suitable safety precautions when given a hazard symbol, and give a reason for the suggestion (Level 7).		Main 2

Maths
Students carry out simple calculations when comparing concentrations of acids.

Literacy
Students use scientific terms correctly when labelling and describing hazards associated with chemicals.

Students summarise information about the properties of acids and alkalis when designing their posters.

APP
Students will identify risks acids and alkalis present to themselves and others, and suggest how to control these risks (AF4).

Key Words
acid, alkali, corrosive, concentrated, dilute

Answers from the student book

In-text questions	**A** hydrochloric acid, ethanoic acid, citric acid **B** Corrosive solutions can burn your skin, and they can burn your eyes. **C** A concentrated solution has more acid particles per litre than a dilute solution. Alternatively, credit suitable hazards. For example, concentrated acids burn skin and eyes but dilute acids only hurt if they make contact with open cuts.
Activity	**Safe handling** Control risks by wearing eye protection and avoiding contact with skin, perhaps by wearing gloves. Mop up spills immediately. Credit any reasonable decision, supported by a suitable reason.

Summary questions	1 taste sour, corrosive, more, more (4 marks) 2 20 g of alkali in 250 cm^3 of solution is equivalent to (20 × 2 = 40 g) of alkali in 500 cm^3 of solution. The other solution has 10 g of alkali in 500 cm^3 of solution. So the first solution is more concentrated. (3 marks) 3 6 mark question. Example answers: Both acids and alkalis can be corrosive, depending on the concentration. This means that both acids and alkalis can, at certain concentrations, burn the skin and eyes. In both acids and alkalis, the more acid or alkali particles there are in a certain volume of solution, the more concentrated the solution. Acids taste sour. Alkalis feel soapy.

Starter	Support/Extension	Resources
Looking at acids and alkalis (10 min) Display a selection of acids and alkalis around the classroom, including household substances such as soap, vinegar, and drain cleaner. Make sure any household containers are empty and thoroughly clean and sealed. Ask students to make a list of the precautions noted on each item and the types of uses seen. **Common acids and alkalis** (5 min) The interactive resource contains a word search where students can familiarise themselves with the chemical names of common acids and alkalis.	**Support**: Students should concentrate on recalling the meaning of each hazard symbol. **Extension**: Students should deduce whether each of the substances contains an acid or an alkali.	**Interactive**: Common acids and alkalis
Main	**Support/Extension**	**Resources**
Introducing acids and alkalis (10 min) Ask students to give their understanding of what acids and alkalis are and where they may have heard of them. Discuss the chemical nature of acids and alkalis and the properties they each have. Discuss that acids and alkalis can have different concentrations, which means that there are different numbers of acid/alkali particles in the solutions. If Starter 1 was not chosen, introduce the fact that some acids and alkalis are safe to ingest and use whereas others are dangerous and can cause serious burns.	**Extension**: Students can be introduced to H^+ for acid particles and OH^- for (most) alkali particles.	
Acids and alkalis (10 min) In this activity students are required to match each hazard symbol to its name and description. Students are then asked to apply this to a laboratory situation, and are asked to identify suitable precautions to risks and hazards.		**Activity**: Acids and alkalis
Whiz bang! (20 min) Students often think that acids and alkalis react together to make an explosion. Demonstrate to them that this is not the case. Then give students 15 minutes to design a poster to summarise the properties of acids and alkalis.	**Extension**: Students should discuss the presence of H^+ and OH^- ions as properties of acids and alkalis.	
Plenary	**Support/Extension**	**Resources**
Memory game (10 min) Go through a list of common acids and alkalis on the board. Students must decide on their mini-whiteboards if the chemical concerned is an acid or an alkali. Remove the list and ask students to recall from memory as many acids and alkalis as possible. **Acid and alkali safety** (5 min) Call out the hazard names associated with most acids and alkalis (corrosive and irritant) and ask students to sketch the symbol from memory on a mini-whiteboard.		
Homework	**Support/Extension**	
Write a short report on the hazard symbols that can be found around the home. For each hazard symbol found, students must sketch the symbol, give a brief description of the hazard, and suggest a precaution to the risk. Ensure students know to do this under adult supervision, that they must not open any containers, and that they must handle all containers carefully.	**Support**: Guide students towards looking at containers in the kitchen or the garden shed.	

4.2 Indicators and pH

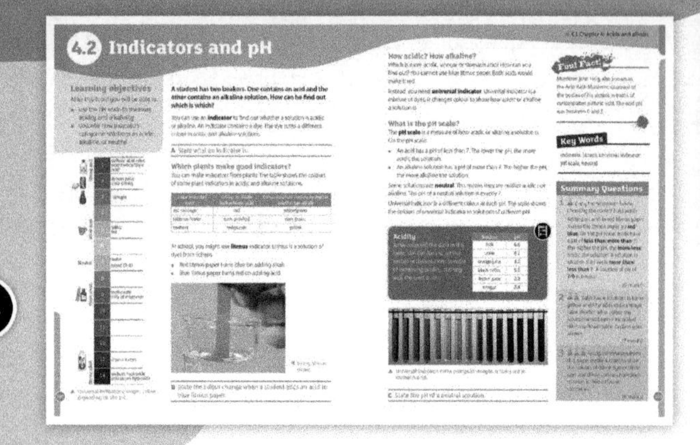

Chemistry NC link:

- the pH scale for measuring acidity/alkalinity; and indicators.

Working Scientifically NC link:

- interpret observations and data, including identifying patterns and using observations, measurements, and data to draw conclusions.

Band	Outcome	Checkpoint	
		Question	**Activity**
Developing	Describe broad colours of universal indicator for acids, alkalis, and neutral solutions (Level 4).		Main 1, Plenary 1, Plenary 2
	State that indicators will be different colours in acids, alkalis, and neutral solutions (Level 3).	A, 1, 2	Starter 2, Main 1, Main 3, Plenary 1, Plenary 2
	Categorise substances as acid, alkali, or neutral using experimental observations (Level 4).		Main 1
Secure	Use the pH scale to measure acidity and alkalinity (Level 5).	C, 1, 3	Main 1, Main 3, Plenary 2
	Describe how indicators categorise solutions as acidic, alkaline, or neutral (Level 5).	A, 1–3	Starter 2, Main 1, Main 3, Plenary 1
	Identify the likely pH of a solution using experimental observations (Level 6).		Main 1
Extending	Use a variety of indicators to measure acidity and alkalinity (Level 7).	1–3	Main 1, Main 2
	Categorise substances as strong or weak acids and alkalis using pH values (Level 7).	1	Main 1, Main 3
	Explain simply how indicators work (Level 7).	A, B, 1–3	Starter 2, Main 3
	Evaluate the accuracy of the pH values chosen through the experimental observations (Level 7).		Main 1

Literacy
Students summarise their knowledge using scientific terms to explain the application and importance of pH testing in farming for their homework.

APP
Students can use practical observations to deduce the approximate pH values of solutions (AF5).

Key Words
indicator, litmus, universal indicator, pH scale, neutral

Answers from the student book

In-text questions	**A** An indicator is a solution that contains a dye that changes colour to show whether a solution is acidic or alkaline. **B** The colour of the litmus paper changes from blue to red. **C** 7
Activity	**Acidity** milk, urine, black coffee, orange juice, vinegar, lemon juice

Summary questions	**1** red, less than, less, more than, 7 (5 marks) **2** The colour with red cabbage juice shows that the solution is alkaline. Hibiscus flower indicator is dark green in alkaline solution. So the predicted colour of the solution with hibiscus flower indicator is dark green. (2 marks) **3** The chart should correctly show the colours of dilute hydrochloric acid and dilute sodium hydroxide solution in five indicators, for example universal indicator, litmus, red cabbage, hibiscus flowers, and beetroot. (6 marks)

Starter	Support/Extension	Resources
Properties of acids and alkalis (5 min) Ask students to list as many properties of acids and alkalis as they can recall from the previous lesson. This can be done on mini-whiteboards and can be run as a competition.	**Support**: A list of properties can be provided for students to categorise.	
Indicator demonstration (10 min) Discuss with students the uses of indicators in everyday life, and that chemical indicators such as litmus paper can be used to identify acids and alkalis. Demonstrate red litmus paper turning blue when alkali is added and blue litmus paper turning red when acid is added. Discuss the term 'indicator' and why these substances are extremely useful to chemists.	**Support**: Although the use of red and blue litmus paper is useful to see the colour change between acids and alkalis, it may be useful to keep to one type of litmus paper to avoid confusing students.	
Main	**Support/Extension**	**Resources**
Using universal indicator (20 min) Students carry out a simple practical using universal indicator (in both paper and solution form) to find the pH of mystery solutions. They then answer questions that follow.	**Support**: A support sheet is available for students to record their observations. **Extension**: Students could be provided with a pH probe during the practical to allow them to consider the difference in accuracy between the two techniques.	**Practical**: Using universal indicator **Skill sheet**: Recording results
Applications of pH testing (10 min) Discuss applications of pH testing, for example, soil testing or determining blood pH. Show students a pH probe and explain why these can provide a more accurate pH value for solutions.		
pH scale (10 min) Students draw and label a pH scale diagram using the student book for guidance.		
Plenary	**Support/Extension**	**Resources**
pH values (10 min) Call out pH values between 1 and 14 randomly and ask students to display acid, alkali, or neutral on a mini-whiteboard. Then ask students to call out the colours of universal indicator expected for these pH values.		
Indicator colours (5 min) The interactive resource includes pictures of solutions after universal indicator has been added. Students must match the correct pH value to each picture.		**Interactive**: Indicator colours
Homework	**Support/Extension**	
Produce a leaflet explaining why pH testing is important for farmers.	**Support**: A hint can be given to students, asking them to consider the type of soil in which plant X will thrive, in order to focus them onto soil acidity/alkalinity.	

4.3 Neutralisation

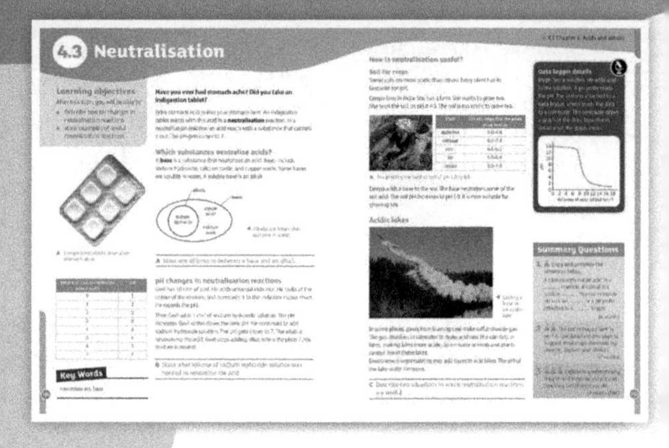

Chemistry NC link:

- defining acids and alkalis in terms of neutralisation reactions.

Working Scientifically NC link:

- select, plan, and carry out the most appropriate types of scientific enquiries to test predictions, including identifying independent, dependent, and control variables, where appropriate.

Band	Outcome	Checkpoint	
		Question	**Activity**
Developing	State simply what happens during a neutralisation reaction (Level 4).	B, 1, 3	Starter 1, Starter 2, Main, Plenary 1, Plenary 2
	Give one example of a neutralisation reaction (Level 3).	C, 3	Starter 1, Starter 2, Main
	Identify independent, dependent, and control variables in an investigation (Level 4).		Main
Secure	Describe how pH changes in neutralisation reactions (Level 6).		Starter 1
	State examples of useful neutralisation reactions (Level 5).	C, 3	Starter 2, Main, Plenary 1, Homework
	Design an investigation to find out which indigestion remedy is 'better' (Level 6).		Main
Extending	Interpret a graph of pH changes during a neutralisation reaction (Level 7).		Main
	Explain why neutralisation reactions are useful in the context of specific examples (Level 7).	3	Starter 2, Main, Plenary 1, Homework
	Justify the method chosen to investigate which indigestion remedy is 'better' (Level 8).		Main

Maths
Students can interpret pH from a graph of pH against volume of acid added to a solution in the student-book activity.

Literacy
Students can summarise information using scientific terminology on neutralisation to explain to gardeners the importance of monitoring soil pH and the science behind chewing gum after meals.

Students will also be tested on their ability to spell key words in the interactive resource.

APP
Students plan an investigation to test indigestion remedies (AF4) and decide which indigestion remedy is 'best' using their results and observations (AF5).

Key Words
neutralisation, base

Answers from the student book

In-text questions	**A** A base is any substance that neutralises an acid. An alkali is a base that is soluble in water. **B** 7 cm^3 **C** Neutralisation reactions are useful for adjusting soil pH to make the soil suitable for particular crops, and for increasing the pH of lakes whose pH is low as a result of acid rain.

Activity	Data logger details
	The pH decreases gradually at first until, when 7 cm^3 of acid has been added, the pH is 13. Then the pH decreases rapidly to pH 5 on the addition of just 2 cm^3 of acid. Then the pH decreases gradually on addition of more acid solution until the pH value is 1.
Summary questions	**1** neutralisation, base, indicator, data (4 marks) **2** She should try growing cabbage and tomato, since the pH data indicate that these crops can grow at pH 7. She could also try growing an apple tree, since this data shows that pH 6.8 is suitable for this plant, and pH 7.0 is only very slightly less acidic. (2 marks) **3** 6 mark question. Example answers: Different crops grow well in soils of different pH. It is useful to measure soil pH to know which plants are more likely to grow well in the soil. Farmers can add acid to a soil to make it more acidic (reduce the pH). Farmers can add bases to a soil to make it less acidic (increase the pH).

Starter	Support/Extension	Resources
Rainbow fizz (10 min) Add universal indicator to a beaker of dilute $NaHCO_3$ and a beaker of dilute HCl. Pour the bicarbonate solution into a clamped burette. Slowly add acid into the burette, and colour changes should occur where the two solutions meet. The fizzing is for added effect and students should be made aware of this. (Note that a large amount of universal indicator will be required for obvious colour changes to be seen inside the burette and that boiling tubes can be used instead of a burette.) **How do indigestion remedies work?** (5 min) Dissolve an indigestion remedy in a beaker of water and use red litmus paper to show the solution is alkaline. Ask students to consider what happens when this is taken for indigestion (i.e., it neutralises excess stomach acid).		
Main	**Support/Extension**	**Resources**
Neutralisation (40 min) Students decide what is meant by the 'best' indigestion remedy. They follow tips provided to plan an experiment to test two indigestion remedies, and use their results for a conclusion. Students then answer the questions that follow on the practical sheet.	**Support**: An access sheet is available where students are not required to plan the method for this investigation.	**Practical**: Neutralisation **Skill sheet**: Planning investigations **Skill sheet**: Recording results
Plenary	**Support/Extension**	**Resources**
Neutralisation conclusion (10 min) Ask students to explain which indigestion remedy they decided would be the 'best' at neutralising stomach acid. How did they decide the criteria for 'best'? **Neutralisation key words** (5 min) The interactive resource consolidates student understanding of acids and alkalis, the pH scale, and neutralisation reactions by asking students to type in key words and figures.		**Interactive**: Neutralisation key words
Homework	**Support/Extension**	
Students write an article in the magazine 'Pearly Whites Monthly' about the science behind why dentists suggest chewing gum after meals, using their knowledge of neutralisation to inform their writing. An alternative WebQuest homework activity is also available on Kerboodle where students research soil pH.	**Support**: Ask students to think about whether food is acidic or alkaline, and then what chewing gum must be in order to make the chewing of gum beneficial.	**WebQuest**: Soil pH

4.4 Making salts

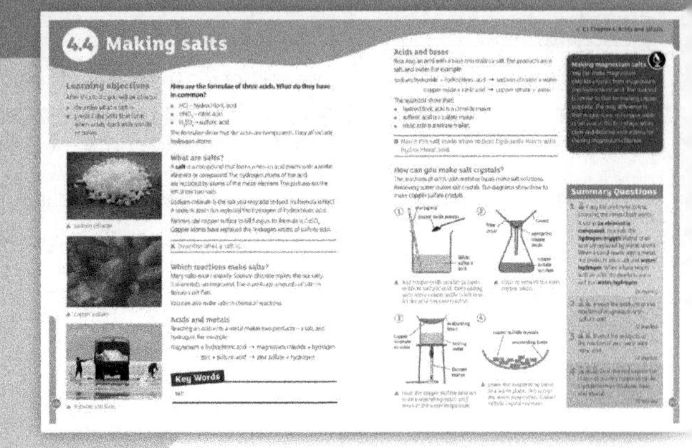
4.4 Making salts

Key Words

Summary Questions

Chemistry NC link:

- reactions of acids with metals to produce a salt plus hydrogen
- reactions of acids with alkalis to produce a salt plus water.

Working Scientifically NC link:

- present observations and data using appropriate methods, including tables and graphs.

Band	Outcome	Checkpoint	
		Question	**Activity**
Developing	State the type of chemical made when an acid and alkali react (Level 3).	A, 1	Main 1
	Match the type of salt that will form from the type of acid used (Level 4).	B, 2, 3	Main 1, Plenary 2, Homework
	Describe the reaction during an investigation by correctly identifying the reactants and products (Level 4).		Main 2
Secure	Describe what a salt is (Level 5).	A, 1	Main 1
	Predict the salts formed when acids react with metals or bases (Level 5).	B, 2, 3	Main 1, Plenary 2, Homework
	Present observations from the practical investigation as word equations (Level 5).		Main 2
Extending	Explain what salt formation displaces from the acid (Level 7).	A, 1	Main 1
	Predict the formulae for products of reactions between acids and metals, or acids and bases (Level 7).		Main 1, Main 2, Plenary 2, Homework
	Construct balanced formula equations for reactions between acids and bases, or acids and metals, including those observed in investigations (Level 8).		Main 2

Literacy
Students organise ideas and information to write a clear and concise scientific method for preparing magnesium chloride crystals.

Students use scientific terms, including the spelling of chemical names correctly, to identify reactants and products, and name the missing substances in word and formula equations.

APP
Students present data appropriately as word and formula equations (AF3).

Key Words
salt

Answers from the student book

In-text questions	**A** Substance in which hydrogen atoms of an acid are replaced by atoms of a metal element. **B** sodium chloride
Activity	**Making magnesium salts** Add small pieces of magnesium (ribbon) to dilute hydrochloric acid in beaker. Continue adding Mg until some remains unreacted in the mixture. Filter mixture to remove excess Mg ribbon, keeping solution. Pour the solution ($MgCl$) into an evaporating dish. Place dish on a tripod and gauze. Heat with a Bunsen burner until half of the water has evaporated. Leave dish and its contents in a warm, dry place for the rest of the water to evaporate, leaving $MgCl$ crystals in the dish.

Summary questions	1 compound, hydrogen, hydrogen, water (4 marks) 2 magnesium sulfate and hydrogen (2 marks) 3 zinc nitrate and water (2 marks) 4 Example answers (6 marks): Add copper oxide (credit hydroxide) to dilute hydrochloric acid in a beaker, one spatula measure at a time. Continue to add copper oxide until some remains unreacted in the mixture. Filter the mixture to remove the excess copper oxide. Keep the solution (filtrate). This has separated excess reactant (copper oxide) from a solution of the product (copper chloride). Pour the filtrate into an evaporating dish. Place the evaporating dish on a tripod and gauze, and heat with a Bunsen burner until about half the water has evaporated. Leave the evaporating dish and its contents in a warm, dry place for the rest of the water to evaporate. Copper chloride crystals remain in the evaporating dish.

Starter	Support/Extension	Resources
An alternative question-led lesson is also available. **Salt facts** (10 min) Ask students to list facts they know about the everyday usage of the word 'salt', for example, table salt or bath salts. Students should consider where they come from, uses, risks, and benefits. Build up a list as a class and discuss why, in particular, table salt is of huge importance globally and biologically (e.g., preservation of food, cooking, chemical industry, nerve conduction in the body). **Why is salt safe to eat?** (5 min) Show students some hydrochloric acid and sodium hydroxide and discuss the hazards of each. Ask students to decide if it would be safe to consume these. Then display sodium chloride (from a table salt container). Explain that it is made from the previous two chemicals – ask students to consider why it is safe to consume.	**Extension**: Students should recognise elements present in table salt given its chemical formula, and the relative quantities of each element in NaCl. **Support**: Students may need a reminder of reactions forming new products, with different properties to the reactants.	**Question-led lesson**: Making salts
Main	**Support/Extension**	**Resources**
How are salts made? (15 min) Discuss with students how the reaction between acids and bases will produce a salt and water, and the reaction between an acid and a metal will produce a salt and hydrogen gas. Students should write down the definition of a salt. Show examples of word and formula equations. Discuss the names of salts – the metal involved followed by the name derived from the type of acid used, for example, chlorides from hydrochloric acid. **Making salts** (25 min) Students carry out the reaction between HCl and NaOH to make table salt crystals. Students note down their observations throughout the reaction and answer the questions that follow, including a question on writing the word equation for this reaction.	**Extension**: Some students may be able to offer balanced formula equations for given salt formation reactions.	**Practical**: Making salts
Plenary	**Support/Extension**	**Resources**
Salt definition (5 min) Ask students to recall from memory the definition of a salt, and write this on their mini-whiteboard. **Name the substances** (10 min) Interactive resource in which students complete word equations of reactions between acids and metals.	**Extension**: Students can be asked to give examples of salts. **Extension**: Encourage students to write balanced symbol equations when given chemical formulae.	**Interactive**: Name the substances
Homework	**Support/Extension**	
Find out the name of the base used to neutralise acids in soils (calcium hydroxide). Find out names of acids present in soils and predict the names of the salts that would form during these reactions, as well as the secondary products of the reactions.		

C1 Chapter 4 Checkpoint

Checkpoint lesson routes

The route through this lesson can be determined using the Checkpoint assessment. Percentage pass marks are supplied in the Checkpoint teacher notes.

Route A (support)
Resource: C1 Chapter 4 Checkpoint: Revision

Students will produce an advisory leaflet for use in hairdressing salons to ensure hairdressers and barbers can use acids and alkalis safely and effectively. The revision activity will suggest how to set out the leaflet, and prompt students on the information required.

Route B (extension)
Resource: C1 Chapter 4 Checkpoint: Extension

Students will produce an advisory leaflet for use in hairdressing salons to ensure hairdressers and barbers can use acids and alkalis safely and effectively. Minimal prompts are provided and students need to work through some extending questions about products involved to include in their leaflet.

Progression to *secure*

No.	Developing outcome	Secure outcome	Making progress
1	Name some common properties of acids and alkalis.	Compare the properties of acids and alkalis.	Students will need to make a clear, visual comparison of acids and alkalis. They should first list the properties of each.
2	Describe, in simple terms, what the key words 'concentrated' and 'dilute' mean.	Describe differences between concentrated and dilute solutions of an acid.	Students will outline the safety precautions needed when acids and alkalis are used and will define what a concentrated and dilute solution is.
3	Describe broad colours of universal indicator for acids, alkalis, and neutral solutions.	Use the pH scale to measure acidity and alkalinity.	Students will include an illustration of the pH scale and include annotations
4	State that indicators will be different colours in acids, alkalis, and neutral solutions.	Describe how indicators categorise solutions as acidic, alkaline, or neutral.	Students will include discussion of indicators and explain how these can be used to identify acidic, alkaline, and neutral substances. Thinking about the level of detail needed for an advisory leaflet will help students come up with fuller descriptions.
5	State simply what happens during a neutralisation reaction.	Describe how pH changes during neutralisation reactions.	Students will describe what a neutralisation reaction is and explain how the pH changes during such a reaction.
6	Give one example of a neutralisation reaction.	State examples of useful neutralisation reactions.	Students are asked to give at least two examples to help the reader relate the information on neutralisation reactions with what they may experience in everyday life.
7	State the type of chemical made when an acid and alkali react.	Describe what a salt is.	Students will define a salt and explain how salts are formed. Students may wish to have access to their notes from the practical 'How are salts made?'.
8	Match the type of salt that will form from the type of acid used.	Predict the salts formed when acids react with metals or bases.	Students will explain how metals react with acids and give examples of word equations showing the metal salts formed.

Answers to end-of-chapter questions

1 Sweat – acidic, blood – alkaline, urine – acidic (3 marks)

2a A (1 mark)

b B and C (2 marks)

c D (1 mark)

3a sweet cherry (1 mark)

b blueberry (1 mark)

c sweet cherry, pineapple, strawberry (3 marks)

d Add an acidic substance to neutralise some of the alkaline substances in the soil (making the pH suitable for growing strawberries). (2 marks)

4 Students should be marked on the use of good English, organisation of information, spelling and grammar, and correct use of specialist scientific terms. The best answers will present clear, well organised, and detailed explanations of the stages of making magnesium chloride crystals (maximum of 6 marks).
Examples of correct scientific points:
Add small pieces of magnesium ribbon to dilute hydrochloric acid in a beaker.
Continue to add pieces of magnesium until some magnesium remains unreacted in the mixture.
Filter the mixture to remove the excess magnesium ribbon. Keep the filtrate.
Pour the filtrate into an evaporating dish. This is magnesium chloride solution.
Place the evaporating dish on a tripod and gauze and heat with a Bunsen burner until about half the water has evaporated.
Leave the evaporating dish and its contents in a warm, dry place for the rest of the water to evaporate. Magnesium chloride crystals remain in the evaporating dish.

Answer guide for Case Study

Developing	Secure	Extending
1–2 marks	3–4 marks	5–6 marks
• The spider diagram includes one use of neutralisation. • The written passage describes one use of neutralisation. It lacks detail and organisation.	• The spider diagram includes at least two uses of neutralisation. It lacks detail or organisation. • The written passage includes descriptions of at least two uses of neutralisation, but lacks detail and organisation.	• The spider diagram includes at least three uses of neutralisation and is well organised and detailed. • The written passage is in a sensible order and includes detailed descriptions of three uses of neutralisation.

kerboodle

C1 Chapter 4 Checkpoint assessment (automarked)
C1 Chapter 4 Checkpoint: Revision
C1 Chapter 4 Checkpoint: Extension
C1 Chapter 4 Progress task (Scientific attitude and measurement)

Physics 1

National curriculum links for this unit	
Chapter	**National Curriculum topic**
Chapter 1: Forces	Forces Balanced forces Forces and motion
Chapter 2: Sound	Observed waves Sound waves Energy and waves
Chapter 3: Light	Light waves
Chapter 4: Space	Space physics

Preparing for Key Stage 4 success

Knowledge Underpinning knowledge is covered in this unit for KS4 study of:	• Motion and forces • Wave properties • Sound in matter • Mass, weight, and gravity
Maths Skills developed in this unit (Topic number).	• Calculate arithmetic means (3.1). • Quantitative problem solving (1.2). • Understand number size and scale, and the quantitative relationship between units (1.1, 1.2, 1.4, 2.1, 3.1). • Plot and draw graphs (line graphs, bar charts, pie charts, scatter graphs, histograms) selecting appropriate scales for the axes (1.2, 1.3, 2.2, 2.3). • Extract and interpret information from charts, graphs, and tables (1.2, 1.3, 1.4, 2.2, 2.3, 4.2, 4.3). • Understand when and how to use estimation (1.1, 2.1, 2.3). • Understand and use direct proportion and simple ratios (1.1, 1.4). • Substitute numerical values into simple formulae and equations using appropriate units (1.4). • Carry out calculations involving $+$, $-$, $\times$, $\div$, either singly or in combination (1.4).
Literacy Skills developed in this unit (Topic number).	• Identify meaning in scientific text, taking into account potential bias (2.1, 4.4, 4.5). • Summarise a range of information from different sources (1.2, 2.1, 2.2, 2.3, 3.5, 4.1, 4.2, 4.3, 4.5). • Use scientific terms confidently and correctly in discussions and writing (all spreads). • Identify main ideas and supporting evidence in text (1.3, 2.1, 2.3, 2.4, 3.4, 3.5, 4.1, 4.2, 4.3, 4.4). • Use largely correct form in a range of writing styles and text, and include information relevant to the audience (3.2, 4.4). • Ideas are organised into well-developed, linked paragraphs. (1.1, 2.3, 2.4, 4.1).
Assessment Skills	• Quantitative problem solving (1.2, 1.4, 2.1, 2.3, 2.4, 3.1, 3.2, 4.2, 4.3, 4.4, 4.5) (end-of-chapter 1 Q5). • Application of Working Scientifically (1.2, 1.3, 2.3, 3.2, 3.5, 4.2, 4.4) (end-of-chapter 1 Q3, end-of-chapter 2 Q8, end-of-chapter 3 Q4).

KS2 Link	Check before	Checkpoint	Catch-up
Unsupported objects fall to the Earth because of the force of gravity acting between the Earth and the falling object.	P1 1.1 Introduction to forces	Ask why dropped objects fall to the ground.	Demonstrate that dropped objects fall simultaneously, and name the force causing this effect as gravity.
Drag forces such as air resistance, water resistance, and friction, that act between moving surfaces to slow objects down.	P1 1.3 Drag forces and friction	Students compare how easy it is to move through water and air at different speeds, giving a reason.	Students compare how easy it is to move their hand in air and in water. Show video clip of ice skater to demonstrate how easily objects move when friction is reduced.
Drag forces such as air resistance, water resistance, and friction act between moving surfaces to slow objects down.	P1 1.3 Drag forces and friction	Ask what happens if a cyclist stops pedalling – students explain why the cyclist stops moving.	Pedalling a bicycle keeps it moving. Applying brakes increases friction and slow the bicycle down. Draw force arrow diagrams showing friction/drag forces in the opposite direction to driving forces.
Vibrating objects make sound, which varies in pitch and loudness, and gets fainter as you move away.	P1 2.2 Sound and energy transfer	Ask students how sounds are made.	Demonstrate this using a vibrating ruler at the end of a table, or by placing a vibrating tuning fork in water.
Light travels in straight lines, which explains the size and shape of shadows.	P1 3.1 Light	Students sketch how light travels from a torch to a book.	Shine light through sheets of cardboard spaced apart, each with a small central hole. Show that the holes must be lined up for light to travel through.
Objects are seen because they give out or reflect light into the eye.	P1 3.1 Light	Students sketch how light travels from a torch to a book to our eyes.	Students group objects as ones that give out light (lit torch bulb, candle) and ones that reflect light (book, mirror).
The Sun, Earth, and Moon are roughly spherical bodies.	P1 4.1 The night sky	Students describe the Sun, Moon, and Earth using three words for each.	Show photographs of the Sun, Moon, and Earth.
The Earth orbits the Sun.	P1 4.2 The Solar System	Students sketch the Sun and Earth using arrows to show how they move relative to each other.	Two students act out the relative motion for the class, or demonstrate using a lamp and a tennis ball.
Earth spins on its axis to create day and night. This causes day length and temperature change during the year.	P1 4.3 The Earth	Students explain in words why we have day and night.	Demonstrate using a globe and lamp.
The Moon orbits the Earth.	P1 4.4 The Moon	Students sketch the Moon and Earth using arrows to show how they move relative to each other.	Two students act out the relative motion for the class, or demonstrate using a globe and a tennis ball.

kerboodle

P1 Unit pre-test
P1 Big practical project (foundation)
P1 Big practical project (higher)
P1 Big practical project teacher notes
P1 Practical project hints: graph plotting
P1 Practical project hints: planning
P1 Practical project hints: writing frame
P1 End-of-unit test (foundation)
P1 End-of-unit test (foundation) mark scheme
P1 End-of-unit test (higher)
P1 End-of-unit test (higher) mark scheme

Answers to Picture Puzzler

Key Words

whistle, astronaut, velcro, eclipse, shadow

The key word is **waves**.

Close Up

magazine fibres

1.1 Introduction to forces

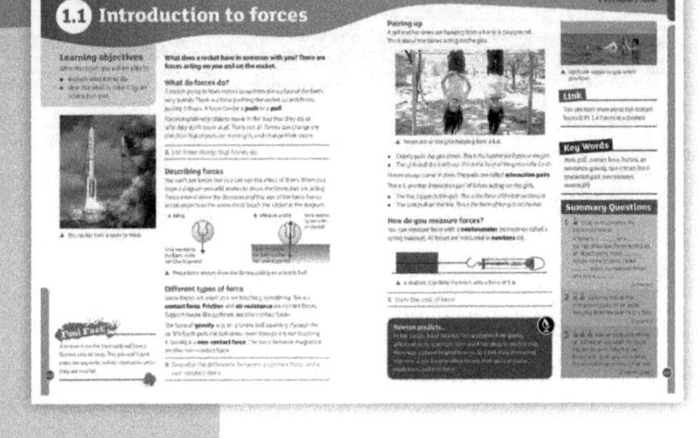

Physics NC link:

- forces as pushes or pulls, arising from the interaction between two objects
- using force arrows in diagrams, adding forces in one dimension
- forces measured in newtons, measurements of stretch or compression as force is changed
- opposing forces and equilibrium: weight supported on a compressed surface.

Working Scientifically NC link:

- make predictions using scientific knowledge and understanding.

Band	Outcome	Checkpoint	
		Question	Activity
Developing	Identify some forces acting on objects in everyday situations (Level 4).		Starter 1, Plenary 1
	Identify an interaction pair (Level 3).	2	Main 1
↓	Use a newtonmeter to make predictions about sizes of forces (Level 4).		Main 1
Secure	Explain what forces do (Level 5).	A	Main 2
	Describe what is meant by an interaction pair (Level 6).	2	Starter 2
↓	Make predictions about forces in familiar situations (Level 5).		Main 2, Plenary 1
Extending	Explain the differences between contact and non-contact forces (Level 6).		Starter 1
	Explain which pairs of forces are acting on an object (Level 7).	3	Main 2
↓	Make predictions about pairs of forces acting in unfamiliar situations (Level 7).		Main 2

Maths

In the student-book activity students use units for force.

Students can use size and scale and the quantitative relationship between units in the practical.

Literacy

In the student-book activity students use scientific terms confidently and correctly in writing about forces.

Students can make clear descriptions of forces when using newtonmeters.

APP

Students can use abstract models to explain forces (AF1).

Students can select appropriate formats to present data (AF3).

Key Words

push, pull, contact force, friction, air resistance, gravity, non-contact force, interaction pair, newtonmeter, newton (N)

Answers from the student book

In-text questions	**A** Forces change the shape, speed, or direction of motion. **B** For a contact force to act the objects have to be touching (e.g., the air and a car for air resistance) but non-contact forces act at a distance. **C** newtons

Summary questions	**1** push, pull, arrows, interaction, newtonmeter (5 marks) **2** The force of the Earth on the apple AND the force of the apple on the Earth OR the force of the tree on the apple AND the force of the apple on the tree. (2 marks) **3** 6 mark question. Example answers: The Earth exerts a force on you. You exert a force on the Earth. The chair exerts a force on you. You exert a force on the chair. These are two interaction pairs. The two forces acting on you are from two different interaction pairs. This means one can be bigger than the other.

Starter	Support/Extension	Resources
What's the force? (10 min) Students recap on what forces are (from KS2), and individually name as many forces as possible. **Who pulls harder?** (10 min) Give groups of students a pair of newtonmeters, linking the hooks together. Ask them to predict the readings on each newtonmeter if one student holds their newtonmeter and the other student pulls theirs away.	**Support**: Show a picture as a prompt for listing forces, for example, forces acting on a cyclist.	
Main	**Support/Extension**	**Resources**
At this point it is important that students are clear on the effects and names of forces, as well as what interactive pairs are.		
Measuring forces (20 min) Introduce students to the idea of a newtonmeter and measuring forces in newtons. Students measure the force needed to carry out different activities (e.g., to lift a pencil case) and record these in a table. Students should compare readings with each other, explaining differences. For accurate readings, the newtonmeter hook should be in line with its spring. **Force arrows** (15 min) Introduce students to force diagrams and force arrows. Give students three arrows of different lengths cut out of card. Students choose an arrow each time they measure a force, showing the direction of the force and comparing its size.	**Support**: Make sure the forces are straightforward to measure. For example, objects with hooks or straps. **Extension**: Students prepare their own table to record results. Students identify several forces acting on one object and explain why they chose these groups, for example, as pairs of interaction forces.	**Practical**: Measuring forces
Plenary	**Support/Extension**	**Resources**
Comparing the size of forces (10 min) Students list at least six situations involving forces and put these in order, ranked by size. This can be done using the list from the interactive resource or non-interactively on the board. **What's the difference?** (10 min) If students have measured the same thing during the practical (for example, lifting a book) ask them to compare results. Students suggest reasons for any different results, for example, linked to technique.	**Support**: Supply a list and ask students to rank these forces by size. **Extension**: Ask students to estimate the size of different forces in newtons.	**Interactive**: Comparing the size of forces
Homework	**Support/Extension**	
Provide students with a strong rubber band stapled to the top of a piece of stiff card, and tie one side of the top of a small sandwich plastic bag to the other end of the rubber band. Attach a piece of paper to the elastic band as a pointer. Students use this to measure forces at home calibrating the scale using their own units, depending on what is available to measure, by placing items in the plastic bag.	**Support**: Calibrate the newtonmeter in the classroom and ask students to use it to measure forces at home. **Extension**: Ask students to make their own newtonmeter using their own design.	

1.2 Squashing and stretching

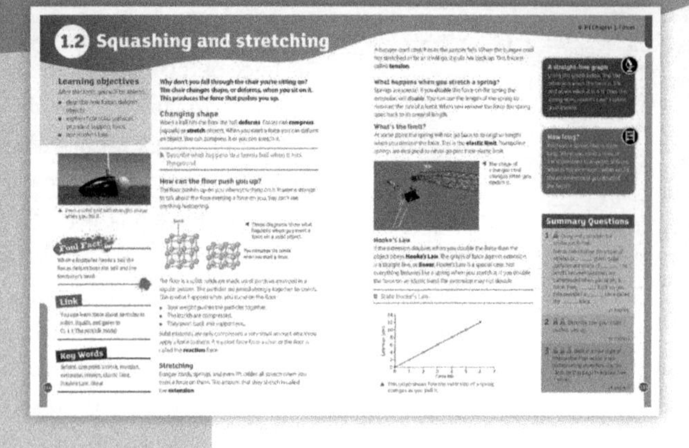

Physics NC link:

- forces: associated with deforming objects; stretching and squashing – springs
- force–extension linear relation; Hooke's Law as a special case
- opposing forces and equilibrium: weight held by a stretched spring
- energy changes on deformation.

Working Scientifically NC link:

- present observations and data using appropriate methods, including tables and graphs.

Band	Outcome	Checkpoint	
		Question	**Activity**
Developing	State an example of a force deforming an object (Level 4).	A, B	Starter 1
	Recognise a support force (Level 4).	1	Starter 2
	Use Hooke's Law to identify proportional stretching (Level 4).		Main 1
	Present data in a line graph and identify a pattern (Level 4).		Main 1
Secure	Describe how forces deform objects (Level 5).	A, B	Starter 1
	Explain how solid surfaces provide a support force (Level 5).	1–3	Starter 2
	Use Hooke's Law to predict the extension of a spring (Level 6).		Maths, Main 1
	Present data on a graph, and identify a quantitative relationship in the pattern (Level 5).		Main 1
Extending	Explain how forces deform objects in a range of situations (Level 7).	A, B	Starter 2, Main 1
	Explain how solid surfaces provide a support force, using scientific terminology and bonding (Level 7).	2, 3	
	Apply Hooke's Law to make quantitative predictions with unfamiliar materials (Level 7).		Maths, Main 1
	Present data in a graph and recognise quantitative patterns and errors (Level 7).		Main 1

Maths

In the student book students complete a maths task using direct proportion, measuring extension for a given force.

In the practical students can plot data on a line graph, or interpret data from a line graph of extension and force.

Literacy

Students read and summarise information about applications of Hooke's Law such as toys or bungee jumping.

Students can use their ideas to explain how a newtonmeter works.

APP

Plan and carry out Hooke's Law experiment (AF4).

Interpret data, conclusion, and evaluation (AF3).

Key Words

deform, compress, stress, reaction, extension, tension, elastic limit, Hooke's Law, linear

Answers from the student book

In-text questions	**A** The shape of the tennis ball changes/is deformed. **B** Hooke's Law says that if you double the force the extension will double.

Activity	**A straight-line graph** When the force is 3 N the extension is 6 cm and when the force is 6 N the extension is 12 cm. This shows that if you double the force the extension doubles. The spring obeys Hooke's Law. **How long** The extension = 6 cm − 4 cm = 2 cm If you doubled the force the extension would be 4 cm.
Summary questions	**1** deform, bonds, support, push, reaction (5 marks) **2** The bonds between the particles in the solid behave like springs When they are compressed they push you back up (2 marks) **3** Example answers (6 marks): Use a range of springs that stretch differently. Some springs would not stretch so much/be stiffer. You would bounce less. Some springs would stretch more. You would bounce more. Different areas of the trampoline could have different springs. You would bounce differently depending on where you were. Would be more fun because the bounce would vary.

Starter	Support/Extension	Resources
An alternative question-led lesson is also available. **Changing shape** (10 min) Hand round a selection of objects, for example, sponge, springs to stretch or squash, plasticine, rubber band, balloon. Students explain what happens when a force is applied and when the force is removed. Introduce the idea of the reaction force, how this is formed, and the energy transfers associated with deformation of material. **Why don't you fall through the floor?** (10 min) Place a heavy ball on the table, on a sponge, and in a beaker of water. Identify similarities and differences (weight acts down – table provides support but not the sponge or water). Explain that some support forces seem invisible but are present. Support forces vary in size. Introduce the idea of the reaction force and how this is formed.	**Support**: Students describe what happens; the teacher explains why in terms of forces. **Extension**: Students identify elastic and non-elastic objects and how to distinguish between them.	**Question-led lesson**: Squashing and stretching
Main	**Support/Extension**	**Resources**
Investigating elastic (35 min) Make two marks 10 cm apart in the middle of the elastic. Loop one end of the elastic from the boss head of the clamp stand. Add the hanger to the loop at the other end of the elastic and measure the new length between the marks. Repeat measurements whilst adding extra masses. Record results in a table and calculate each change in length. Students then plot a line graph of change in length against force, draw a line of best fit, and describe the pattern. This is done as part of the questions on the practical sheet. A partially labelled graph grid may be used to support students and to speed up the process. Introduce Hooke's Law.	**Support**: A support sheet is available with a pre-drawn table. **Extension**: Students understand that extension should be proportional to force and use their graph to predict extension for different masses.	**Practical**: Investigating elastic **Skill sheet**: Choosing scales **Skill sheet**: Calculating means **Skill sheet**: Recording results
Plenary	**Support/Extension**	**Resources**
Bungee jumpers (10 min) Show a video clip of a bungee jumper. Explain that the rope is elastic. Students explain how to calculate the right length of rope to use, and what happens if you get it wrong.	**Support**: Students describe what happens to the rope in the video and why it helps to keep the jumper safe.	
Stretching experiment (10 min) Interactive resource that can be used as a recap for the experiment carried out in the lesson.	**Extension**: Students explain problems caused if the wrong spring or elastic is chosen.	**Interactive**: Stretching experiment
Homework	**Support/Extension**	
Students research one idea about the application of springs. They must find out why the elastic behaviour is used, how it is controlled, how problems are avoided, and the energy changes that occur on deformation of the spring.	**Support**: Students can be supported by coming up with uses of springs during the lesson.	

1.3 Drag forces and friction

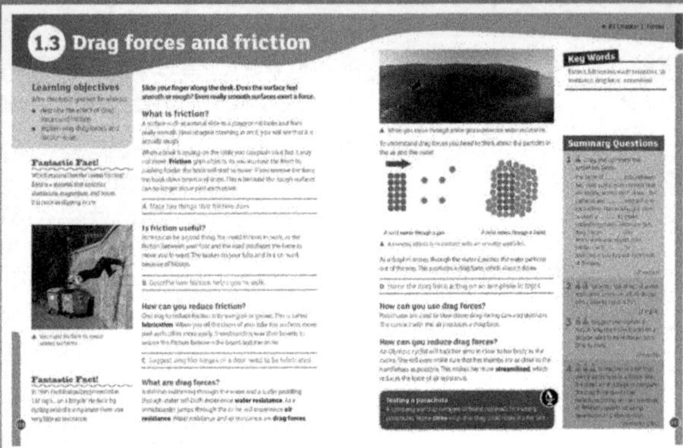

Physics NC link:

- forces: associated with rubbing and friction between surfaces, with pushing things out of the way; resistance to motion of air and water.

Working Scientifically NC link:

- select, plan, and carry out the most appropriate types of scientific enquiries to test predictions, including identifying independent, dependent, and control variables, where appropriate.

Band	Outcome	Checkpoint	
		Question	**Activity**
Developing	Identify examples of drag forces and friction (Level 3).	C, 1	
	Describe how drag forces and friction arise (Level 4).	A, B	Starter 1
	Carry out an experiment to test a prediction of friction caused by different surfaces (Level 4).		Main 1
Secure	Describe the effect of drag forces and friction (Level 5).		Main 2, Homework
	Explain why drag forces and friction arise (Level 6).		Main 1
	Plan and carry out an experiment to investigate friction, selecting suitable equipment (Level 5).		Main 1
Extending	Explain the effect of drag forces and friction in terms of forces (Level 7).	3, 4	
	Explain why drag forces and friction slow things down in terms of forces (Level 7).	3, 4	
	Plan and carry out an experiment, stating the independent, dependent, and control variables (Level 7).		Main 2

Maths
In the practical students plot and draw graphs selecting appropriate scales for the axes when representing their results.

Literacy
In the student-book activity students write up their practical, planning and adapting writing style to suit audience and purpose.

APP
In the student-book activity students plan to test a parachute (AF4).

Investigate designs used to reduce drag forces (AF3).

Interpret data, conclusion, and evaluation (AF5).

Key Words
friction, lubrication, water resistance, air resistance, drag force, streamlined

Answers from the student book

In-text questions	**A** Friction can stop something moving or it can slow down something that is moving. **B** The friction produces the force between your foot and the floor that means that you can walk forwards. **C** You need to lubricate surfaces to reduce friction. **D** air resistance
Activity	**Testing a parachute** Keep these things the same: • the weight of the object beneath the parachute • the area of the parachute • the thickness of the material.

Summary questions	1 friction, rough, force, air resistance, water resistance, air/gas, water (7 marks) 2 Water resistance slows the bird down. (1 mark) 3 The brake blocks become worn away because of friction between the surfaces. (2 marks) 4 6 mark question. Example answers: Air resistance depends on area. Bigger area means that more molecules hit the parachute. The air resistance is bigger with a bigger parachute. Air resistance depends on speed. Bigger speed means that more molecules hit the parachute. The air resistance is bigger with a bigger speed. The biggest air resistance will act on a large parachute attached to a fast car.

Starter	Support/Extension	Resources
Slipping and sliding (10 min) Students name surfaces that are slippery/non-slippery and compare them. They list features of the best surfaces to slide on with the idea of reducing friction.	**Support**: Show images of different surfaces (e.g., icy road, wet road, a slide, tarmac). Group these as high/low friction.	
Friction and drag (10 min) Students list three or four objects (or animals) that move easily through water. The interactive resource can then be used to identify features that change friction and drag.	**Extension**: Students suggest how birds alter their shape to change their speed or stop quickly.	**Interactive**: Friction and drag
Main	**Support/Extension**	**Resources**
Investigating friction (35 min) Students use newtonmeters to pull a box with masses in it along different surfaces. They record and analyse their results, drawing a graph of their results. OR **Streamlining** (optional practical) Students drop 1 cm^3 of plasticine in a column of water. They change its shape and compare how the shape affects the time taken to fall a fixed distance, and link this with forces involved. The plasticine can be retrieved using thread. Students present data in a table. Resources have not been provided for this practical.	**Support**: An access sheet is available with a given method and results table. **Extension**: Students measure the cross-sectional area for each shape. They look for a relationship between area and time, plotting a suitable graph.	**Practical**: Investigating friction **Skill sheet**: Choosing scales **Skill sheet**: Planning investigations **Skill sheet**: Recording results **Skill sheet**: Drawing graphs
Plenary	**Support/Extension**	**Resources**
Phonebook friction (10 min) Interleave the pages of two magazines or phonebooks. Ask students to hold the spines and pull them apart.	**Extension**: Students explain why it is hard to separate the magazines (each page in contact contributes to the total friction to be overcome).	
Shoes for the job (10 min) Students match features of different sport shoe soles with the surfaces and movement (e.g., football, rugby, ice skating, running, ballet).	**Support**: Students identify if soles of shoes have a large/small surface area, and if they are rough or smooth. Teacher links this to the sport's requirements.	
Homework	**Support/Extension**	
Students write a short article about how the design of sportswear for athletes, swimmers, and runners helps them move faster.	**Support**: Students list design features of sportswear that increase speed. **Extension**: Students link specific features of clothes to how it reduces drag, for example, close fitting or smooth.	

1.4 Forces at a distance

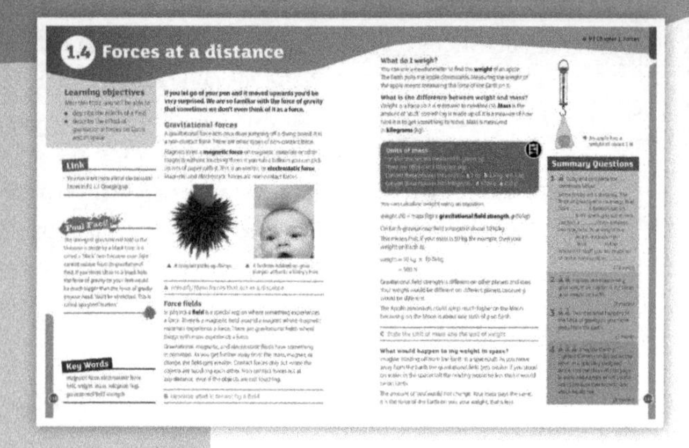

Physics NC link:

- non-contact forces: gravity forces acting at a distance on Earth and in space
- gravity force, weight = mass × gravitational field strength (g), on Earth g = 10 N/kg, different on other planets and stars.

Working Scientifically NC link:

- present observations and data using appropriate methods, including tables and graphs.

Band	Outcome	Checkpoint	
		Question	**Activity**
Developing	Identify gravity as a force that acts at a distance (Level 3).	A	
↓	State that gravity changes with distance (Level 4).		Starter 1
	With help, draw a table and present results (Level 3).		Main 1
Secure	Describe the effect of a field (Level 5).	1	
↓	Describe the effect of gravitational forces on Earth and in space (Level 5).	3	Main 2, Plenary 1
	Present results in a simple table (Level 4).		Main 1
Extending	Apply the effects of forces at a distance to different fields (Level 7).		Starter 1, Main 2, Plenary 1
↓	Explain how the effect of gravity changes moving away from Earth (Level 7).		Main 1, Main 2
	Present results in a table, ensuring they are reliable (Level 6).		Main 1

Maths

In the student book students use number size and scale, and the quantitative relationship between units of mass and weight.

In the practical students extract and interpret information from graphs and tables they have produced.

Literacy

Students communicate ideas and information to a wide range of audiences by writing holiday brochures for different planets for homework.

Students collaborate and use exploratory talk when they present ideas for the Olympics in Space.

APP

Use an abstract model of forces to explain gravitational force (AF1).

When doing the practical, repeat sets of observations or measurements where appropriate, selecting suitable ranges and intervals (AF4).

Interpret data from the Gravity cups practical, recognising obvious inconsistencies (AF5).

Key Words

magnetic force, electrostatic force, field, weight, mass, kilogram (kg), gravitational field strength

Answers from the student book

In-text questions	**A** magnetic forces, electrostatic forces, and gravitational forces/gravity **B** A field is a region where something experiences a force. It doesn't have to be touching the thing to produce the force. **C** Mass is measured in kg, weight is measured in newtons.
Activity	**Units of mass** **a** 2000 g **b** 3500 g **c** 400 g **d** 4.7 kg **e** 0.25 kg

Summary questions	1 mass, electrostatic, magnetic, force, newtons, mass, kilograms (7 marks) 2 The gravitational field on Jupiter is bigger. Weight increases with gravity. Mass does not change. (3 marks) 3 Gravity gets weaker. (1 mark) 4 Example answers (6 marks): Events that involve throwing something a distance would produce new records, javelin/shot put/hammer, Because the gravitational field strength is less, Events that involve lifting things would produce new records, weightlifting, Because the gravitational field strength is less, Objects will travel further before they hit the ground, Events that are affected by air/water resistance would not be affected, cycling/swimming

Starter	Support/Extension	Resources
The levitating paperclip and spinning pepperoni (10 min) Students list similarities and differences between a levitating paperclip and a spinning pepperoni sausage, naming forces involved. Tie thread to the paperclip, attach thread to the bench, hold a magnet so the paperclip levitates. Suspend a pepperoni sausage from a clamp stand using thread. Hold an electrostatically charged balloon near the pepperoni sausage – it turns. Although this does not involve gravity, this can show how forces get weaker with distance.	**Support**: Demonstrate the scenarios and ask students which non-contact force was used. **Extension**: Students explain what happens if the other pole of the magnet faces the paperclip, or different materials are moved between the magnet and paperclip.	
Contact and non-contact forces (10 min) Students group forces given on the interactive resource into contact and non-contact forces as a recap and introduction to this lesson.		**Interactive**: Contact and non-contact forces
Main	**Support/Extension**	**Resources**
Gravity cups (25 min) Prepare sealed containers (e.g., drinking chocolate containers) by placing different masses of sand in each to represent different celestial bodies. For example, 100 g for Earth, 17 g for the Moon, 270 g for Jupiter, 38 g for Mars, and 120 g for Saturn. Students weigh the containers, and use $W = mg$ to decide on which planet/Moon the container would weigh that amount. Students present data in a table. It is extremely important at this stage to distinguish between g (gravitational field strength) and g (for grams).	**Support**: A support sheet is available with a pre-drawn table for results, and a step-by-step guide to work out the identity of each station. **Extension**: Students explain why the mass of the container varies.	**Practical**: Gravity cups
A meal on the Moon (15 min) Provide a graph showing mass (x-axis) against weight on the Moon (y-axis). Students weigh items of food and use this and the graph to calculate the weight of each food on the Moon.	**Support**: Students explain if an astronaut gains or loses mass if their meal weighs less on the Moon.	
Plenary	**Support/Extension**	**Resources**
Match the weight (5 min) Provide a list of 5 masses (and 5 equivalent weights) on the Earth and on the Moon. Students link the correct masses and weights.	**Support**: Present data for one mass at a time. **Extension**: Students use the idea of gravity and weight to explain their answer.	
Olympics in space (5 min) Ask students to compare an astronaut doing sport on the Earth and on the Moon (wearing the same clothes) – long jump, high jump, basketball, and so on.		
Homework	**Support/Extension**	
Write a holiday brochure for a trip to another planet. Explain what the conditions would be like, and how to prepare for the trip.	**Support**: Provide summary data about a specific planet (temperature, atmosphere, surface, distance). **Extension**: There is scope for a detailed discussion linking the conditions and preparations needed.	
An alternative WebQuest homework activity is also available on Kerboodle where students research the International Space Station.		**WebQuest**: International Space Station

1.5 Balanced and unbalanced

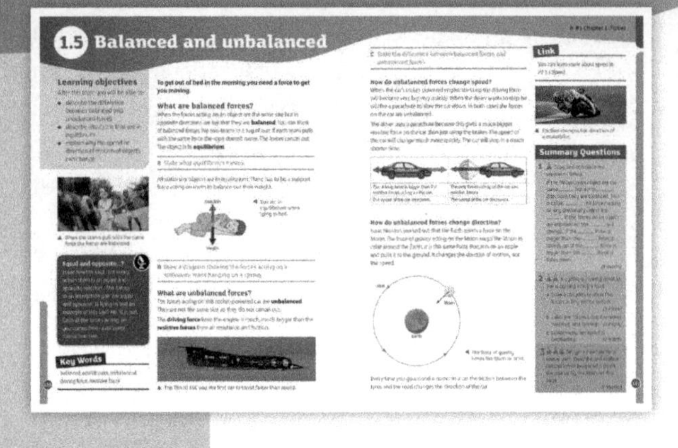

Physics NC link:

- using force arrows in diagrams, adding forces in one dimension, balanced and unbalanced forces
- forces being needed to cause objects to stop or start moving, or to change their speed or direction of motion (qualitative only)
- change depending on direction of force and its size
- opposing forces and equilibrium: weight held by a stretched spring or supported on a compressed surface.

Working Scientifically NC link:

- present observations and data using appropriate methods, including tables and graphs.

Band	Outcome	Checkpoint	
		Question	**Activity**
Developing	Identify familiar situations of balanced and unbalanced forces (Level 4).	1	
	Define equilibrium (Level 4).	A	
	Identify when the speed or direction of motion of an object changes (Level 4).		Main 1, Starter 1
	Present observations in a table with help (Level 3).		Main 1
Secure	Describe the difference between balanced and unbalanced forces (Level 6).	C	Main 1, Plenary 1
	Describe situations that are in equilibrium (Level 5).	B	
	Explain why the speed or direction of motion of objects can change (Level 6).	2	Starter 2
	Present observations in a table including force arrow drawings (Level 6).	B	Main 1
Extending	Explain the difference between balanced and unbalanced forces (Level 7).	2	
	Describe a range of situations that are in equilibrium (Level 7).	B	Main 1
	Explain why the speed or direction of motion of objects can change using force arrows (Level 7).		Main 1
	Predict and present changes in observations for unfamiliar situations (Level 7).		Main 1

Maths
In the student-book activity students use proportion when estimating force arrows.

In the practical activity students can carry out calculations involving +, −, ×, ÷, either singly or in combination.

Literacy
Students make connections within/across a range of texts when reading an account of Newton's work on forces.

APP
Use abstract ideas such as force arrows to explain how resultant forces affect motion (AF1).

Plan and use investigative approaches to compare forces (AF4).

Key Words
balanced, equilibrium, unbalanced, driving force, resistive forces

Answers from the student book

In-text questions	**A** An object is in equilibrium if the forces on it are balanced. **B** Diagram of mass with arrow pointing up labelled 'tension' and the same size arrow pointing down labelled 'weight'. **C** Balanced forces cancel out/are equal in size and opposite in direction. Unbalanced forces are not of equal size/direction/do not cancel out.
Summary questions	**1** size, opposite/opposing, equilibrium, balanced, speed, driving, resistive, resistive, driving (9 marks) **2a** Force diagram with an arrow showing that the resistive force is bigger than the driving force. (1 mark) **b** Arrow pointing backwards labelled resistive, arrow pointing forwards labelled driving. (1 mark) **c** The forces are unbalanced. (1 mark) **3** Example answers (6 marks): An object speeds up or slows down when the forces acting on it are unbalanced. An object is stationary or moving at a steady speed when the forces acting on it are balanced. Ride will be exciting if there are lots of sections where the forces are unbalanced. The force of gravity acts at all times so there will need to be a mechanism for lifting people up. You can use gravity to accelerate people on different sections of the ride. People will need restraints so that they are safe when they accelerate/decelerate.

Starter	Support/Extension	Resources
Forces and sport (10 min) Show a short video of a sports activity. Students list what happens as the motion of a person or object changes, for example, the ball was kicked or the player swung a racket.	**Extension**: Students identify the type and direction of forces changing the motion.	
Changing speed (10 min) Students describe their motion on a short car/bus journey, explaining how the driver changed the motion, for example, braked, accelerated, turned the steering wheel.		
Main	**Support/Extension**	**Resources**
Force circus (40 min) Students identify forces acting on several experiments in a circus, deciding if they are balanced or not, and describing the different forces acting on the object. As part of the practical sheet, students sketch the force diagram for each experiment showing the size and direction of the forces acting on the object.	**Support**: The support sheet provides a pre-drawn table. **Extension**: Students identify the relative size and direction of unbalanced forces, linking this to the motion.	**Practical**: Force circus **Skill sheet**: Scientific apparatus
Plenary	**Support/Extension**	**Resources**
Riding a bicycle (5 min) Students describe and act out how to change motion when you ride a bicycle, linking the ideas to the forces.	**Support**: Name the forces and ask students to identify the direction, and if one force is larger or smaller than another. **Extension**: Students estimate the size of the different forces.	
Balanced and unbalanced forces (5 min) Interactive resource where students sort statements describing the motion of a football being kicked into balanced or unbalanced forces.		**Interactive**: Balanced and unbalanced forces
Homework	**Support/Extension**	
Students list different situations at home where forces are balanced or unbalanced. Students name the forces involved in each case, identifying the direction and relative size.	**Support**: Students identify if the forces are balanced or unbalanced. **Extension**: Students name the forces involved and prepare force arrow diagrams.	

P1 Chapter 1 Checkpoint

Checkpoint lesson routes

The route through this lesson can be determined using the Checkpoint assessment. Percentage pass marks are supplied in the Checkpoint teacher notes.

Route A (support)
Resource: P1 Chapter 1 Checkpoint: Revision

Students will work through a series of mini experiments and a revision activity that allows them to gradually revisit and consolidate their understanding of forces.

Route B (extension)
Resource: P1 Chapter 1 Checkpoint: Extension

Students need to produce a storyboard for a film explaining the forces acting on a car in a car chase (drag/air resistance, friction on the wheels and brakes, thrust from engine). They will need to draw a series of pictures showing how these forces change as the car is moving and changing direction.

Progression to *secure*

No.	Developing outcome	Secure outcome	Making progress
1	Identify some forces acting on objects in everyday situations.	Explain what forces do.	In Task 1 students should explain what a number of forces do. To help with this, demonstrate objects experiencing the forces listed. Ask students to say what the effect of the named force is.
2	Identify an interaction pair.	Describe what is meant by an interaction pair.	In Task 2 students consider some basic interaction pairs. Demonstrate examples of interaction pairs and ask students to identify pairs of forces involved. Start with an example of a book, which is the first part of Task 2.
3	State an example of a force deforming an object.	Describe how forces deform objects.	In Task 3 Experiment 1, students complete sentences using key words to form their descriptions. Demonstrate to students how to deform a rubber band. Allow students to deform sponges. They can complete their own description for this.
4	Recognise a support force.	Explain how solid surfaces provide a support force.	In Task 3 Experiment 2, students describe situations where objects are supported in the classroom (e.g., a book on a bench) and state what supports the object.
5	Use Hooke's Law to identify proportional stretching.	Use Hooke's Law to predict the extension of a spring.	In Task 3 Experiment 1, allow students to stretch rubber bands with a newtonmeter. They predict the length when the force is doubled using the support in the sheet.
6	Identify examples of drag forces and friction.	Describe the effect of drag forces and friction.	Talk with students about the difference between running through water and running on a road. Encourage them to use key words and write a description in Task 3.
7	Describe how drag forces and friction arise.	Explain why drag forces and friction arise.	To demonstrate this concept to students, you can draw pictures of the particle arrangement of a gas and a liquid. Students are given diagrams in Task 3 to annotate.
8	Identify gravity as a force that acts at a distance.	Describe the effect of gravity on an unsupported mass.	In Task 3 Experiment 2, provide students with pieces of paper to drop. They should describe what they observe, then describe what happens to an unsupported object using key terms.
9	Describe how gravity forces affect an unsupported object.	Describe how gravity forces change the weight of an object on different planets.	Before completing Task 3 students should watch a brief video of people dropping objects on the Moon and compare this with people dropping objects on Earth.
10	Identify familiar situations of balanced and unbalanced forces.	Describe the difference between balanced and unbalanced forces.	In Experiments 2 and 3 you can demonstrate different situations with balanced and unbalanced forces. Examples given are dropping a piece of paper and rolling a ball across a bench.

11	Define equilibrium.	Describe a range of situations that are in equilibrium.	In Task 4 discuss with students situations that are in equilibrium. Before writing their descriptions students should annotate the diagrams provided.
12	Identify when the speed or direction of motion of an object changes.	Explain why the speed or direction of motion of objects can change.	This can be a difficult concept for students to understand and is best demonstrated physically before explanations are produced. Guidance is provided in Task 5.

Answers to end-of-chapter questions

1 Contact: friction, air resistance, upthrust. Non-contact: gravitational force, magnetic force, electrostatic force. (6 marks)

2a unbalanced (1 mark) **b** balanced (1 mark) **c** unbalanced (1 mark)

3a surface (1 mark) **b** height of ramp (1 mark) **c** size, material, and shape of block (1 mark) **d** One of the variables (the surface) is categorical, not continuous. (2 marks)

4a Diagram showing a reaction force up and weight down. The force arrows are the same size. (2 marks)

b When the cyclist sits on the seat it deforms and pushes back on her. (2 marks) **c** unbalanced (1 mark)

5a Measure the length of the spring with no force on it. Measure the length with a certain force on it. Subtract the length with no force on it from the length with a force on it to find the extension. (3 marks)

b A mass of 100 g is a measure of how much force it takes to make it move. A weight of 1N is a measure of the gravitational force of the Earth on the mass. (2 marks)

c The graph is a straight line. This means that if you double one thing then the other thing doubles.
In this case the graph shows that if the force doubles, the extension doubles. This is Hooke's Law. (2 marks)

6 Students should be marked on the use of good English, organisation of information, spelling and grammar, and correct use of specialist terms. The best answer will be organised clearly in paragraphs, linking ideas and reasoning correctly to provide a full explanation (maximum of 6 marks).
Examples of correct scientific points:
A newtonmeter measures force.
A bigger force produces a bigger extension.
An elastic band would get longer.
The extension of the elastic band would not be proportional (does not obey Hooke's Law).
So if you doubled the force the extension would not double.
The extension of a spring is proportional to the force (obeys Hooke's Law).

Answer guide for Big Write

Developing	Secure	Extending
1–2 marks	3–4 marks	5–6 marks
• Describes motion but with little explanation or attention to the text type (blog). • Example points made: Rocket takes off because of thrust. There is gravity acting on the rocket. Some forces slow it down. It accelerates at the start, and again as it approaches Mars.	• Explains motion with some indication they have paid attention to the text type. • Example extra points made: There is a gravitational force on the rocket due to the Earth at all times. As the rocket takes off, it accelerates because the forces on it are unbalanced. If the forces on the rocket are balanced it will move at a steady speed. The spacecraft needs fuel to accelerate away from Mars to get home.	• Explains motion in detail, paying attention to the text type. • Example of extra points made: There is an interaction pair between the rocket and the Earth. In space, if the engine stops it will slow down because the force of the Earth is acting on it. As it approaches Mars, the force of gravity due to the interaction between Mars and the rocket will speed it up.

kerboodle

P1 Chapter 1 Checkpoint assessment (automarked)
P1 Chapter 1 Checkpoint: Revision
P1 Chapter 1 Checkpoint: Extension
P1 Chapter 1 Progress task (Handling information)

2.1 Waves

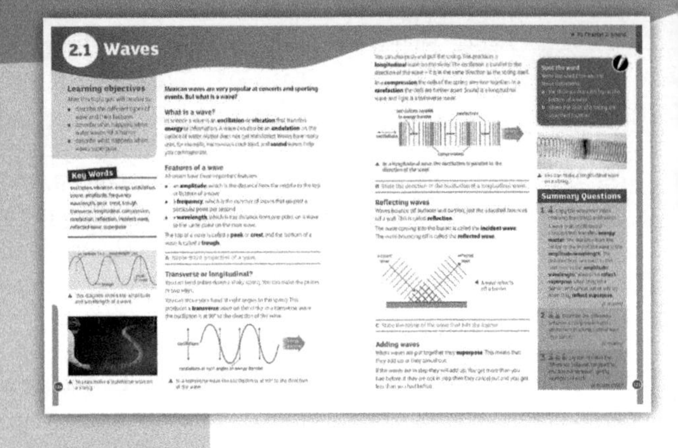

Physics NC link:

- waves on water as undulations which travel through water with transverse motion; these waves can be reflected, and add or cancel – superposition
- using physical processes and mechanisms, rather than energy, to explain the intermediate steps that bring about changes in systems.

Working Scientifically NC link:

- interpret observations and data, including identifying patterns and using observations, measurements, and data to draw conclusions.

Band	Outcome	Checkpoint	
		Question	Activity
Developing	State some features of waves (Level 4).	A, B, 1, 2	Main 2, Plenary 1
	State what happens when waves hit a barrier (Level 4).	1	Main 2
	State that waves in the same place affect each other (Level 4).	1	
↓	Record observations from wave experiments (Level 4).		Main 2
Secure	Describe the different types of wave and their features (Level 5).	A–C, 1, 2	Lit, Main 2, Plenary 1
	Describe what happens when water waves hit a barrier (Level 5).	1	Main 2
	Describe what happens when waves superpose (Level 6).	1	
↓	Identify patterns in observations from wave experiments (Level 5).		Main 2
Extending	Compare the properties of waves and their features (Level 7).	1	Main 2, Plenary 1
	Explain how reflection of a wave occurs (Level 7).	1	Main 2
	Explain one effect of superposition of waves (Level 7).	3	
↓	Use observations of waves to draw conclusions about longitudinal and transverse waves (Level 7).		Main 2

Maths
Students draw waves in a graphical form, interpreting the y-axis as amplitude and the x-axis as wavelength.

Literacy
Students match key words to definitions in the student-book activity.

APP
Models are used when discussing and explaining wave behaviour (AF1).

Students use observations to draw a conclusion (AF5).

Key Words
oscillation, vibration, energy, undulation, sound, amplitude, frequency, wavelength, peak, crest, trough, transverse, longitudinal, compression, rarefaction, reflection, incident wave, reflected wave, superpose

Answers from the student book

In-text questions	**A** amplitude, wavelength, frequency **B** parallel to the direction of the wave **C** incident wave
Activity	**Spot the word** **a** amplitude **b** compression

Summary questions	**1** energy, amplitude, wavelength, reflect, superpose (5 marks) **2** In a compression, the links of the spring are close together. In a rarefaction, they are far apart. (2 marks) **3** 6 mark question. Example answers: The direction of the oscillations in longitudinal and transverse waves are different. In a transverse wave the oscillation is at right angles (at 90°) to the direction of the wave. In a longitudinal wave the oscillation is in the same direction (parallel) to the direction of the wave. Both types of waves can reflect off a surface and can add together (superpose).

Starter	Support/Extension	Resources
Students often think that energy *and* the substance it passes through are travelling with a wave. This is not true – particles vibrate but only the energy is transferred with the wave.		
What are waves? (10 min) Students describe what they think a wave is. They may give examples of waves or describe something travelling up/down or in a particular direction. Students should jot down key ideas in their books. Explain how waves transfer energy through the medium it travels in.	**Support**: Provide examples so students can decide if something is a wave or not.	
Examples of waves (10 min) Use the interactive resource to identify examples of waves. Students can think of some examples themselves. Then explain to students how waves are formed and how they transfer energy.	**Extension**: Students explain why their examples are examples of waves.	**Interactive**: Examples of waves
Main	**Support/Extension**	**Resources**
Students do not always realise that energy is transferred along the slinky/water, so it is important to point out the *direction* of vibration. Point out to students that waves do not always reflect, although they do in these experiments.		
Comparing waves (40 min) Demonstrate water waves using a fish tank of water with corks floating on the surface. Students can see the undulation moving along the surface towards the sides of the tank. Point out that the energy is transferred but the corks bob up and down, and identify wavelength and amplitude. Demonstrate longitudinal waves, using a slinky spring being pushed back and forth, and ask students to compare features of this (longitudinal) wave with the (transverse) water waves. Students then complete questions on the activity sheet.	**Support**: An access sheet is available with simpler, more structured questions based on observations from the demonstration.	**Activity**: Comparing waves
Plenary	**Support/Extension**	**Resources**
Drawing waves (5 min) Students draw a transverse wave and label its wavelength and amplitude.	**Extension**: Students can be asked to draw multiple waves while changing frequency or amplitude.	
What are waves? (revisited) (5 min) Students check their answers from the start of the lesson and make corrections based on what they have learned. You should use these answers to clear up outstanding issues and consolidate the key terms used this lesson.	**Support**: Students could be given a series of statements to decide if these are true or false.	
Homework		
Students list ten examples of waves, giving reasons for their choice and describing them as longitudinal or transverse.		

2.2 Sound and energy transfer

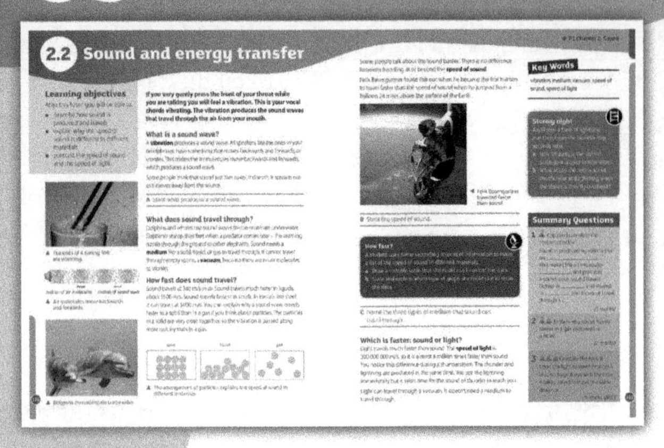

Physics NC link:

- sound needs a medium to travel, the speed of sound in air, in water, in solids
- sound produced by vibrations of objects, in loud speakers.

Working Scientifically NC link:

- present reasoned explanations, including explaining data in relation to predictions and hypotheses.

Band	Outcome	Checkpoint	
		Question	**Activity**
Developing	Name some sources of sound (Level 3).	1	Starter 1, Starter 2
	Name materials that sound can travel through (Level 4).	C, 1	Main
	State that sound travels more slowly than light (Level 3).	1	Main
	Use data to compare the speed of sound in different materials (Level 4).		Main
Secure	Describe how sound is produced and travels (Level 5).	1	Starter 1, Starter 2, Main
	Explain why the speed of sound is different in different media (Level 6).	1, 2	Main
	Contrast the speed of sound and the speed of light (Level 5).	1, 3	Maths
	Compare the time for sound to travel in different materials using data given (Level 5).		Main
Extending	Explain what is meant by supersonic travel (Level 7).		Plenary 2, Homework
	Describe sound as the transfer of energy through vibrations and explain why sound cannot travel through a vacuum (Level 8).		Main
	Compare the time taken for sound and light to travel the same distance (Level 7).	3	Maths
	Explain whether sound waves from the Sun can reach the Earth. (Level 7).		Main

Maths
Students calculate speeds of light and sound using simple calculations of distance and time.

Literacy
For homework students write about supersonic travel, linking key concepts and scientific terminology gained from the lesson.

APP
Students decide on the best method to present data in the student-book activity (AF3).

Students interpret secondary data to draw conclusions and apply these to questions (AF5).

Key Words
vibration, vocal chords, medium, vacuum, speed of sound, speed of light

Answers from the student book

In-text questions	**A** vibrations **B** 340 m/s **C** solids, liquids, and gases
Activity	**How fast?** **a** Table should have two columns, with headings 'material' and 'speed (m/s)'. **b** A bar chart because one of the variables is categoric. **Stormy night** **a** 1.32 km **b** There would be no time difference between seeing the lightning and hearing the thunder.

Summary questions	1 vibrating, vibrate, solids, gases, vacuum (5 marks) 2 The particles in a gas are further apart than the particles in a liquid. The vibration is not passed on so quickly. (2 marks) 3 Example answers (6 marks): Light travels much faster than sound. So the light reaches you first. It takes about 0.03 seconds for the sound to reach you. The speed of sound is about 300 m/s. It would take 0.000 000 03 seconds for light to reach you. The speed of light is 300 million m/s. So light is about 1 million times faster than sound. The time it takes light to reach you is about a millionth of the time it takes sound to reach you.

Starter	Support/Extension	Resources
An alternative question-led lesson is also available. **Sources of sound** (5 min) Students list five sources of sound, explaining how the sounds are caused. They should identify the source of the vibration (which is not always obvious, for example, in the loudspeaker). **Good vibrations** (5–10 min) Students hum with their hand resting on their throat to feel the larynx vibrating. When students are quiet, hit a tuning fork on the bench so it vibrates and produces a sound, then dip the tips of its prongs just under the surface of water to show it is vibrating. Explain that all sounds are caused by vibrations and travel through a medium.	**Extension**: Students describe how the sound can be controlled. **Extension**: Use several tuning forks and ask students for the link with pitch and size, or as a recap on superposition of waves.	**Question-led lesson**: Sound and energy transfer
Main	**Support/Extension**	**Resources**
The speed of sound (40 min) Explain that sound travels at different speeds in different materials. Students often think (wrongly) that sound travels slowest in solids but in fact it travels slowest in gases. It travels faster in solids due to the proximity of particles making the transfer of vibrations easier. Review the particle arrangement in solids, liquids, and gases. Explain that sound waves transfer energy from particle to particle. You should emphasise the need for particles in sound vibrations (and so sound cannot travel through a vacuum). Students predict whether sound travels fastest in solids, liquids, or gases, then complete the questions on the activity sheet.	**Support**: Sketch diagrams of particle arrangements for students to identify as solid, liquids, or gases. **Extension**: Students make clear links with the arrangement of particles and the transfer of energy by sound waves.	**Activity**: The speed of sound
Plenary	**Support/Extension**	**Resources**
Vibrations and energy (10 min) The interactive resource involves students linking up sentences to consolidate the ideas of the lesson. **Faster than the speed of sound** (10 min) Explain that *supersonic* means faster than the speed of sound. Show video clips of supersonic objects, for example, Concorde, rockets, Thrust SSC (land speed world record holder), and remind students how fast these objects are travelling (the speed of sound in air is 340 m/s).	**Support**: Pause the video at points where features of supersonic travel can be emphasised. **Extension**: Students can suggest how an observer could tell something was supersonic (the object is ahead of the sound).	**Interactive**: Vibrations and energy
Homework		
Students explain what is meant by supersonic travel, and how the objects are designed to travel faster than the speed of sound. Students suggest what the implications of supersonic travel are, and present their ideas on the benefits (e.g., being able to travel greater distances or reduce journey time) and drawbacks (e.g., cost) of supersonic travel.		

2.3 Loudness and pitch

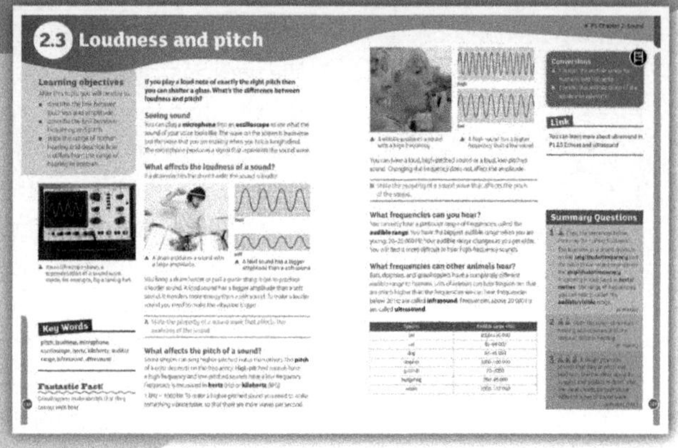

Physics NC link:
- auditory range of humans and animals
- frequencies of sound waves, measured in hertz (Hz).

Working Scientifically NC link:
- make predictions using scientific knowledge and understanding.

Band	Outcome	Checkpoint	
		Question	**Activity**
Developing	State the link between loudness and amplitude (Level 4).	A, 1	Main 1, Plenary 1
	State that frequency is measured in hertz (Level 4).	1	Maths
	State the range of human hearing (Level 4).		Maths, Main 1
	Predict how sounds will change in different situations (Level 4).	3	Main 1
Secure	Describe the link between loudness and amplitude (Level 6).	2	Starter 2, Main 1
	Describe the link between pitch and frequency (Level 6).	2	Starter 2, Main 1
	State the range of human hearing and describe how it differs from the range of hearing in animals (Level 5).	3	Maths, Main 1
	Explain how sounds will differ in different situations (Level 6).		Main 1, Plenary 1
Extending	Compare and contrast waves of different loudness using a diagram (Level 7).		Main 1, Plenary 1
	Compare and contrast waves of different frequency using a diagram (Level 7).		Main 1, Plenary 1
	Explain how animals hear the same sounds differently (Level 7).	3	Main 1
	Present a reasoned prediction using data of how sounds will be differently heard by different animals (Level 7).		Main 1

Maths
In the student-book activity students carry out simple conversions between Hz and kHz, demonstrating their understanding of number size and scale and the quantitative relationship between units.

Literacy
Students explain in writing how mosquito alarms are used for their homework.

APP
Students use secondary data to make further predictions (AF5).

Key Words
pitch, loudness, microphone, oscilloscope, hertz, kilohertz, audible range, infrasound, ultrasound

Answers from the student book

In-text questions	**A** amplitude **B** frequency
Activity	**Conversions** **a** 0.02 kHz–20 kHz **b** 1 kHz–123 kHz

Summary questions	1 amplitude, frequency, hertz, audible (4 marks) 2 Human hearing range is 20–20 000 Hz. Dolphins hear frequencies much higher than humans but cannot hear as low frequencies as humans. (2 marks) 3 6 mark question. Example answers: Vocal chords vibrate to produce sound. Sound waves are made when air is squashed and stretched. Pitch depends on frequency. To make a higher note her vocal chords vibrate more times per second. That makes the frequency of a sound wave higher. Loudness depends on amplitude. To make a louder note her vocal chords vibrate with a bigger amplitude. That makes the amplitude of a sound wave bigger.

Starter	Support/Extension	Resources
Loudness and pitch (5 min) The interactive resource asks students to categorise ways to change the pitch or loudness of sounds based on everyday observations and musical instruments.	**Extension**: Students supply their own suggestions to add to the lists.	**Interactive**: Loudness and pitch
Sound rulers (5–10 min) This can be done either as a demonstration or as a quick practical activity (depending on the number of rulers available). Securely hold the ruler overhanging the end of a bench and twang the free end to produce a sound. Show how to change the pitch by changing the length of the ruler that is overhanging, and the loudness by changing the size of vibration or by increasing the force.	**Extension**: Students investigate sound from rulers independently and state a clear relationship between the variables.	
Main	**Support/Extension**	**Resources**
Wave diagrams (30 min) Students find drawing wave diagrams difficult so a lot of practice of this skill is essential. Use simple examples, changing one factor at a time to begin with. Keep checking diagrams drawn to make sure students keep wavelengths and amplitudes consistent. Connect the signal generator and loudspeaker to the output of an oscilloscope. Show the shape of the wave for a frequency of about 400–600 Hz. Change the pitch to demonstrate how the wavelength changes and change the volume to demonstrate how the amplitude changes. Students then complete the activity sheet.	**Support**: A support sheet is available as a reference for key terms used during this activity. **Extension**: Students should be able to draw wave diagrams where both pitch and loudness are changed.	**Activity**: Wave diagrams **Skill sheet**: Converting units
Human hearing (10 min) Explain that there is a limit to the pitch of notes we can hear. Use the signal generator to generate a sound that is audible – the lowest frequency is about 20 Hz. Increase the pitch until students cannot hear the sound (about 20 000 Hz). Be aware some pitches are unpleasant – ask students to indicate noises that cause discomfort – and move quickly through these. Near the upper range students indicate when they stop hearing the sounds. This can be between 15 kHz and 20 kHz. Explain that 1 kHz is 1000 Hz. Older adults may not be able to hear the upper ranges in pitch.		
Plenary	**Support/Extension**	**Resources**
Changing waves (10 min) Students sketch a wave on a mini-whiteboard and then draw a louder wave. Check answers, then repeat but ask students to draw a higher pitched wave, and so on.	**Support**: Present a choice of waves for students to choose the loudest, the highest pitched, and so on.	
What do you know? (10 min) Students write down three things they have learned this lesson. This is a useful chance to check misconceptions, for example, confusing amplitude with wavelength.		
Homework		
Students write a short paragraph explaining how high-pitched 'mosquito' alarms can be used to deter anti-social teens from loitering outside shops.		

2.4 Detecting sound

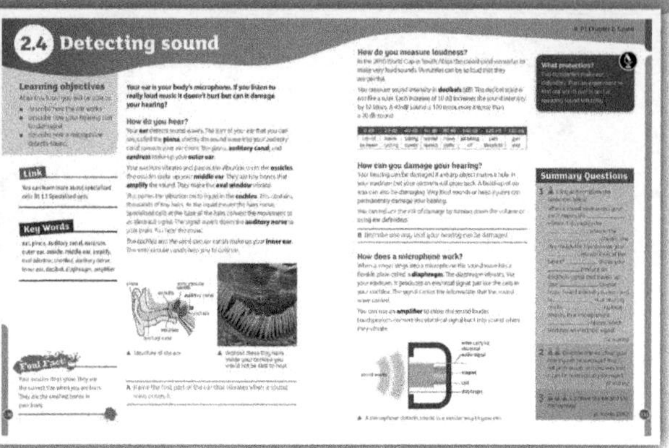
2.4 Detecting sound

Learning objectives

How do you hear?

How do you measure loudness?

How can you damage your hearing?

How does a microphone work?

Link

Key Words

What protection?

Summary Questions

Physics NC link:

- pressure waves transferring energy; waves transferring information for conversion to electrical signals by microphone
- sound produced by vibrations of objects, in loudspeakers, detected by their effects on microphone diaphragm and the ear drum.

Working Scientifically NC link:

- evaluate risks.

Band	Outcome	Checkpoint	
		Question	**Activity**
Developing	Name some parts of the ear (Level 4).	A, 1	Main 2
	State some ways that hearing can be damaged (Level 4).	B, 2	Main 2
	State that a microphone detects sound waves (Level 4).	1	Main 1
↓	Describe some risks of loud music (Level 4).		Main 2
Secure	Describe how the ear works (Level 5).	1	Main 2, Plenary 1
	Describe how your hearing can be damaged (Level 5).	B, 2	Main 2
	Describe how a microphone detects sound (Level 5).	1, 3	Main 1
↓	Explain some risks of loud music (Level 6).		Main 2, Plenary 2
Extending	Explain how parts of the ear transfer vibrations (Level 7).	1	Main 1, Main 2, Plenary 1
	Explain how your hearing can be damaged (Level 7).	2	Main 2, Plenary 2
	Compare and contrast the ear and the microphone (Level 7).	3	Main 1
↓	Explain, in detail, risks of hearing damage linked to sound level and time of exposure (Level 8).		Main 2, Plenary 2

Literacy

For homework students summarise information from this lesson in a leaflet on the dangers of loud music.

Students extract information from text, and use this information when answering comprehension questions in the activity.

APP

In the student-book activity students plan an experiment and suggest variables when testing ear defenders (AF4).

Students make suggestions to reduce risks to hearing on the activity sheet (AF4).

Students use appropriate terminology in communicating ideas to primary school children in their leaflet for homework (AF3).

Key Words

ear, pinna, auditory canal, eardrum, outer ear, ossicles, middle ear, amplify, oval window, cochlea, auditory nerve, inner ear, decibel, diaphragm, amplifier

Answers from the student book

In-text questions	**A** ear drum **B** One of: inserting a sharp object, exposure to a very loud sound, wax build-up
Activity	**What protection?** Example: somebody wears the ear defenders, another person reduces a loud sound until the person with the ear defenders cannot hear it. Change ear defenders and repeat. The independent variable is the ear defenders. The control variables are person, distance to loudspeaker, frequency of sound. Repeat with different people and compare the results.

Summary questions	1 ear drum, ossicles, oval window, cochlea, hairs, cochlea, auditory nerve, decibels, damaged, diaphragm (10 marks) 2 Not permanent: ear wax, perforated ear drum, ear infection. Permanent: listening to loud music, head injury. (2 marks) 3 6 mark question. Example answers: Both detect vibration. Both produce an electrical signal. The ear contains bones/membranes/liquid and the microphone does not. The ear amplifies the sound and the microphone does not. The ear contains cells that produce a signal and the microphone does not. A microphone contains magnets and wire and the ear does not. A microphone can be attached to an amplifier and the ear already amplifies sound. The ear drum in the ear is like the diaphragm in the microphone.

kerboodle

Starter	Support/Extension	Resources
Measuring loudness (10 min) Display a decibel scale, which indicates safe sound levels and everyday examples. Discuss the display, explaining how loudness is measured in decibels and suggest ways to reduce harm.	**Extension**: Discuss whether the link between decibels and exposure-time is as clear-cut as diagrams suggest.	
Parts of the ear (10 min) As a class, play hangman using the names of the different parts of the ear (e.g., pinna, eardrum, cochlea). As students guess each part, identify where it is within the ear, and how vibrations pass through the different parts of the ear.	**Support**: Students describe parts of the ear rather than naming them. **Extension**: Discuss additional structures in the ear and balance.	
Main	**Support/Extension**	**Resources**
Detecting sounds (10 min) Connect the microphone to the input of the oscilloscope. Demonstrate sound waves produced when a noise is made. Explain links between the microphone and ear (if possible, unscrew the microphone's cover to show the diaphragm corresponding to the human ear drum). Recap the parts of the ear and how sounds are measured in decibels.	**Support**: Keep to the obvious comparisons between the microphone and ear to avoid confusion.	
Hearing and how it is damaged (30 min) If a sound level meter is available, measure sound levels during the lesson. Students complete the activity sheet identifying parts of the ear and then extract information from text to identify ways the ear can be damaged, suggesting methods to reduce harm.	**Extension**: Students may choose to add descriptions to their diagram explaining the function of each part of the ear.	**Activity**: Hearing and how it is damaged
Plenary	**Support/Extension**	**Resources**
Hearing (5 min) Students rearrange sentences to explain how sounds travel from the pinna to the brain in the interactive resource.	**Extension**: Ask students to give additional details	**Interactive**: Hearing
How loud was the lesson? (10 min) Display sound levels during the lesson against a decibel scale. Discuss implications, for example, duration and levels, impact on concentration, the need to reduce levels so instructions can be heard, and so on.	**Extension**: Discuss implications in more detail (e.g., varied impact on people, factors beyond control).	
Homework		
Students write a leaflet for primary students on the dangers of loud music and list ways to reduce the harm.		
An alternative WebQuest homework activity is also available on Kerboodle where students research the science of music.		**WebQuest**: The science of music

2.5 Echoes and ultrasound

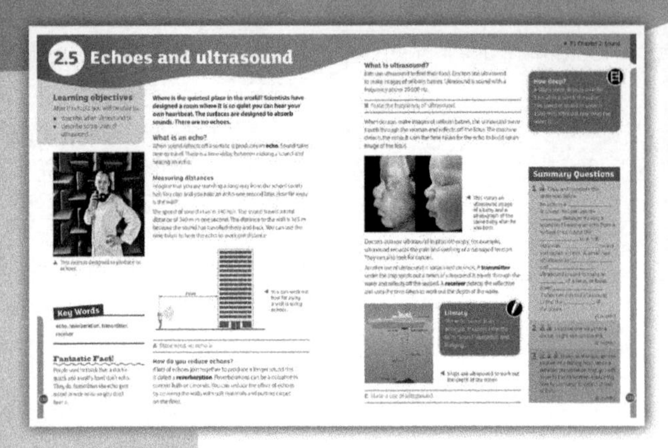
2.5 Echoes and ultrasound

Learning objectives

What is an echo?

Measuring distances

Key Words

Fantastic Fact!

How do you reduce echoes?

What is ultrasound?

How deep?

Literacy

Summary Questions

Physics NC link:

- pressure waves transferring energy; use for cleaning and physiotherapy by ultra-sound
- frequencies of sound waves measured in hertz (Hz); echoes, reflection, and absorption of sound.

Working Scientifically NC link:

- present reasoned explanations, including explaining data in relation to predictions and hypotheses.

Band	Outcome	Checkpoint	
		Question	**Activity**
Developing	State simply what ultrasound is (Level 4).		Plenary 1
	State some uses of ultrasound (Level 4).	C, 1	Starter 1, Main, Plenary 1, Plenary 2
↓	Suggest reasons why animals use ultrasound (Level 4).		Main
Secure	Describe what ultrasound is (Level 5).	B	Main, Plenary 1
	Describe some uses of ultrasound (Level 5).	1, 3	Starter 1, Main, Plenary 1, Plenary 2
↓	Explain, with reasons, why animals use echolocation (Level 6).		Main
Extending	Explain how ultrasound can be analysed (Level 7).	3	Maths, Main
	Explain some uses of ultrasound (Level 7).	3	Starter 1, Main, Plenary 2
↓	Explain, with reasons, different ways animals use echolocation (Level 7).		Main

Maths
In the student-book activity students carry out simple calculations, substituting numerical values in the speed–time equation to deduce the depth of the sea, given values for speed and time.

Literacy
Students extract information from text and apply this information to answer questions on examples of echolocation.

For homework students summarise what they know about echoes, using a range of scientific terminology and diagrams.

APP
Draw valid conclusions that utilise more than one piece of supporting evidence, including numerical data and line graphs (AF4).

Key Words
echo, reverberation, transmitter, receiver

Answers from the student book

In-text questions	**A** A reflection of sound. **B** sounds above 20 000 Hz **C** One of: to make an image of a fetus/find the depth of the ocean/find fish/find cancer/destroy kidney stones.
Activity	**How deep?** Total distance travelled = 1.6 s × 1500 m/s = 2400 m So the distance to the bottom = 2400 m ÷ 2 = 1200 m

Summary questions	1 reflection, time, distance, absorb, communicate, hunt, image, kidney stones, depth (9 marks) 2 To image a newborn baby by ultrasound waves reflecting off the fetus, with the differing time taken to detect the echo is used to build an image of the fetus. (2 marks) 3 Example answers (6 marks): Fix a transmitter and receiver to a boat. Use ultrasound not sound. Ultrasound is more focused than sound. Use a transmitter to send out a pulse of ultrasound. Time how long it takes to hear the echo. Work out the distance. Divide by two. Ignore later echoes as they could be from the sea floor. Characteristics of a reflected wave change dependent on the material it is reflected from.

Starter	Support/Extension	Resources
Ultrasound scans (10 min) Show an image or video clip of an ultrasound scan. Explain ultrasound are sound waves too high pitched to hear. The image is created because ultrasound waves partly reflect from different surfaces.	**Extension**: Discuss other uses of ultrasound, for example, in engineering.	
Echoes (10 min) Students write down three things they know about echoes. Compare their answers to bring out these points: echoes are sound reflections, the echo is the same as the original sound but quieter and heard later, echoes are heard where there are lots of hard surfaces. Make sure students realise there must be a sound wave and a reflecting surface.	**Extension**: Students give examples of echolocation. They may realise that echoes from more distant reflecting surfaces arrive later or that soft surfaces will absorb sound.	
Main	**Support/Extension**	**Resources**
Using echoes (35 min) Demonstrate that a dropped ball takes longer to fall, bounce, and return to its original height when it falls a greater distance. Explain distances can be measured using echoes, where the ball is replaced by a sound wave. Remind students the signal travels to the surface and returns, so times measured are twice the time taken to reach the surface. Discuss uses of echolocation (bats, whales, sonar, finding flaws inside materials, scanning a patient) and how hard surfaces reflect waves, whilst soft surfaces absorb waves. Remind students that ultrasound is very high frequency (above 20 000 Hz). Students then complete tasks and questions on the activity sheet.	**Support**: An access sheet is available with simpler text and supporting comprehension questions. **Extension**: Students can evaluate the safety of medical scans that use ultrasound.	**Activity**: Using echoes
Plenary	**Support/Extension**	**Resources**
Ultrasound and echoes (5 min) Interactive resource in which student link together sentences on ultrasound, echoes, and their uses.	**Extension**: Students can suggest further halves of sentences for others in the class to match.	**Interactive**: Ultrasound and echoes
Ultrasound or echoes (10 min) Present some applications and ask students to identify the ones which use echoes (sonar, echolocation) and the ones which use ultrasound (medical scans).	**Support**: Stress whether the sound can be heard in each application. **Extension**: Students prepare lists of uses of echoes/ultrasound.	
Homework		
Students prepare a sheet summarising what they have learned about ultrasound and echoes using diagrams and text to explain their ideas.		

P1 Chapter 2 Checkpoint

Checkpoint lesson routes

The route through this lesson can be determined using the Checkpoint assessment. Percentage pass marks are supplied in the Checkpoint teacher notes.

Route A (support)
Resources: P1 Chapter 2 Checkpoint Revision
Students will work through a revision activity that allows them to gradually revisit and consolidate their understanding of sound and waves.

Route B (extension)
Resources: P1 Chapter 2 Checkpoint Extension
Students will be asked to prepare a poster explaining how people hear music at a concert in detail. They will use scientific language to include full explanations accompanied by diagrams.

Progression to *secure*

No.	Developing outcome	Secure outcome	Making progress
1	State some features of waves.	Describe the different types of waves and their features.	Demonstrating longitudinal and transverse waves using a slinky spring will help students to visualise the two types of waves. Students can then begin to complete Task 1.
2	State what happens when a wave hits a barrier.	Describe what happens when water waves hit a barrier.	Using a tray of water, remind students what happens when waves hit a barrier. Students are then able to start the cloze activity in Task 2.
3	State that waves in the same place affect each other.	Describe what happens when waves superpose.	The tray of water can again be used for demonstration. Students can complete the sentence about superposition in the cloze activity in Task 2.
4	Name some sources of sound.	Describe how sound is produced and travels.	Students complete a description using key words of how sound is produced in the cloze activity in Task 2.
5	Name materials that sound can travel through.	Explain why the speed of sound is different in different media.	Before completing the cloze activity in Task 3, students should draw diagrams of particle arrangements in the boxes provided.
6	State that sound travels slower than light.	Contrast the speed of sound and the speed of light.	Show students video clips of lightning and thunder reaching the observer at different times.
7	State the link between loudness and amplitude.	Describe the link between loudness and amplitude.	Demonstrate the link between loudness and amplitude using an oscilloscope, signal generator, and loudspeaker if available. Students often confuse amplitude with wavelength. Students should write a full description of the link in Task 4.
8	State that frequency is measured in hertz.	Describe the link between pitch and frequency.	Demonstrate the link between pitch and frequency using an oscilloscope, signal generator, and loudspeaker. Students can complete descriptions in Task 4.
9	State the range of human hearing.	State the range of human hearing and describe how it differs from the range of hearing in animals.	A basic graphical representation of hearing ranges is given in the support sheet. Students can then complete Task 5.
10	Name some parts of the ear.	Describe how the ear works.	In Task 6, students can annotate a diagram of the ear and describe the role of each part.
11	State some ways that hearing can be damaged.	Describe how your hearing can be damaged.	In Task 6, students first complete a table of parts of the ear and how they can be damaged. They can then use this information to write a full paragraph.
12	State that a microphone detects sound.	Describe how a microphone detects sound.	Students need to consider the sequence to write a full description. Guidance is provided in Task 7.
13	State simply what ultrasound is.	Describe what ultrasound is.	Give students the frequency range of ultrasound, and ask students to look back to the hearing range information in Task 5. Students can then work through Task 7.
14	State some uses of ultrasound.	Describe some uses of ultrasound.	Students can complete a guided paragraph to describe uses of ultrasound in Task 7.

Answers to end-of-chapter questions

1 Diagram with correct label of amplitude and correct label of wavelength. (2 marks)

2a Diagram with the same wavelength but larger amplitude. (1 mark)

b Diagram with the same amplitude but smaller wavelength. (1 mark)

3 400 (1 mark)

4a it reflects (1 mark)

b They add up or cancel out. (2 marks)

5a The oscillation is at 90° to the direction of travel. (1 mark)

b The oscillation is parallel to the direction of travel. (1 mark)

6 Credit a sensible situation, such as a concert. (1 mark)

7a C (1 mark) **b** B (1 mark)

c The particles in C are closer together than the particles in A. The particles in A are closer together than the particles in B. Sound travels better through materials where the particles are closer together. (3 marks)

8a How does the intensity of a sound vary with distance from the source? (1 mark)

b Independent – distance from sound source; dependent – loudness of sound; controls – frequency and loudness of sound from source (1 mark)

c line graph (1 mark)

9 Students should be marked on the use of good English, organisation of information, spelling and grammar, and correct use of specialist scientific terms. The best answers will have scientific ideas clearly and correctly organised to give a detailed description of sound travel (maximum of 6 marks).

Examples of correct scientific points:

The loudspeaker vibrates/moves in and out.

This squashes and stretches the air.

This is a longitudinal wave, with compressions (where air molecules are close together) and rarefactions (where they are far apart).

The wave travels through the air as the molecules pass on the vibration.

The wave is guided into your auditory canal by the pinna.

This makes your ear drum vibrate.

This makes the ossicles vibrate.

This makes the oval window vibrate.

This makes the liquid in the cochlea vibrate.

Produces an electrical signal.

The signal travels up your auditory nerve to your brain.

Answer guide for Sound campaign

Developing	Secure	Extending
1–2 marks	3–4 marks	5–6 marks
• Includes basic ideas related to each situation e.g., vibrating source, older people don't hear higher frequencies, barriers reflect sound, loud sounds can damage hearing. • Lacks organisation and detail.	• Includes more complex ideas e.g., defines wave properties, links frequency to pitch and amplitude to loudness, defines ultrasound and how images are produced. • Lacks some detail and organisation.	• Includes complex ideas related to each situation e.g., changes in cochlea to hearing in old age, explanation of scanning in terms of echoes and linking to distance, reduction of risk of damage by using material to shield houses from the road. • The written passage is organised and detailed.

kerboodle

P1 Chapter 2 Checkpoint assessment (automarked)
P1 Chapter 2 Checkpoint: Revision
P1 Chapter 2 Checkpoint: Extension
P1 Chapter 2 Progress task (Maths)

3.1 Light

Physics NC link:

- the similarities and differences between light waves and waves in matter
- light waves travelling through a vacuum; speed of light
- the transmission of light through materials: absorption, diffuse scattering, and specular reflection at a surface.

Working Scientifically NC link:

- evaluate data, showing awareness of potential sources of random and systematic error.

Band	Outcome	Checkpoint	
		Question	**Activity**
Developing	Describe some ways that light interacts with materials (Level 4).	A, B, 1	Starter 2, Main
↓	State that light travels very fast (Level 4).		Starter 1
	Compare results with other groups, stating if there is a spread in results (Level 4).		Plenary 2
Secure	Describe what happens when light interacts with materials (Level 5).	A, B, 1–3	Starter 1, Starter 2, Main
↓	State the speed of light (Level 5).	2	
	Compare results with other groups, suggesting reasons for differences (Level 5).		Plenary 1
Extending	Predict how light will interact with different materials (Level 7).		Starter 2, Main, Plenary 2
↓	Calculate the distance travelled by light in a light-year (Level 7).	C	
	Evaluate results suggesting reasons for errors (Level 7).		Plenary 1

Maths
The student-book activity asks students to compare light-time to sound-time, carrying out simple calculations and change of units.

Students also extract and interpret information and from tables.

Literacy
The literacy activity in the student book requires students to use scientific terms accurately in a given context.

APP
Carry out an experiment to investigate properties of different materials, displaying data in a table (AF4).

Interpret light intensity/resistance data to group results obtained, form a conclusion, and evaluate the experiment (AF5).

Key Words
source, emit, reflect, eye, absorb, luminous, non-luminous, transmit, transparent, translucent, opaque, vacuum, wave, light-time

Answers from the student book

In-text questions	**A** Emit means to give out light, transmit means to allow light to pass through it. **B** You can see clearly through a transparent material but not through a translucent material, even though light travels through both. **C** The distance light travels in a year.

Activity	**How long? How far?** Sound takes a million times longer: 8 million minutes 8 000 000/(60 × 24 × 365) = 15.2 years **Sort those words** For example, the light bulb emits light because it is luminous. The flower reflects light because it is non-luminous and opaque. This light is then absorbed by your eye. The water transmits light and is transparent.
Summary questions	**1** luminous, emits, reflects, non-luminous, opaque (5 marks) **2** Light is absorbed by water even though you can see through it. Only a small amount is absorbed, so you need a lot of water for it to become dark. (2 marks) **3** 6 mark question. Example answers: The Sun emits light. The light travels through space to the Earth. The light travels through the air. The light (is refracted as it) goes into the water. The fish reflects light. The light (is refracted as it) comes out of the water. The light enters your eye and is absorbed.

Starter	Support/Extension	Resources
Sun's light (5 min) Discuss how the Sun's light travels into the classroom and how we see it. Key points**:** It travels through a vacuum, air, and glass; it takes about 8 minutes to reach us; it reflects off surfaces into our eyes. (Students may not realise there is a vacuum between Earth and the Sun.)	**Support**: Make sure key terms are understood (e.g., vacuum). **Extension**: Discuss how we can see the Moon, planets, and stars other than the Sun.	
Types of material (5 min) Students use the interactive resource to classify different objects using the terms translucent, opaque, and transparent. Discuss answers to check understanding.	**Extension**: Students can offer further examples of materials in each category.	**Interactive**: Types of material
Main	**Support/Extension**	**Resources**
How bright is the light? (40 min) Measure the light transmitted through different materials using a light dependent resistor (LDR) and multimeter to measure resistance, or a light meter. Many light meters give readings in lux. An LDR is a resistor with lower resistance for higher light levels. Set the multimeter to read resistance and aim the LDR towards the light source. Resistance is not directly proportional to light levels, so this is best for ranking materials rather than quantitative comparisons. Students check equipment by seeing how light levels vary in the room first. Use clamp stands to fix the LDR/light meter and light source about 5–10 cm apart. Place samples of different materials between the light and LDR/light meter and record measurements. Students rank materials on a scale from transparent to opaque.	**Support**: A suggested results table is provided, using a simplified practical procedure. **Extension**: Students can investigate the effect of thickness on opacity using layers of tissue paper.	**Practical**: How bright is the light? **Skill sheet**: Recording results **Skill sheet**: Accuracy and precision **Skill sheet**: Calculating means
Plenary	**Support/Extension**	**Resources**
Comparing results (10 min) Students compare results from their experiment. Discuss why results vary, suggesting improvements.		
Comparing materials (5–10 min) Students compare materials that light or sound travels easily through. These may not be the same (e.g., double glazing does not transmit sound well but does transmit light well).	**Support**: Students have a list of materials and they have to decide whether the material will let light or sound through.	
Homework		
Students list 10 materials used at home, classifying them as opaque, transparent, and translucent. They write a sentence for each material, explaining why being opaque, transparent, or translucent makes it suitable for its purpose.		

3.2 Reflection

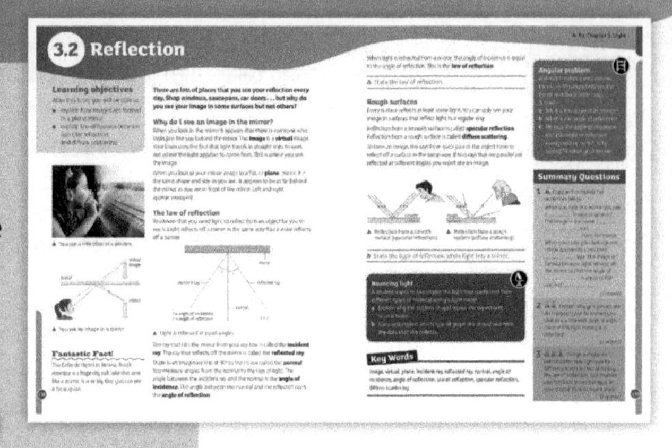
3.2 Reflection

Learning objectives

Why do I see an image in the mirror?

The law of reflection

Fantastic Fact!

Rough surfaces

Angular problem

Summary Questions

Key Words

Physics NC link:

- the transmission of light through materials: absorption, diffuse scattering, and specula reflection at a surface
- use of ray model to explain imaging in mirrors
- differential colour effects in absorption and diffuse reflection.

Working Scientifically NC link:

- use appropriate techniques and apparatus during fieldwork and laboratory work, paying attention to health and safety.

Band	Outcome	Checkpoint	
		Question	**Activity**
Developing	Describe the features of a mirror image (Level 4).	1	Starter 1
	Identify examples of specular reflection and diffuse scattering (Level 4).	B, 2	Starter 2
	Use appropriate equipment safely with guidance (Level 4).		Main
Secure	Explain how images are formed in a plane mirror (Level 5).	1	Plenary 2
	Explain the difference between specular reflection and diffuse scattering (Level 6).		Main
	Use appropriate equipment and take readings safely without help (Level 6).		Main
Extending	Draw a ray diagram showing how an image is formed in a plane mirror (Level 7).		Plenary 2
	Extend the concept of specular reflection and diffuse scattering by applying this to models and other examples (Level 8).	3	Main
	Take accurate readings using appropriate equipment and working safely (Level 7).		Main

Maths
Students carry out simple calculations with angles in the student-book activity, applying existing knowledge of geometry.

Literacy
Students use scientific terminology in explaining their reflection experiment and when answering corresponding questions.

APP
In the student-book activity students must choose the correct graph to use when investigating reflection (AF3).

Students carry out experiments to investigate concepts in reflection (AF4).

Students interpret data to explain and evaluate the reflection experiment and form a conclusion (AF5).

Key Words
image, virtual, plane, incident ray, reflected ray, normal, angle of incidence, angle of reflection, law of reflection, specular reflection, diffuse scattering

Answers from the student book

In-text questions	**A** When light is reflected from a mirror, the angle of incidence is equal to the angle of reflection. **B** specular reflection
Activity	**Angular problem** **a** 50 ° **b** 50 ° **c** No, the angle of incidence is equal to the angle of reflection and the angle between them can be anything from nearly 180 ° to 0 °.

	Bouncing light **a** Repeating readings helps to eliminate the effect of random errors and makes results more precise. **b** A bar chart, because the data are categorical (name of material) and are not both continuous.
Summary questions	**1** virtual, size, shape, distance, right, incidence, reflection (7 marks) **2** The light hits the wall and is reflected at lots of different angles. The light needs to reflect in a regular way to form an image. (2 marks) **3** Example answers (6 marks): A design showing an uneven surface, made by footballs lined up in a row. A marble can be reflected from the surface of the footballs. At each part of the surface the marble is reflected according to the law of reflection. The surfaces of the footballs are at different angles to each other so the marble ends up scattered in lots of directions.

Starter	Support/Extension	Resources
Mirror images (5 min) Hand students mirrors and ask them to describe the image of an object, for example, which way up, which way round, its size.	**Support**: Ask structured questions, for example, which way up is it? **Extension**: Students explain why the image is the same size, right way up, and laterally inverted.	
Different reflections (10 min) Explain the difference between specular reflection (as in mirrors) and diffuse scattering (as from rougher surfaces). Students classify examples, for example, specular reflection from surface of still water, from mirrors, or from glass surfaces. Diffuse scattering from painted walls, from clothes, from whiteboards, or pages in a book.	**Support**: Show images that students can classify as specular reflection or diffuse scattering.	
Main	**Support/Extension**	**Resources**
Investigating reflection (40 min) This works best if black out blinds are used. Start by demonstrating the law of reflection using a mirror. Students predict and explain results. Students follow this by investigating specular reflection and diffuse scattering. They shine a torch onto a selection of different flat surfaces and observe the reflected light on a nearby white surface. The experiment shows that a clear image will form from a mirror (specular reflection) and that coloured surfaces reflect their own colour of light, while dull, dark surfaces absorb light.	**Support**: Students are given a choice of reflected rays on the practical sheet when considering specular reflection. Demonstrate the practical procedure for diffuse scattering beforehand to ensure students understand the task fully.	**Practical**: Investigating reflection
Plenary	**Support/Extension**	**Resources**
Reflection experiment (5 min) Interactive resource where student choose words to complete a paragraph on the reflection experiment.		**Interactive**: Reflection experiment
Forming images in mirrors (10 min) Demonstrate how mirror images are formed. Draw a triangle on one half of an OHP sheet. Fold the plastic down the centre (the fold represents the mirror). Trace the triangle on the other half of the sheet. Unfold the sheet to compare the image's position, size, and so on with the object. Add lines to represent the path of the rays of light. Students copy down the ray diagram.	**Extension**: Students apply this concept to explain how a kaleidoscope works.	
Homework	**Support/Extension**	
Set questions showing the position of an object and the position of a mirror. Students draw the position they expect to see the images formed in the mirror, and check their answers using a mirror if possible.	**Extension**: Students should add light rays to their diagrams.	

3.3 Refraction

Physics NC link:

- the refraction of light and action of convex lens in focusing (qualitative); the human eye.

Working Scientifically NC link:

- present observations using appropriate methods, including tables and graphs.

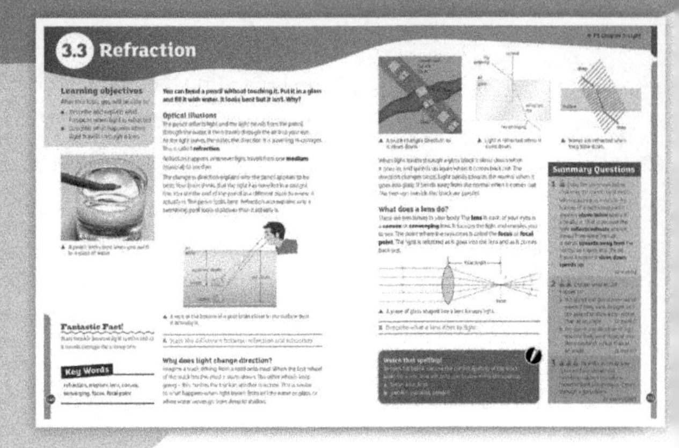

Band	Outcome	Checkpoint	
		Question	**Activity**
Developing ↓	Describe what happens when light is refracted (Level 4).	1	Starter 1, Main, Plenary 1
	Describe features of the image formed by a lens (Level 4).		Plenary 2
	Record some observations as a diagram with help (Level 4).		Main
Secure ↓	Describe and explain what happens when light is refracted (Level 6).	1	Starter 1, Main, Plenary 2
	Describe what happens when light travels through a lens (Level 6).	B	Plenary 2
	Record observations using a labelled diagram (Level 5).		Main
Extending ↓	Predict the path of light using a model of light refraction (Level 7).	2, 3	Plenary 1
	Explain what happens when light travels through a lens (Level 7).	B	Plenary 2
	Record observations using labelled diagrams, and apply this to other situations (Level 7).		Main

Literacy

Students identify the correct spellings of key words in the student-book activity.

APP

Students carry out an experiment to investigate refraction, displaying observations using ray diagrams (AF4).

Students interpret results obtained from the refraction experiment to draw a conclusion (AF5).

Key Words

refraction, medium, lens, convex, converging, focus, focal point, critical angle, total internal reflection, optical fibres, endoscope

Answers from the student book

In-text questions	**A** In reflection light bounces off something, in refraction it changes direction. **B** A lens focuses or bends the rays of light to a focal point.
Activity	**Watch that spelling!** **a** lens **b** parallel

Summary questions	1 above, refracts, away from, speeds up (4 marks) 2 **a** Speed would decrease; direction would stay the same. (2 marks) **b** Speed would decrease; direction would stay the same. (2 marks) 3 6 mark question. Example answers: Draw a line on the ground to show the boundary between air and glass. Draw another one further on to show the boundary between glass and air. Make lines of people about a metre apart. They march at an angle towards the line on the ground. As they get to the line on the ground they slow down. The people who reach it first slow down first. This changes the direction that they are marching in. As they cross the second line they speed up. This changes the direction again. They should be marching in the same direction as they were originally.

kerboodle

Starter	Support/Extension	Resources
Becoming invisible (5 min) We can only see transparent objects if light changes direction (refracts) when it passes through them. Place a test tube in a beaker. Pour glycerol in the beaker. Then pour glycerol inside the test tube – the test tube becomes invisible. Explain light doesn't refract (change direction) when it travels between the test tube and the glycerol, so we cannot detect the test tube. **Key words in light** (5 min) The interactive resource provides a crossword on key words from this topic so far for students to complete.	**Extension**: Show that the test tube is not invisible if water is used, even though both the test tube and the water are transparent. Ask for suggestions why (light refracts when travelling from one medium to another).	**Interactive**: Key words in light
Main	**Support/Extension**	**Resources**
Investigating refraction (40 min) Students investigate the path of light through a glass or perspex block, changing the angle of incidence. For accuracy, students mark the path of each emerging ray using dots, then remove the block and draw the rays using a ruler. Students then complete practical sheet questions. The ray of light arriving along the normal (at right angles to the block) goes straight through; light arriving at an angle changes direction at the boundary. It moves towards the normal. It emerges parallel to the original ray.	**Support**: An access sheet is available where students are required to carry out the experiment along pre-drawn incident rays, then answer a series of multiple-choice statements.	**Practical**: Investigating refraction
Plenary	**Support/Extension**	**Resources**
What is happening? (10 min) Students can model refraction by marching in groups of three towards a boundary. As each row passes a boundary marked on the floor, it slows down to simulate light travelling in a medium. If all students in the row arrive simultaneously, their row does not change direction. If one side of the row reaches the boundary first, this end slows down and the row changes direction. To keep rows in line, students can hold a metre ruler horizontally. **Water lenses** (5 min) Place a drop of water on an image drawn on a shiny surface (e.g., mini-whiteboard with a small picture on it). The water magnifies the image. Explain that this is due to refraction through the lens.	**Support**: Help students spot which part of the row slows down and predict the change in direction. **Extension**: Students explain how this activity relates to a ray of light travelling through a glass block. Students predict how the angle changes if they approach at different angles. **Extension**: Students explain why the lens magnifies the image.	
Homework		
Students identify equipment that uses lenses (or refraction) at home. They write a sentence explaining what the job of the lens is in each example.		

3.4 The eye and the camera

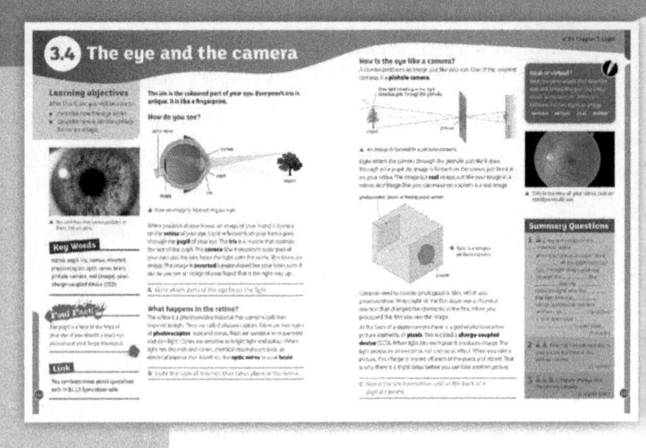
3.4 The eye and the camera

Learning objectives

How do you see?

Key Words

What happens in the retina?

How is the eye like a camera?

Summary Questions

Physics NC link:

- light transferring energy from source to absorber leading to chemical and electrical effects; photo-sensitive material in the retina and in cameras
- use of ray model to explain the pinhole camera
- the refraction of light and action of convex lens in focusing (qualitative); the human eye.

Working Scientifically NC link:

- use appropriate techniques, apparatus, and materials during fieldwork and laboratory work, paying attention to health and safety.

Band	Outcome	Checkpoint	
		Question	**Activity**
Developing	Name parts of the eye (Level 4).	A, 1	Starter 2, Main
	Name parts of the camera (Level 4).	C	Starter 2, Main
↓	Use suitable materials to make models of the eye and the camera (Level 4).		Main
Secure	Describe how the eye works (Level 5).	B, 1	Main, Plenary 1
	Describe how a simple camera forms an image (Level 5).		Main
↓	Choose suitable materials to make models of the eye and the camera (Level 5).		Main
Extending	Explain how the eye forms an image (Level 7).	1	Plenary 1
	Compare a simple camera with the eye (Level 7).	4	
↓	Justify the choice of materials used to make models of the eye and the camera (Level 7).		Main

Literacy
In the student-book activity students use scientific terminology to explain the difference between real and virtual images. Students describe how parts of the eye and camera are similar and different. Students research about the eyes of other animals and write a short summary with a labelled diagram.

APP
Students use models to explain how the eye and camera work (AF1).

Key Words
iris, retina, pupil, cornea, inverted, photoreceptors, optic nerve, brain, pinhole camera, real (image), pixel, charge-coupled device (CCD)

Answers from the student book

In-text questions	**A** the cornea and the lens **B** chemical reaction **C** charge-coupled device (CCD)
Activity	**Real or virtual** A real image is an image that you can put on a screen whereas a virtual image is one that you see in a mirror.

Summary questions	**1** reflects, pupil, cornea, lens, retina, real, electrical, optic nerve (9 marks) **2** The camera in your phone contains a CCD not a screen. The camera stores an image but the pinhole camera does not. (2 marks) **3** 6 mark question. Example answers: Similarities: They both have a hole at the front to let the light in. There is a pinhole in the camera and a pupil in the eye. Both have a screen or place where the image is formed. Differences: There is no focusing of the image in the pinhole camera. The retina has light-sensitive cells where there is a chemical reaction. The eye produces an electrical signal. Lots of people can see the same image on the screen of the camera but only you can see the image on your retina.

Starter	Support/Extension	Resources
An alternative question-led lesson is also available. **What do lenses do?** (10 min) Students look through convex lenses and describe the images seen when objects are varying distances away. Nearby objects are magnified, distant objects are smaller. If they are focused on a screen, images are upside down.	**Support**: Target students with easier questions. **Extension**: Link shape of lens (thickness) with focal length.	**Question-led lesson:** The camera and the eye
The camera and the eye (5 min) The interactive resource allows students to sort parts of the eye, parts of the camera, and parts that appear in both.	**Support**: Allow students to use the image in the student book. **Extension**: Students match parts of the eye to their function.	**Interactive**: The camera and the eye
Main	**Support/Extension**	**Resources**
Modelling the eye and the camera (40 min) Explain that the eye and the camera perform similar jobs. Explain what each part of the eye and the camera do, and identify these on a diagram. Students then make a model of an eye and a model of a camera, describing similarities and differences. Each model has an aperture, a lens, a light-detecting surface, and a space between the lens and light-detecting surface. It is important to explain that the cornea and the fluid inside the eyeball help focus light, as well as the lens. Compare changing the distance between the lens and the film in a camera with changing the shape of the lens in the eye to focus on different objects. At the end of the activity students should draw ray diagrams of the camera and the eye in their books.	**Support**: The support sheet includes a list of parts of the camera and the eye to help students label diagrams, and to help them decide on parts to show on their models.	**Activity**: Modelling the eye and the camera
Plenary	**Support/Extension**	**Resources**
The journey through the eye (5 min) Students describe how light travels from an object to the retina using scientific terminology.	**Support**: Use the list on the support sheet provided for the main activity.	
Why we have two eyes (10 min) Students view an object across the room using each eye in turn, then both eyes. Ask how the image seemed to change, for example, if it seemed to change position, appear 2D rather than 3D, and so on. Discuss why we need two eyes, for example, to judge the speed of approaching objects.	**Extension**: Students discuss why predators have eyes at the front of their heads and prey have eyes at the side of their heads.	
Homework		
Students research eyes of another animal to write a short article with a labelled diagram. The article should include comparisons between the ray diagram for the eye and that of the pinhole camera.		

3.5 Colour

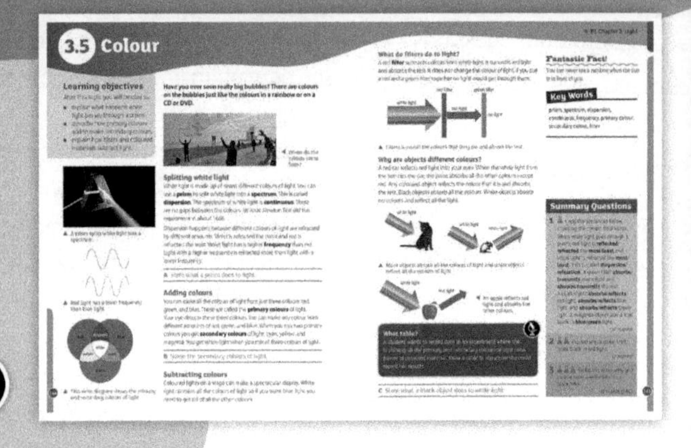

Physics NC link:

- colours and the different frequencies of light, white light, and prisms (qualitative only); differential colour effects in absorption and diffuse reflection.

Working Scientifically NC link:

- make predictions using scientific knowledge and understanding.

Band	Outcome	Checkpoint	
		Question	**Activity**
Developing	State what happens to light when it passes through a prism (Level 4).	1	Starter 1, Starter 2
↓	State the primary and secondary colours of light (Level 4).	A	Main, Plenary 2
	State the effect of coloured filters on light (Level 4).	1	Main
	Predict how red light will appear on a white surface (Level 4).		Main
Secure	Explain what happens when light passes through a prism (Level 6).	1	Starter 1, Starter 2
↓	Describe how primary colours add to make secondary colours (Level 6).		Main, Plenary 2
	Explain how filters and coloured materials subtract light (Level 6).	1, 2	Main, Plenary 1
	Predict the colour of objects in red light and the colour of light through different filters (Level 6).		Main, Plenary 1
Extending	Explain why a prism forms a spectrum (Level 7).	1, 3	Starter 1, Starter 2
↓	Explain the formation of secondary colours (Level 8).		Main, Plenary 1
	Predict how coloured objects will appear given different coloured lights and filters (Level 7).	1	Main, Plenary 1
	Predict the colour of objects in lights of secondary colours, giving a reason for the prediction (Level 7).		Main, Plenary 1

Literacy
Students use scientific terminology to explain how filters work in summary questions, on their practical sheet, and in their homework.

APP
Students suggest a suitable table of results given an experiment on primary and secondary colours in the student-book activity (AF3).

Students make predictions and carry out an experiment to investigate colour mixing (AF4).

Students interpret observations and data from their experiments to draw a conclusion, and apply this to other scenarios (AF5).

Key Words
prism, spectrum, dispersion, continuous, frequency, primary colour, secondary colour, tertiary colour, filter

Answers from the student book

In-text questions	**A** Splits white light into a spectrum **B** cyan, yellow, magenta **C** A black object absorbs all colours of light.
Activity	**What table?**

Colour of material	Appearance in red light	Appearance in green light	Appearance in blue light	Appearance in cyan light	Appearance in magenta light

Summary questions	1 refracted, least, most, dispersion, transmits, absorbs, absorbs, reflects, reflects, green (10 marks) 2 The green shirt only reflects green light. It absorbs the red light and reflects no light, which we see as black. (2 marks) 3 6 mark question. Example answers: Filters subtract colours from white light. You cannot subtract a colour and still have white. White consists of all the colours mixed together. A white filter would be like a piece of transparent material, like glass. To see black there must be no light reaching your eye. A black filter would absorb all the colours. A black filter would be like an opaque material like brick.

Starter	Support/Extension	Resources
Big prism (10 min) Use a very bright light source (e.g., the Sun, an OHP) to project a spectrum using a prism. This is dispersion. Ask why the colours appeared (white light travelling through the prism is a mixture of coloured light). The prism does not create coloured light – it splits white light into a spectrum.	**Support**: Prompt students towards the colours seen (and link to a rainbow). **Extension**: Students give examples of other spectra, for example, rainbows in waterfalls.	
Rainbows (10 min) Class discussion: Where do we see rainbows? Why do they occur? This can be used as a consolidation of refraction as well as a short introduction to dispersion.	**Support**: Prompt students with 'Under what circumstances do you see rainbows?' to help students make the link between water, light, and refraction.	
Main	**Support/Extension**	**Resources**
Colour mixing (40 min) Introduce the concept by asking students to look around the room using coloured filters. They should see that objects appear different colours. Students then carry out the experiment on the practical sheet. This works best if black out blinds are used. If these are not available, place the experiments in boxes. Remind students we see light reflecting off objects. Explain black is not a colour – black objects absorb all light. Students predict the colour of a red object in different coloured light and predict the colour of light through two coloured filters. They then test their predictions. Students then move on to testing colours of objects by shining different coloured lights onto them, against a black background.	**Support**: The support sheet includes a suggested table of results, guiding students through a simpler experimental procedure. **Extension**: Some students may be able to predict a pattern based on the preliminary experiment.	**Practical**: Colour mixing
Plenary	**Support/Extension**	**Resources**
How can you see colours? (5 min) Students suggest ways to make an object appear red (e.g., it is red so it reflects red light, a red light source shines on a red or white object, or white light passes through a red filter onto a red or white object).		**Interactive**: Types of colours
Types of colours (5 min) Interactive resource where students sort colours into primary, secondary, or neither.	**Extension**: Students suggest additional ways to make something appear yellow (combining two primary colours).	
Homework		
Students write a guide telling police how to collect accurate witness statements for crimes committed in yellow street light, suggesting mistakes witnesses may make describing colours. An alternative WebQuest homework activity is also available on Kerboodle where students research how lights can be used during concerts on stage.		**WebQuest**: Stage lighting

P1 Chapter 3 Checkpoint

Checkpoint lesson routes

The route through this lesson can be determined using the Checkpoint assessment. Percentage pass marks are supplied in the Checkpoint teacher notes.

Route A (support)
Resources: P1 Chapter 3 Checkpoint Revision.

Students will work through a revision activity that allows them to gradually revisit and consolidate their understanding of reflection and refraction, coloured light, and the eye and camera. Include simple demonstrations throughout the lesson to reinforce different points.

Route B (extension)
Resources: P1 Chapter 3 Checkpoint Extension.

Students will be asked to prepare a poster describing the journey of light when a person looks at a view through a window. This allows students to describe in detail how sunlight is reflected, travels through the glass, and into the person's eyes or a camera. Students should use scientific language in their poster to explain how the image is formed and describe what happens at the different stages.

Progression to *secure*

No.	Developing outcome	Secure outcome	Making progress
1	Describe some ways that light interacts with materials.	Describe what happens when light interacts with materials.	In Task 1 students can complete a cloze activity using the key words they need for a full description.
2	State that light travels very fast.	State the speed of light.	Task 2 is a cloze activity using numbers. Students will need to consider the magnitude of each number. The speed is given in metres per second. Students may have previously met it in kilometres per second or miles per hour.
3	Describe what happens when light is reflected.	State the law of reflection.	Students should complete a labelled ray diagram in Task 2 and state the law of reflection. They will use the law of reflection to complete the cloze activity. Students may benefit from repeating simple reflection light experiments.
4	Identify examples of specula and diffuse reflection.	Compare specula and diffuse reflection.	Students may struggle with the correct use of terminology for diffuse and specula reflection. Students should complete the cloze activity in Task 3, and then note down ways of remembering the two terms in the space provided.
5	Describe what happens when light is refracted.	Describe and explain what happens when light is refracted.	For students to understand this enough to produce an explanation, they need to think about light travelling as a wave. Draw a diagram for students, or demonstrate with a water tray or ripple tank if available. Students can write a full explanation in Task 5.
6	Describe features of the image formed by a lens.	Describe what happens when light travels through a lens.	Students should draw and annotate a diagram in Task 5. They should then write a description.
7	Name parts of the eye.	Describe how the eye works.	In the table in Task 6, students will need to describe what each part of the eye does. They can use this information to form a full description, supported by prompts in Task 6.
8	Name parts of the camera.	Describe how a simple camera forms an image.	Students complete a similar task to the previous outcome in Task 6. Students may benefit from having a video clip available to watch during this part of the activity.
9	Name some parts in the eye and in the camera.	Compare the eye and the camera.	The table in Task 6 will help students to draw comparisons between the eye and the camera.
10	State what happens to light when it passes through a prism.	Explain what happens when light passes through a prism.	Students should be able to remember what happens with a prism visually, and then need to ensure they have the correct vocabulary for a description. Support is given in Task 7.
11	State the primary and secondary colours of light.	Describe how primary colours add to make secondary colours.	Students will benefit from visual demonstrations and representations of colour. If available, provide students with coloured lenses and reinforce key points with coloured board pens. Students can then complete Task 7.
12	State the effect of coloured filters on light.	Explain how filters and coloured materials subtract light.	Students can complete the table in Task 7. They can use the information given in the table to help them write a full explanation.

Answers to end-of-chapter questions

1 A, H, I, M, O, T, U, V, W, X, Y (1 mark)

2a Blue jacket and red trousers. All colours are in white light, the blue jacket reflects blue and the red trousers reflect red. (2 marks)

b Black jacket and black trousers. The blue jacket and red trousers would absorb green light so no light is reflected. (2 marks)

3a The light is refracted so the image of the fish is below where it really is. (2 marks)

b The light does not change direction so the fish is below the bird. (2 marks)

4a angle of incidence (1 mark)

b mass of plastic (1 mark)

c angle of refraction (1 mark)

d The bigger the mass, the smaller the angle of refraction. (1 mark)

e Put the results in order of increasing mass. (1 mark)

5 Rays brought to focus, as shown on page 143 of the Student Book. (4 marks)

6 Angle would be bigger in water. Water slows light down less. (2 marks)

7 Students should be marked on the use of good English, organisation of information, spelling and grammar, and correct use of specialist scientific terms. The best answers would present clear, detailed, and well organised descriptions and explanations of light through the lenses (maximum of 6 marks).

Examples of correct scientific points:

Light is refracted as it goes from air into each of the materials.

The materials would refract light by different amounts.

A lens is a piece of glass that focusses light.

The rays cross at the focal point.

If the material slows light down more, it would refract light more.

Diamond slows down light the most, so would refract light the most.

The focus would be closest for a diamond lens.

Glass would refract light the least because it slows light down the least.

The focus would be furthest for glass.

Answer guide for the Big write

Developing	Secure	Extending
1–2 marks	3–4 marks	5–6 marks
• Uses coloured lights to 'change' the colours of clothing, writing on posters, and writing on programmes. • Shows an understanding of how mirrors reflect light. • Plan lacks detail and organisation.	• Uses simple ideas about reflection to suggest ways to use mirrors to produce images that the audience could see. • Produce examples of materials that could be used on a programme/poster that would change colour. • Plan lacks organisation of ideas.	• Uses ideas of partial reflection in glass to explain how to produce a ghostly image e.g., pepper's ghost where you could have an image and a person in the same place. • Describes in detail how it could be done practically. • Plan is clearly organised and has sufficient detail.

kerboodle

P1 Chapter 3 Checkpoint assessment (automarked)
P1 Chapter 3 Checkpoint: Revision
P1 Chapter 3 Checkpoint: Extension
P1 Chapter 3 Progress task (Literacy)

4.1 The night sky

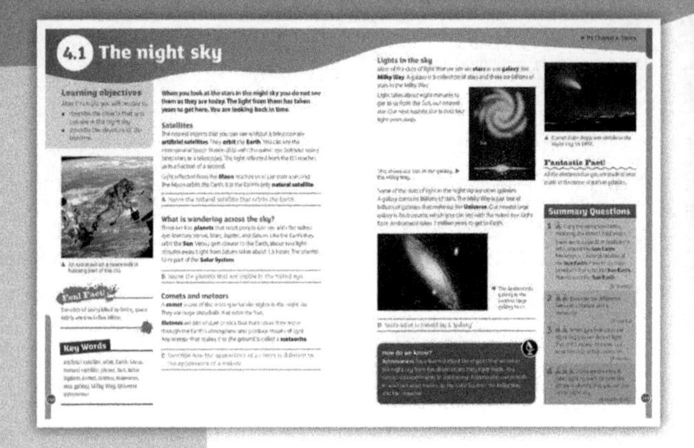
4.1 The night sky

Learning objectives

Satellites

What is wandering across the sky?

Comets and meteors

Key Words

Lights in the sky

Fantastic Fact!

Summary Questions

How do we know?

Physics NC link:

- our Sun as a star, other stars in our galaxy, other galaxies
- the light year as a unit of astronomical distance.

Working Scientifically NC link:

- understand that scientific methods and theories develop as earlier explanations are modified to take account of new evidence and ideas, together with the importance of publishing results and peer review.

Band	Outcome	Checkpoint	
		Question	**Activity**
Developing	Name some objects seen in the night sky (Level 3).	A, 3	Starter 1, Starter 2
	Place some objects seen in the night sky in size order (Level 4).		Plenary 2
↓	Identify scientific evidence from secondary evidence (Level 4).		Starter 1
Secure	Describe the objects you can see in the night sky (Level 5).	D, 1	Starter 1, Starter 2, Main 1
	Describe the structure of the Universe (Level 5).	B	Main 1
↓	Draw valid conclusions that utilise more than one piece of supporting evidence (Level 5).		Main 2
Extending	Use the speed of light to describe distances between astronomical objects (Level 7).	4	Plenary 1
	Describe the structure of the Universe in detail, in order of size and of distance away from the Earth (Level 7).		Main 1, Plenary 2
↓	Assess the strength of evidence, deciding whether it is sufficient to support a conclusion (Level 7).		Main 2

Maths

Understand number size and scale with reference to a billion.

Literacy
Read information from a range of sources about the objects in the night sky and prepare a podcast for the public.

APP
Draw valid conclusions that utilise more than one piece of supporting evidence such as photographs of objects in space (AF4).

Key Words
star, artificial satellite, orbit, Earth, Moon, natural satellite, planet, Sun, Solar System, comet, meteor, meteorite, star, galaxy, Milky Way, Universe, astronomer

Answers from the student book

In-text questions	**A** the Moon **B** Mercury, Venus, Mars, Jupiter, Saturn **C** A comet is an object with a tail that stays in the night sky and returns. A meteor produces a streak of light that lasts a very short time. **D** A galaxy contains millions of stars.

Summary questions	**1** Earth, Earth, Sun, Sun (4 marks) **2** A meteor is a piece of rock or dust that burns up in the atmosphere. A meteorite is a piece of rock that reaches the ground. (2 marks) **3** Any two from: stars, galaxies, planets **4** 6 mark question. Example answers: It takes fractions of a second for light to reach us from objects in orbit around the Earth, such as satellites or the International Space Station. Light takes minutes to reach us from planets close to us in the Solar System, such as Mercury, Venus, Mars, Jupiter. Light takes hours to reach us from distant planets in the Solar System. Light takes years to reach us from stars in the Milky Way galaxy. Our nearest star is about 4 light-years away. Light takes millions of years to reach us from other galaxies.

Starter	Support/Extension	Resources
What is in the night sky? (10 min) Students list what they can see in the night sky. Then use the interactive resource where students match items in the night sky with their definition. Discuss why there objects are visible.	**Support**: Suggest ideas and ask students what they have seen. **Extension**: Students identify reasons why they cannot see things well at night, for example, light pollution, clouds, or buildings.	**Interactive**: What is in the night sky?
What is in the sky tonight? (5–10 min) Use a star map to show what is visible in tonight's sky (e.g., from the National Schools Observatory website) or show a current video of Tonight's Sky from Hubble's website. Free downloadable programs such as Celestia and Stellarium make good alternatives.	**Extension**: Discuss if it is possible to tell between planets or stars using a telescope.	
Main	**Support/Extension**	**Resources**
What is in the Universe? (20 min) Use the Hubble website image gallery to show objects in the night sky (planets, nebulae – gas clouds where stars form, stars, black holes – remnant of collapsed giant stars, galaxies). Explain how objects fit together to form the Universe. This can be prepared in advance as a slide show with images and titles. Use the activity sheet to reinforce student perception of our place in the Universe.	**Support**: Show animations of satellites. An access sheet is available with easier text and comprehension questions. Graph paper is useful to give students an idea of one billion.	**Activity**: What is in the Universe? **Skill sheet**: Converting units
Satellites (20 min) Define a satellite as a smaller object orbiting a larger one. Give examples of natural satellites such as the Moon orbiting the Earth or planets orbiting stars. Remind students satellites always move and that they orbit the widest point of Earth but not necessarily over the equator. Discuss uses of manmade satellites and describe how scientists share data from these.	**Extension**: Discuss different orbits for satellites (vary in height, orientation, uses), for example, geostationary orbits, low polar orbits. Ask students to suggest benefits for scientists of sharing their ideas.	
Plenary	**Support/Extension**	**Resources**
How far are they? (10 min) Students rank objects in order of distance from Earth and matching distances in light-time, for example, Sun (8 light-minutes), Moon (1 light-second), Proxima Centuri (our nearest star, 4 light-years). Planet light-times vary as position in orbit varies, for example, Neptune (4 light-hours ±8 light-minutes) or Mars about 4–20 light-minutes.	**Support**: Provide a diagram for reference. **Extension**: Students estimate distances in light-time before you provide a list.	
What is in the Universe? (5 min) Students list objects found in the Universe. Rank them in size order, (e.g., Moon, planet, star, black hole, galaxy, Universe).	**Support**: Provide the list for students to rank.	
Homework	**Support/Extension**	
Make a model of a satellite identifying solar panels for power, rockets to control direction, communication antenna, and battery for power supply.	**Support**: Use Met Office template for satellite model, available from their website. **Extension**: Model a named satellite.	

4.2 The Solar System

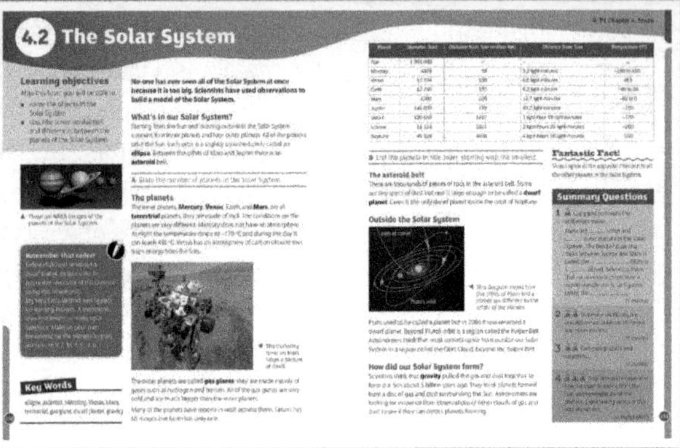
4.2 The Solar System

Physics NC link:

- gravity force, gravity forces between Earth and Moon, and between Earth and Sun (qualitative only).

Working Scientifically NC link:

- interpret observations and data, including identifying patterns and using observations, measurements and data to draw conclusions.

Band	Outcome	Checkpoint	
		Question	**Activity**
Developing	Name some objects in the Solar System (Level 3).		Starter 1, Plenary 1
↓	Name the planets in the Solar System (Level 4).	A, B	
	Identify some patterns in the Solar System (Level 3).		Main 2
Secure	Describe how objects in the Solar System are arranged (Level 5).	1	Main 1, Main 2
↓	Describe some similarities and differences between the planets of the Solar System (Level 5).	2	Main 2
	Identify patterns in the spacing and diameters of planets (Level 6).		Main 2
Extending	Explain how the properties and features of planets are linked to their place in the Solar System (Level 7).		Main 2, Plenary 2
↓	Compare features of different objects in the Solar System (Level 7).	2, 3	
	Use data to make predictions about features of planets (Level 7).		Main 2

Literacy

Students retrieve and collate information from a range of sources on space exploration, exploring the advantages and disadvantages of space travel, to summarise the information in a table.

APP

Students use the model of the orrery to explain the movement of the Earth and the Moon relative to the Sun (AF1).

Students choose different methods of representing scientific data in the activity, transferring data from a table to a graph (AF3).

Key Words

ellipse, asteroid, Mercury, Venus, Mars, terrestrial, gas giant, dwarf planet, gravity

Answers from the student book

In-text questions	**A** There are eight planets in the Solar System. **B** Mercury, Mars, Venus, Earth, Neptune, Uranus, Saturn, Jupiter
Activity	**Remember that order!** Students should choose a suitable mnemonic with the correct initial letters.
Summary questions	**1** four, four, asteroid belt, dwarf, Oort Cloud (5 marks) **2** Similarities: They all orbit the Sun. They are round. Differences: The inner planets are made of rock, the outer planets, of gas. Outer planets are colder. You cannot see some of the outer planets with the naked eye. (2 marks) **3** Planets and asteroids both orbit the Sun. Some of the planets are made of rock like some asteroids. Asteroids are not spherical. **4** 6 mark question. Example answers: As you move away from the Sun the temperature decreases. Less light reaches objects that are further away. Less energy is transferred from the Sun to objects that are further away. More distant planets should be colder than nearer planets. Venus should be colder than Mercury because it is further from the Sun. It is hotter than Mercury because it has an atmosphere that traps energy transferred the Sun.

Starter	Support/Extension	Resources
What do you know? (5 min) Students sketch a diagram showing the objects they think are in the Solar System and their orbits. Use this to assess prior knowledge and draw out misconceptions.	**Support**: Provide a diagram for students to add labels to.	
Models of the Solar System (10 min) Show the video clip 'Models of the Solar System – Earth, Sun and Moon' from the Institute of Physics website. Students list 3–5 points from the video.	**Support**: Point out models of Sun, Moon, and Earth in video. **Extension**: Students explain why we see 'wandering stars' (planets).	
Main	**Support/Extension**	**Resources**
The moving Solar System (15 min) Students make an orrery (moving model of Sun, Earth, and Moon) in their books. This can also be done as a large demonstration model. One paper fastener fixes the Sun and the longer paper strip to the page so the strip can turn. The other paper fastener fixes Earth and the short strip to the other end of the longer strip, so Earth orbits the Sun. Glue the Moon to the other end of the shorter paper strip so it orbits Earth. Students use the orrery to explain phenomena in the Solar System. They suggest improvements to their models, for example, scale.	**Extension**: Students add another planet, and use the orrery to explain why it seems to move forwards and backwards relative to Earth.	
The Solar System to scale (25 min) At this point, it is important to introduce the difference between inner planets and outer planets, in particular about the materials they are made from. This can be done from the student book. Using a long, narrow strip of paper, students can display relative distances of planets from the Sun by folding the paper, or by using a scale diagram. Discuss patterns in the separations and the scale of the Solar System. Students then work through the activity sheet individually.	**Support**: Introduce the idea of scale and give students 30-cm rulers. The support sheet includes a table of data to help students answer the questions. **Extension**: Calculate space-time to planet, discussing problems with space travel.	**Activity**: The Solar System to scale **Skill sheet**: Choosing scales
Plenary	**Support/Extension**	**Resources**
Objects in the Solar System (5 min) Interactive resource where students order objects in the Solar System according to size. **What planet am I?** (5 min) Each student writes down clues so their partner can guess which planet they are thinking of.	**Support**: Ask students to focus on the relative sizes of the Sun, Earth, and Moon.	**Interactive**: Objects in the Solar System
Homework	**Support/Extension**	
Students research benefits and costs of space travel (e.g., spin-off technology, cost of manned versus unmanned expeditions). An alternative WebQuest homework activity is also available on Kerboodle where students research the planets of the Solar System.	**Support**: Students fill out a table with two columns: advantages and disadvantages. **Extension**: Students can add extra columns based on evidence and evaluation.	**WebQuest**: Solar System tourist

4.3 The Earth

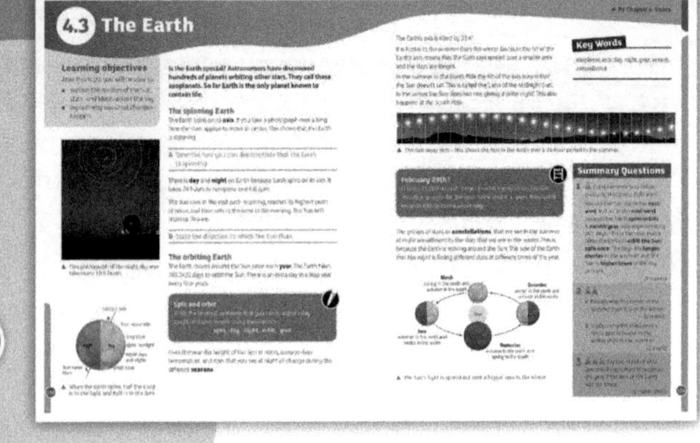

Physics NC link:

- the seasons and the Earth's tilt, day length at different times of the year, in different hemispheres.

Working Scientifically NC link:

- interpret observations and data, including identifying patterns and using observations, measurements, and data to draw conclusions.

Band	Outcome	Checkpoint	
		Question	Activity
Developing	Describe differences between seasons (Level 3).	2	Starter 1
↓	Describe the motion of the Sun, stars, and Moon across the sky (Level 4).	B, 1	Starter 2
	Describe patterns in data linking day-length and month (Level 4).		Main 3
Secure	Explain the motion of the Sun, stars, and Moon across the sky (Level 5).	A, B, 1	
↓	Explain why seasonal changes happen (Level 6).		Main 1, Main 2
	Use data to show the effect of the Earth's tilt on temperature and day-length (Level 5).		Main 3
Extending	Predict the effect of the Earth's tilt on temperature and day-length (Level 7).		Main 3
↓	Predict how seasons would be different if there were no tilt (Level 7).	3	Plenary 2
	Interpret data to predict how the Earth's tilt affects temperature and day-length (Level 7).		Main 3

Maths

The student-book activity allows students to carry out simple calculations to work out the occurrence of a leap year.

During the activity students extract and interpret information from charts, graphs, and tables. They also represent changes in temperature and day-length with changes in season graphically.

In order to answer questions, students must interpret graphs comparing day-length, temperature, and season.

Literacy

The student-book activity asks students to summarise information using key words.

Students explain to each other phenomena caused by the moving Earth.

For homework students write an account of changes experienced travelling from the equator to the North Pole.

APP

Use of globes, paper Pole Stars, and thermofilm to explain phenomena when explaining the seasons (AF1).

Students display tabulated data as graphs to show trends and patterns (AF3).

Key Words

exoplanet, axis, day, night, year, season, constellation

Answers from the student book

In-text questions	**A** Take a picture of the night sky over many hours. The stars make circular tracks. **B** east
Activity	**Spin and orbit** For example, one day is the time it takes for the Earth to spin once. The half of the Earth where sunlight does not reach is night. One year is the time it takes the Earth to orbit the Sun once. **February 29th?** $21\,600 \times 4 = 86\,400$ so $86\,400 \div (24 \times 60 \times 60)$ days $= 1$ day

Summary questions	**1** east, west, spins, year, orbit the Sun, longer, higher (7 marks) **2 a** It is hotter because the days are longer so the Sun warms the Earth for longer. The rays from the Sun are more concentrated than they are in winter. (2 marks) **b** The Sun is lower in the sky in the winter so shadows are longer. (1 mark) **3** 6 mark question. Example answers: You would not have seasons. Days and nights would be equal length throughout the year. Shadow-length at noon would be the same throughout the year. The height of the Sun in the sky at noon would be the same throughout the year. There would be no difference between the angle at which the Sun's rays hit the Earth at different times of the year. Temperature changes depend on the Sun's rays spreading out over a bigger area in the winter than the summer.

Starter	Support/Extension	Resources
An alternative question-led lesson is also available. **Different seasons** (5 min) Students list differences in seasons, for example, day-length, position of Sun, and weather. Students suggest why changes happen.	**Support**: Students identify differences in day-length and temperature. **Extension**: Students suggest differences on the same date in different parts of the Earth.	**Question-led lesson**: The Earth
The Pole Star (5 min) Discuss navigation without a compass. The North Pole always points towards the Pole Star because Earth tilts that way. Use a video clip from the Internet to show how to find the Pole Star and navigate using it.		
Main	**Support/Extension**	**Resources**
Why we have seasons (15 min) Ensure students know the Earth always tilts towards the Pole Star, not towards the Sun. Use a paper star on a wall as the Pole Star. Move a globe (Earth) to tilt towards this star as it orbits around a central lamp (Sun). The North Pole tilts towards the Sun for part of the year only. Add a sticker on the globe to show the UK. Students should identify when the UK has winter and summer, and predict changes in day-length.	**Extension**: Students design their own model on paper to show this idea.	
Seasons and temperature (10 min) Students may think winter is cooler because the Earth is further away from the Sun but it is because the Sun's rays spread over a larger area when Earth tilts away from the Sun. Stick a 1-cm wide strip of thermofilm from pole to pole, including the UK. Tilt the globe towards the lamp. The thermofilm by the UK warms up changing colour (summer). Tilt the globe away from the lamp, light spreads over a larger area and the thermofilm is cooler (winter). It is important to keep the separation of the lamp and section of the globe the same.		
The seasons (20 min) Students complete questions on the activity sheet.	**Support**: A support sheet is provided with labelled graph grids and fewer sets of data.	**Activity**: The seasons
Plenary	**Support/Extension**	**Resources**
The Sun and the seasons (5 min) Students complete the gap fill on the interactive resource to explain how seasons occur.	**Support**: Set as cloze exercise. **Extension**: Students draw diagrams explaining why some countries are cooler.	**Interactive**: The Sun and the seasons
A changing tilt (5 min) Students predict what would be different if Earth was not tilted (we would still be cooler than the equator but day-length/temperature would be the same all year).	**Support**: Structure using questions with yes/no answers. **Extension**: Predict changes if Earth's tilt were greater.	
Homework		
Give students the temperature and day-length in a particular month for four countries between the equator and the North Pole. They write an account or postcards describing changes from the point of view of a tourist.		

4.4 The Moon

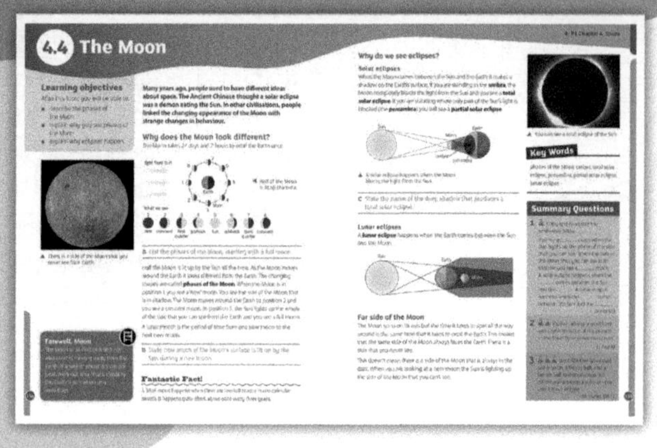

Physics NC link:

- use of ray model.

Working Scientifically NC link:

- make predictions using scientific knowledge and understanding.

Band	Outcome	Checkpoint	
		Question	**Activity**
Developing	Name some phases of the Moon (Level 4).	A, 1	
	Explain simply why we see the Moon from Earth (Level 4).		Main
	Describe what a total eclipse is (Level 4).	1	
	Show the different phases of the Moon using models provided (Level 4).		Main
Secure	Describe the phases of the Moon (Level 5).	1	Main, Starter 2, Plenary 2
	Explain why we see the phases of the Moon (Level 6).		Main
	Explain why total eclipses happen (Level 6).	1, 3	Main
	Explain phases of the Moon using the models provided (Level 6).		Main
Extending	Predict phases of the Moon at a given time (Level 7).		Plenary 1
	Explain how total eclipses are linked to phases of the Moon (Level 8).		Main
	Explain why it is possible to see an eclipse on some of the planets in the Solar System but not others (Level 7).	2	
	Predict the phases of the Moon using models provided (Level 8).		Main

Maths
The student-book activity asks students to carry out a simple calculation to work out the distance between the Moon and the Earth at a given time.

Literacy
Students use scientific vocabulary when writing about the phases of the Moon in the starter and plenary tasks.

Students summarise scientific text for key ideas in their homework.

APP
Use of models to demonstrate the phases of the Moon (AF1).

Students choose appropriate methods to present observations (AF3).

Key Words
solar eclipse, phases of the Moon, total eclipse, partial eclipse, lunar eclipse

Answers from the student book

In-text questions	**A** full moon, waning gibbous, last quarter, waning crescent, new moon, waxing crescent, first quarter, waxing gibbous **B** Half the Moon is lit up at all times. **C** umbra
Activity	**Farewell, Moon** Distance = your age × 3.8 cm/year = 11 years × 3.8 cm/year = 41.8 cm

Summary questions	1 full, new, Moon, Earth, Earth, Moon (6 marks) 2 There will be eclipses on any other planet that has one or more moons. 3 6 mark question. Example answers: Put the torch on the desk and switch it on. Label the tennis ball 'Moon'. Label the beach ball 'Earth'. For a solar eclipse, hold the tennis ball between the beach ball and the torch. There is a shadow cast by the tennis ball on the beach ball. For a lunar eclipse, hold the beach ball between the tennis ball and the torch.

Starter	Support/Extension	Resources
Check the facts (5 min) Check misconceptions/prior knowledge with five short questions. Students may think that the Moon changes shape or clouds change its appearance, that it always appears in the same part of the sky, and that it gives out its own light. Possible questions: Does the Moon change shape? Is the Moon bigger/closer than the Sun? What is a full/new moon? Is the Moon seen in the same place each night/during the night? **How does the Moon change?** (5 min) Students write down how the Moon changes in as much detail as possible, for example, timescale, what they see, where it is, and when it is seen.	**Support**: Provide multiple choice answers. **Extension**: Students explain answers and offer more detail.	
Main	**Support/Extension**	**Resources**
The Moon and eclipses (40 min) Students model the phases of the Moon and eclipses using the instructions on the practical sheet. Students then answer the questions on the practical sheet.	**Support**: Clarify these concepts using animations and diagrams. A support sheet is available with partially drawn diagrams for students to complete. **Extension**: Students suggest why we don't see eclipses every day/month.	**Practical**: The Moon and eclipses
Plenary	**Support/Extension**	**Resources**
What does it look like? (10 min) Draw a phase of the Moon (e.g., full moon). Students describe its appearance in future or the past, for example, in a week's time/two weeks' time/a week ago. This can be done in conjunction with the interactive gap fill as a summary. **How does the Moon change? (Part 2)** (5 min) Students revisit their answers at the start of the lesson to see how much more detail they can add.	**Support**: Provide cards with images to sort. **Extension**: Predict appearance (phases) of Earth for an astronaut on the Moon.	**Interactive**: What does it look like?
Homework	**Support/Extension**	
Provide students with accounts to read from people/news articles of solar or lunar eclipses. Students must then write a summary paragraph explaining what was seen.	**Extension**: Students should relate their summary to the relative positions of the Sun, Earth, and Moon.	

P1 Chapter 4 Checkpoint

Checkpoint lesson routes

The route through this lesson can be determined using the Checkpoint assessment.

Percentage pass marks are supplied in the Checkpoint teacher notes.

Route A (support)
Resource: P1 Chapter 4 Checkpoint Revision

Students will create a poster about space, using the prompts and questions provided in the revision activity, to help them revisit and consolidate their understanding of this chapter.

Route B (extension)
Resource: P1 Chapter 4 Checkpoint Extension

Students will be asked to write an account of a journey through the Solar System playing attention to the forces involved, and comparing the planets they visit. Prompts and guidance are given in the extension sheet.

Progression to *secure*

No.	Developing outcome	Secure outcome	Making progress
1	Name some objects seen in the night sky.	Describe the objects you can see in the night sky.	Before completing this section of their poster students can complete the cloze activity in Task 1.
2	Place some objects seen in the night sky in size order.	Describe the structure of the Universe.	Key words are given as prompts in Task 1 for students to add to their poster. Task 3 looks at the numbers involved in describing the Universe.
3	Name some objects in the Solar System.	Describe how objects in the Solar System are arranged.	In Task 2 prompts are given for the students to draw and annotate objects in the Solar System.
4	Name the planets in the Solar System.	Describe some similarities and differences between the planets of the Solar System.	Students are encouraged to include facts and comparisons in their poster using the prompts given in Task 2.
5	Describe differences between seasons.	Explain why seasonal changes happen.	Students may benefit from a model demonstration using a globe and a light source. They should write clear explanations on the poster. Further support is given in Task 4.
6	Describe the motion of the Sun, stars, and Moon across the sky.	Explain the motion of the Sun, stars, and Moon across the sky.	You may wish to demonstrate relative movement by getting students to stand and turn round in their places to see objects in the room appear to move. Support is given in Task 5.
7	Name some phases of the Moon.	Describe the phases of the Moon.	Students could include a Moon calendar, with named phases, in their poster. Support is given in Task 5.
8	Explain simply why we see the Moon from Earth.	Explain why we see the phases of the Moon.	You may wish to demonstrate different phases of the Moon using a light source, globe, and ball.
9	Describe what a total eclipse is.	Explain why total eclipses happen.	You may wish to demonstrate how eclipses occur using a light source, globe, and ball. Support is given in Task 5.

Answers to end-of-chapter questions

1 Orbit the Earth: Moon, satellite, International space station.
Orbit the Sun: planet, asteroid, comet. (2 marks)

2a One mark for each correct label. (3 marks)
b winter (1 mark)
c 9 (1 mark)

3a Left of diagram labelled east and sunrise. Centre of diagram labelled noon. Right of diagram labelled west and sunset. (2 marks)
b Winter path has the same shape as the summer path but will be lower in the sky (2 marks)
c Earth orbits around the Sun in one year, and rotates around a tilted axis. (2 marks)

4a light-second away: Moon (1 mark)
light-years away: galaxy (1 mark)
b It would take minutes or hours for the signal to reach the spacecraft. There would be a long delay between asking a question and receiving an answer. (2 marks)

5 Students should be marked on the use of good English, organisation of information, spelling and grammar, and correct use of specialist scientific terms. The best answers will be well presented and clearly organised, making references to the information provided in the table as well as to their scientific knowledge (maximum of 6 marks).
Examples of correct scientific points:
The seasons would be would be longer or shorter depending on the angle.
The angle of tilt of Mars, Saturn, and Neptune is about the same as Earth.
The seasons on Mars, Saturn, and Neptune would be similar to Earth.
The axis of Mercury is not tilted.
Mercury would not have seasons.
You would hardly notice the seasons on Jupiter – the angle of tilt of Jupiter is so small.
Seasons are longer for planets further from the Sun because it takes longer for the planet to orbit the Sun.
Uranus has an angle of tilt of nearly 90 degrees, so rolls like a barrel on its axis as it moves around the Sun – seasons would last about 6 months.
Venus has very little difference between the seasons because the angle is very small – it is just spinning the other way.

Answer guide for Big Write

Developing	Secure	Extending
1–2 marks	3–4 marks	5–6 marks
• Student picks out obvious points from the table given (e.g., year length is shorter, day length is longer) but little or no comparisons to other planets in the Solar System.	• Student shows comprehension that conditions probably too hot for life and that the same side would always face the star. • Some basic comparison with other planets in the Solar system.	• Student connects the idea that temperatures not suitable for liquid water so unlikely to have life. • Compares with other planets in the Solar System, e.g., rolls like Uranus.

kerboodle

P1 Chapter 4 Checkpoint assessment (automarked)
P1 Chapter 4 Checkpoint: Revision
P1 Chapter 4 Checkpoint: Extension
P1 Chapter 4 Progress task (Maths)

Index

OXFORD
UNIVERSITY PRESS

Great Clarendon Street, Oxford, OX2 6DP, United Kingdom

Oxford University Press is a department of the University of Oxford. It furthers the University's objective of excellence in research, scholarship, and education by publishing worldwide. Oxford is a registered trade mark of Oxford University Press in the UK and in certain other countries

© Oxford University Press 2013

The moral rights of the authors have been asserted

First published in 2013

All rights reserved. No part of this publication may be reproduced, stored in a retrieval system, or transmitted, in any form or by any means, without the prior permission in writing of Oxford University Press, or as expressly permitted by law, by licence or under terms agreed with the appropriate reprographics rights organization. Enquiries concerning reproduction outside the scope of the above should be sent to the Rights Department, Oxford University Press, at the address above.

You must not circulate this work in any other form and you must impose this same condition on any acquirer

British Library Cataloguing in Publication Data
Data available

978-0-19-839259-0

11

Paper used in the production of this book is a natural, recyclable product made from wood grown in sustainable forests.
The manufacturing process conforms to the environmental regulations of the country of origin.

Printed in Great Britain by CPI Group (UK) Ltd,
Croydon CR0 4YY

Acknowledgements
The publisher and the authors would like to thank the following for permissions to use their photographs:

Cover image: Sebastian Tomus/Shutterstock

Although we have made every effort to trace and contact all copyright holders before publication this has not been possible in all cases. If notified, the publisher will rectify any errors or omissions at the earliest opportunity.

Links to third party websites are provided by Oxford in good faith and for information only. Oxford disclaims any responsibility for the materials contained in any third party website referenced in this work.